Like a **Phoenix** *from the* **Ashes**

Phoenix
Vlam in mij, laai weer op;
hart in mij, heb geduld,
verdubbel het vertrouwen –
vogel in mij, laat zich opnieuw ontvouwen
de vleugelen, de nu nog moede en grauwe;
o, wiek nu op uit de verbrande takken
en laat den moed en uwe vaart niet zakken;
het nest is goed, maar het heelal is ruimer.
              – Hendrik Marsman, 1899–1940

Flame in me, blaze up again;
heart in me, be patient,
double the trust –
bird in me, let itself unfold again
the wings, the now weary and gray ones;
oh, now rise from the burned branches
and do not let down courage and your speed;
the nest is good, but the universe is wider.
              – translation by Philip Mees

ANNEJET RÜMKE

Like a Phoenix *from the* Ashes

EXERCISES FOR RECOVERING FROM
AND PREVENTING BURNOUT

Printed with support from the Waldorf Curriculum Fund

Published by
Waldorf Publications at the
The Research Institute for Waldorf Education
351 Fairview Avenue
Suite 625
Hudson, NY 12534

Title: *Like a Phoenix from the Ashes*
     Exercises for Recovering from and Preventing Burnout
Author: Annejet Rümke
With contributions from Arianne Collee and Natalie Peters
A translation of the Dutch original, *Als een feniks uit de as. Herstellen en voorkomen van burnout. Een oefenboek*
Published by Uitgeverij Christofoor, Zeist, Netherlands, 2008

Translation: Philip Mees
Cover image: painting from *Gold Collection* by Ursula Stone,
     with permission of the artist
Drawings page 71: Teun Berserik
Proofreader/copy editor: Melissa Merkling
Layout: Ann Erwin

Table of Contents

The Myth of the Phoenix

Once upon a time, so long ago that the stories are all but forgotten, a bird was living in Paradise. Its name was Simurg. This bird was one of a kind, both male and female. Its wings were as wide as the clouds, and its feathers gold and yellow like living fire. It was all-wise and possessed all words.

In the middle of Paradise, in the center of the earth, it had its nest, high in the sacred saena tree, the Tree of Life, the mother of all trees. From this tree flows all life, and the seeds of all plants in the world grow in the saena tree. When Simurg beats its broad, sparkling wings, the seeds from the Tree of Life fly over the entire earth. Next to the saena tree grows a bush that can cure all wounds and illnesses.

In Paradise, the human being did not know the difference between life and death. Dying and being born was rather a kind of breathing in and breathing out. Not until we left Paradise and entered into a deeper connection with the earth did we experience death, illness, pain and suffering. But Simurg did not obey the laws of mortality, and this is why it was cherished by human beings. They were always hoping to catch a glimpse of it. If you found one of its golden, glowing feathers you were very lucky, because they possessed magical healing powers. But people rarely saw the bird.

Simurg was known to almost all people on the earth. In ancient Persia, people still knew that Simurg was related to the Sun God, Ahura Mazdao. In ancient Egypt she was called Bennu; she had creative powers and was related to the soul of the Sun God Ra. Where Bennu alighted on the Bennu Tree was the most sacred place on earth. In Jewish mythology this bird is a male, in Russia it is the firebird, and in China the dragon.

In the West, we know this bird by the name it was given in ancient Greece: the Phoenix. The Phoenix is one of a kind. Every five hundred years it feels that its forces are declining. Then it gathers fragrant herbs, such as incense, cinnamon and myrrh, with which it builds its nest and sits on it. When the sun is at its strongest, it fans the heat with its wings until the nest bursts into flame. The flames flare up and burn everything.

Some say that the Phoenix lays an egg and hatches it in the heat of the fire; others say that it fertilizes its nest. Be this as it may, when everything has been burned to ashes, when the flames have spent themselves and are extinguished and the last glowing embers have turned black, when everything has become gray and cold, something stirs in the ashes. The new Phoenix rises up from the ashes and spreads its wings anew. It leaves the old behind and flies up, reborn, full of new life and strength.

Introduction

Burnout means burned up. But what is it actually that is burned up, and how did it get to that point? When you are burned up, how can you recover and rise from the ashes? Preferably not just as you were before, but with renewed strength and capacities? These are the questions considered in this book.

This book deals with burnout as an illness of our time, connected with our lifestyle and work culture, but also with individual character traits and customs. Biological and psychological factors that play a role in burnout will receive special attention, as will the differences between men and women. The last part of the book describes many exercises to help you recover from burnout and to help you avoid getting burned out to begin with.

This book was written especially for people who are suffering from burnout or are on their way to it. It offers insights and exercises that can help prevent burnout. Burnout is a radical event of great importance and happens to tens of thousands of people every year. It often happens that people sit at home for months, gloomy and tired, without getting significant help. This creates insecurity and inhibits recovery.

Deliberately working toward recovery means that you have started to climb out of the pit, and that there is a prospect of getting better, even in a literal sense, namely that you will be functioning better than before. Burnout is a crisis, but if you handle it well, it also offers potential for change and growth. Change and growth can take place because you get to know yourself better, because you develop a different lifestyle that fits you better than the hectic life you had before, and perhaps also because you find different values in life.

This book is for people who want to understand what burnout is, how it comes about, and especially how to recover from it or, even better, avoid it. I was once burned out myself, and in that period I decided to organize my life as a physician and my practice in a different way. I stopped making concessions and remained faithful to my own values. That is why I look back on that period as a difficult but precious phase in my life that was essential for the direction I eventually chose in my work.

In the past twenty-five years I have treated many people with burnout and other stress-related complaints. The beginning of the therapy is always an explanation of the processes that are taking place in body and soul in cases of burnout. Working together to figure out a clear approach offers hope and the prospect of getting better by following a path of exercises. It is wonderful to see how someone who comes in exhausted and gloomy, after a few months to a year, rises up as a phoenix from the ashes and finds a more individual direction in life.

Like a Phoenix from the Ashes focuses on recovery and prevention and gives many examples. The exercises strengthen the capacity of self-healing. The book therefore also brings hope and supports individual growth.

This book is also for professionals who work with people who are burned out. In the past twenty-five years I have given many training sessions in psychiatry and professionalism for counselors, physicians, psychotherapists and other therapists, all of them people who help others professionally and are always looking for new approaches in their work with clients who are burned out. At the same time, these therapists are at high risk of burnout themselves. In addition to insights, this book offers concrete suggestions for better understanding and counseling people with burnout. The exercises can be used in practice and may, I hope, inspire readers to develop their own variations and new exercises.

The examples interspersed throughout the text describe real people and their struggles with stress and burnout. They can be followed through the book in their process of recovery. These real-life stories give the theory a face, and you might recognize yourself in others who are going through something you are experiencing if you are burned out yourself. For people who are working as professionals with burnout clients, the examples offer possibilities to identify with situations and provide guidelines for therapeutic support.

What follows is a brief description of how this book is organized so that you can easily find your way through the chapters. At the back of the book is an index of the case studies presented throughout the text.

PART 1, *Burning to Ashes*, describes in Chapter 1 what the experience of burnout is like and gives a first review of the societal and personal context.

In Chapter 2 the symptoms of burnout are described on four levels: (1) What are typical physical symptoms and ailments? (2) How is your vital energy affected and what are the consequences? (3) What psychological changes are witnessed? (4) Finally, how does burnout affect the capacity to set your own course in life? Burnout is also compared to other complaints of fatigue.

PART 2, *Fuel for the Fire*, describes the underlying causes of burnout from a broad perspective. You may read this whole part or select the chapters that are relevant to your particular situation. You may also choose to skip Part 2 for now and go on to Part 3 to discover how you can work on recovery and do the exercises in Part 4. You can then return to the "preconditions" chapter when you feel better.

Chapter 3, *Your Work: Does It Energize You or Burn You Out?* takes a look at work and the factors that either increase your risk of getting burned out or, conversely, tend to protect you from it. In certain professions and under certain conditions, for example job restructuring, you run more risk of getting burned out; however, the organization of your work, your position in the company, and the company's management style are important factors in the creation of either stress or enjoyment in the workplace. In this chapter we also examine the importance of support and solidarity among colleagues and the consequences of harassment and trauma at work. We also discuss the protection of your boundaries between personal life and work.

In Chapter 4, *Complex Interactions between Brain and Body*, the biological processes that support stress regulation and their disturbance in people living chronically under stress are described systematically. This chapter demonstrates how, through several neurological and hormonal circuits, our brain serves our physical and psychological well-being and how our conscious and unconscious processes influence each other. The active and balancing role of the heart in stress regulation is examined, as are the reasons why chronic stress diminishes our resistance to negative outside influences.

Chapters 5, 6, 7 and 8 deal with factors within us that contribute to burnout, such as natural predispositions, habits, psychological processes and motivation. Chapter 5, *Failing Vitality*, describes the life body as the carrier of our vitality. How is our life energy strengthened or undermined? How do personality differences influence vital energy, and how can you protect and strengthen yourself?

Chapter 6, *Soul Life*, is about psychological factors leading to burnout. What is the role of our personality? How do old patterns work in new situations and what role do such fixed patterns play in burnout? We can view our personality as built up from partial personalities or "selves" consisting of certain character traits, feelings and behavior. They each have their own energy and play their own role in our inner and outer life. These part-personalities have different, often contradictory voices in our psyche. This chapter describes, in a playful manner, a number of dominant soul traits that frequently occur in people with burnout, as well as "selves" in us that lead a repressed and neglected existence. You get to know them in such a way that you can begin to pick up their voices in yourself. This will not only help you understand yourself better, but you will also become able to make more conscious choices and keep a better balance between your inner life and the demands of the world around you.

Chapter 7, *Setting Your Course in Life*, deals with the "I," the inner authority that, as the director of our biography, manages and guides the soul and the life force. Human development is not possible without a balance between change and adaptation, between ideals and a sense of reality. Our capacity for reflection and self-reflection enables us to find our own direction. Inner motivation and creativity form a source of life energy here. If that source dries up, the result is cynicism and indifference, and you run more risk of burnout.

Burnout is not just something related to your work; your home life may also be an important factor. Chapter 8 is focused on *Personal Circumstances Influencing Burnout*. It deals with problems and habits at home that undermine vitality and phases in our biography that create risks of burnout.

Chapter 9, *An Emancipated Woman Is Not a Man*, was written especially for women. Burnout happens more often to women than to men. Why is that? We explore the biological, psychological and social differences between men and women. We also look at cultural changes and the demands on working women. We briefly discuss the effects of stress on unborn children.

Chapter 10, *If You Are Not Busy, You Are Not Important*, concludes Part 2. It reviews the cultural patterns, customs and expectations we live with. What are the consequences of stress regulation for our lifestyle, in which we constantly need to stay informed and available at all times? And what are the consequences of increasing fear and anxiety for our peace of mind? What are the effects of screen culture (the TV, computer, tablet, cell phone), and what is the influence of stressed parents and teachers on children on the one hand, and of stressed children on parents and teachers on the other?

In PART 3, *Rising up out of Ashes*, the emphasis is on recovery and prevention. When you realize that you are overstressed and don't want to get burned out, how can you then work toward recovery? What can you change in yourself so you stay healthy? To what extent can you influence your work and home situations so they become less exhausting? How can you keep your enthusiasm for what you are doing and, at the same time, protect your boundaries? How can you keep your balance in little everyday ways? This part includes three interviews in which experienced therapists give their personal views from different angles on working with people with burnout.

Chapter 11, *Getting Better Step by Step*, goes into the general principles of recovery and the role of a good coach in this process.

Chapter 12, *Life Forces: Nourishment, Boundaries, Protection*, focuses on restoration of vitality and the qualities needed for it, such as healthy rhythms, meaningful movements, and nourishing inner images.

Chapter 13, *The Soul: Finding a New State of Balance*, is about learning to handle stress and dealing more consciously with our different selves. By entering into conversation with your inner selves, you will learn to become less dependent on all kinds of situations and people outside yourself.

Chapter 14, *In Search of Your Own Motivation*, is about retrieving your own direction and autonomy in life, and about the art of integrating these in your own (working) life.

Chapter 15, *Burnout as Challenge for Change*, outlines the process for going back to work and preventing another burnout.

PART 4 consists of exercises that correspond to the previous chapters. By doing the exercises you will put the content of this book into practice. The different types of exercises are also very useful when you are on the path of recovery and contemplating the future, as well as for the prevention of burnout. You don't need to do all of them; simply pick the ones that appeal to you and that you find promising.

At the beginning of Chapter 16, *The Ingredients of the Exercises*, you will find questions that will help you determine the extent of your burnout. And you'll be able to use basic exercises, such as grounding, visualizing and observing, to develop a lifestyle that offers more balance and less stress. There is also an exercise to help you actively relax.

The exercises in Chapter 17, *Observing Yourself*, are intended for self-examination. Learn how to observe yourself and your stress at work and at home. This kind of exercise will help you notice how your body and soul react to different situations. By registering what you think, feel and do, and by more consciously perceiving how you react to situations at work and at home, you will discover what causes stress and what relaxes you. In this way you can become more conscious of your own lifestyle and make new choices that enable you to find a balance between your capacities, needs and character on the one hand, and the demands of your work and surroundings on the other.

Chapter 18 contains *Exercises Focused on the Life Forces* that are helpful in acquiring a more relaxed lifestyle. These exercises and suggestions will help you strengthen your vitality, sleep better, and nourish yourself with healthy images.

Chapter 19, *Exercises Focused on the Soul*, contains exercises for the soul and the inner selves that live there. These are of a rather exploratory nature; they aim to develop more insight into unconscious motives and fixed patterns from the past that contribute to a lifestyle involving too much stress. What keeps you from taking good care of yourself? To what degree are you run by forces outside yourself? What expectations of yourself and of others put you over the edge? How can you learn to let yourself make mistakes and stop brooding? What roles do your inner children play?

Chapter 20 presents exercises to help you find your own course again and stick to it. How can you stand more positively in life and connect with what you are doing in the here and now? Also included is an explanation of meditation.

In Chapter 21 you'll find several short First Aid For Stress exercises that are easy to practice daily and will help reduce your stress levels.

PART 1

Burning to Ashes:
What Is Happening?

"Good morning. Why have you just put out your lamp?"

"Those are the orders," replied the lamplighter. "Good morning."

"What are the orders?"

"The orders are that I put out my lamp. Good evening."

And he lighted his lamp again.

"But why have you just lighted it again?"

"Those are the orders," replied the lamplighter.

"I do not understand," said the little prince.

"There is nothing to understand," said the lamplighter. "Orders are orders. Good morning."

And he put out his lamp.

Then he mopped his forehead with a handkerchief decorated with red squares.

"I have a terrible profession. In the old days it was reasonable. I put the lamp out in the morning, and in the evening I lighted it again. I had the rest of the day for relaxation and the rest of the night for sleep."

"And the orders have been changed since that time?"

"The orders have not been changed," said the lamplighter. "That is the tragedy! From year to year the planet has turned more rapidly and the orders have not been changed!"

"Then what?" asked the little prince.

"Then—the planet now makes a complete turn every minute, and I no longer have a single second for repose. Once every minute I have to light my lamp and put it out!"[1]

---

1 Antoine de Saint-Exupéry, *The Little Prince*, New York, 1943.

1 Burnout: Burned up and run down

Burnout is a stress disease that is often related to overload at work; but situations in private life can also lead to burnout. Caretakers and teachers run a higher than average risk of burnout, especially if their work is combined with family obligations or caring for relatives. If you recognize the symptoms of excessive stress in time, and take adequate measures, you can avoid much suffering. For this reason, this is a book of exercises not only for people who are recovering from burnout, but also for those who are experiencing chronic stress overload. This book describes the preconditions and precursors to burnout, and provides exercises that will help you clearly perceive your situation and manage the hectic circumstances of your life in a more relaxed way.

1.1 What is burnout?

Burnout is a serious and long-lasting condition of exhaustion. A person with burnout has both physical and psychological symptoms. Frequent colds and flu, muscle pains, lowered resistance, digestive problems, headaches, stomachaches, and decreased libido may occur in the run-up to burnout. Great fatigue, reduced power of concentration and decreased ability to organize are accompanied by a feeling of dejection. Self-esteem becomes fragile and vulnerable.

Burnout is a slow, drawn-out process. From prolonged excessive stress and lack of relaxation, the balance in life is upset, vital processes are disturbed, and psychological equilibrium becomes fragile. Slowly but surely, the body itself is undermined. Recovery takes place slowly, and frequently the previous level of energy doesn't come back. Even people who normally glow with a zest for life and self-confidence can burn out. The cause often lies in years of faulty stress management.

The experience of burnout is a major personal crisis. People experiencing burnout may no longer recognize themselves; they may think they are going crazy or feel completely exhausted. Their lowered resistance and general distress are demoralizing and may lead to fear of physical deterioration. Psychological instability and the inability to cope reinforce feelings of being helplessly out of control. The mechanisms that used to help "get over things" don't work any longer. Self-image is affected.

1.2 Burnout and stress

Positive and Negative Stress

Excessive stress, but also a lack of any tension, have a negative influence on our moods, our energy and our performance. Positive stress is the kind of tension that helps us concentrate and focus fully on a task, allowing us to be and do our best. Positive stress occurs, for instance, when we have an important exam, when we have to write an article with a fixed deadline, or right before an important event or appearance. You charge yourself up for the best possible performance; a certain amount of tension comes with that, just as the bow has to be drawn for the arrow to fly.

In the case of negative stress, there is so much distress that concentration becomes impossible, you lose control of your nerves, and the capacity to perform declines as a result. Because of nervousness you don't pay enough attention to the exam questions and give a wrong answer, you forget your lines in a play, or the dreaded deadline causes so much stress that you can't write anymore. Similarly, chronic stress also undermines performance, for instance if you always have too much to do, have to function beyond your ability, or work too many hours a day without time to properly recover.

However, when we are not sufficiently challenged, when life is boring and the pace too slow, or if there is not enough potential for development, our inner state of balance is undermined and eventually we lose all motivation to perform. This happens, for instance, to gifted children when they are constantly bored in class, or to a creative worker stuck in a dull office job.

Persistent negative stress undermines the inner state of balance and, eventually, also the biological balance that forms the basis for a healthy soul life. The optimum level of stress necessary for good performance varies from person to person. What for one person is still a comfortable tension may be unbearable for another; what seems to you like a reasonable work atmosphere may be too fast or slow for a coworker. Constantly being hurried along by your boss, parents or partner can result in negative stress, but so can a dull, uninspiring home or work environment. If the bow is always drawn too tight, it will lead to burnout; if it's too loose, it is more likely to lead to depression or dropping out.

1.3   Is burnout a disease of our culture?

Yes! Burnout is a typical disease of our culture with its hectic pace, its emphasis on cerebral work, and few moments for recharging, rest and introspection. Studies have shown that in up to eighty percent of stressed-out people, work situations are to blame. But even without scientific studies we all know that it is considered the norm always to be busy, and that many people constantly feel tired and often even exhausted. Evidently, burnout has to do not only with individual work situations, but also with the mind-set of our time, the structures of our organizations, and the demands of our culture as a whole.

The concept of burnout as we now know it was first used in 1974 by the American psychiatrist Herbert Freudenberger, when he described exhaustion in young, idealistic caretakers in an alternative clinic for drug addicts and psychiatric patients.[2] He was the first to do systematic research into burnout, and since then hundreds of articles and many books about burnout and stress have appeared, often based on the authors' own experiences or focused on particular groups. Workers in people-oriented professions such as education, health care and personal services are particularly vulnerable to burnout, but executives and politicians are also at risk.[3] There is no doubt that the phenomenon of burnout not only has an impact on the individual, but it also has serious consequences in society and the economy. People who can't work due to burnout see their incomes reduced; disability payments go up; and those who help diagnose and treat burnout see their incomes increase.

---

2 Herbert J. Freudenberger, "Staff Burnout," in: *Journal of Social Issues* 60, 1974, 159–165.
3 Compared with other professions, burnout occurs most frequently in education. One study showed that more than 13% of teachers develop burnout.

1.4 Burnout as personal crisis

At the individual level, burnout is a personal crisis that brings suffering with it and a struggle with life circumstances, ideals and capacities. But it is also a learning process that eventually can lead to a deepening and enrichment of life. It creates a necessity to take a fresh look at life and reconsider choices made. It can lead to new directions for our lives, whether at work or at home, that are a better match for us in terms of goals, ideals and abilities and are less determined by outside factors. In this way a period of burnout also opens a potential for personal growth and the achievement of greater autonomy as a human being.

1.5 Burnout: The balance disturbed

Every healthy organism maintains a state of equilibrium between building up and breaking down. This is true of great ecosystems such as the ocean and primeval forests, but also for the human body and the human being as a social being. Just as the problems for the ecosystem of overfishing at sea or cutting down trees in primeval forests become visible only after a certain time, human beings may also live for a long time under breakdown conditions and use up their constructive forces without being aware of it. The many examples in this book bear witness to this.

Replenishing and building up our energy happens when we take care of ourselves, and in a balanced situation, this will counteract life's destructive effects. In itself, breaking down is a necessary process that belongs to an active life. But in many areas of modern life, there is an excess of breakdown processes. The chart on the next two pages outlines constructive and destructive processes.

Our health depends on effectively functioning life forces, which depend on the balance between building up and breaking down. Cultural factors and our situations at work and at home have inter- acting roles in this balance. When you burn out, you are in the final stages of a process that has been going on for years, in which breakdown has outpaced buildup. Because stress builds up only gradually, you become used to it; the feeling of fatigue seems normal, and symptoms of exhaustion are therefore not so noticeable. Moreover, people who

The Balance between Building up and Breaking down

Buildup	Balance	Breakdown
Nourishing and constructive impressions, e.g., beauty of architecture and residential surroundings, nature. Activities engendering inner pictures such as reading, musing, making music, listening to stories.	**Impressions**	Sensory overload: noise, visual stimuli, stench, ugly buildings, too much TV, computer, radio. Images and sounds in which the spectator or listener is passive.
Alternation between activity and rest. Time for recovery. Sufficient rhythm and predictability in your life.	**Action/Rest**	Physical overload. Chaos at work and at home. Irregular times and places for sleep, meals and work. Insufficient time to recover.
Active interest in and time for things other than work and chores: sports, music, gardening, literature, etc.	**Relaxation/ Tension**	No activities besides work and chores. Constant pressure from outside. Unresolved tension and frustration at work and/or in pesonal life.
Sufficient time for sleep. Good quality sleep.	**Sleeping/Waking**	Chronic shortage of sleep, disturbed sleep, waking up, frequent nightmares.
Right quantity and good quality of nutrition, restful time to eat and digest.	**Eating and Digesting**	Too little too much, too hurried, unhealthy food, irregular mealtimes.
Living quarters and work environments in which you feel safe and comfortable.	**Home and Workplace**	Living where you don't feel safe or at home. Unhealthy, threatening or dull workplace.
Sufficient meaningful movement.	**Movement**	Repetitive mechanical motions, or being passive while moving through a stressful environment, e.g., in a car in heavy traffic.
Active wonder[4] and enjoyment in encounters with nature and/or culture.	**Wonder/Fear/ Alertness**	A constant stream of negative and alarming news. The need to be constantly alert, e.g., to survive in traffic.

---

4 See Chapter 20, exercise 20.6.

Buildup	Balance	Breakdown
Meaningful work in which you can grow and develop yourself.	Work	Work that exhausts and overloads you, or work that is dull and monotonous.
Good, loving relationships with partner, children, relatives, friends and colleagues.	Relationships	Tension in family relationships; criticism, quarrels, bullying.
Encouragement, support and constructive feedback from people around you.	Social Support	Destructive criticism and lack of support and appreciation from the people around you.
Inner motivation for your daily tasks. Looking forward to the things you have to do.	Motivation	Lack of interest in what you have to do.
Reflecting with regularity on yourself and your situation.	Reflection	Taking no time to reflect on yourself and your situation.
The feeling that you are a good director of your own life.	Direction	Too little control over processes in which you are closely involved. Chronic feeling of falling short and fear that nothing is ever finished.
Experiencing yourself as capable. The feeling of being able to handle the tasks you are assigned.	Self-Esteem	Experiencing powerlessness and chronic overload in a work or personal situation.
Contentment with what and who you are while also seeing a goal to live toward, potential for inner growth.	Contentment	Having to satisfy social-cultural norms such as performance, career, expectation of staying "young, pretty and nice."
Daily moments of living in the here and now, full attention for what you are doing. Regular times for meditation.	Attention/Worry	Constant worrying, regrets, looking back. Being prey to concerns, e.g., finances, illness of yourself and others, insecurity about work and colleagues.

burn out have a tendency to systematically ignore and deny all signs of overload. They don't want to fail; they want to look strong. As a result, the balance is upset more and more.

Burnout is thus more a process than a static condition. Because mutually reinforcing symptoms of overload develop at different levels, we witness a vicious cycle: increasing stress to perform, more time at work and less time off, resulting in more stress and making it ever harder to jump off the merry-go-round. As you gradually get used to the chronic dejection and fatigue, you increasingly realize you can't keep going this way.

The first complaints are generally about loss of vitality and growing fatigue, which no longer respond to the usual amount of rest and relaxation. Like expanding circles in water, physical complaints and inner unease occupy an ever-growing place in daily life.

Early warning signals may include increased irritability, anxiety, disillusionment at work, and anger at coworkers. Burnout may also announce itself in an actual physical illness such as mononucleosis, thyroid problems, heart attack, hernia, and others. Because people with burnout are usually enormously energetic, they tend to never give up. Instead, they feel shame at their lack of initiative and apparent weakness and strive ever harder to live up to the image they've set for themselves. Instead of noticing how they feel and taking seriously the signs of fatigue and impending breakdown, people caught in the vicious cycle just tend to work more and harder. In the end this leads to total exhaustion, not only of their vitality, but of their physical resistance and psychological resilience, so that life loses all meaning.

EXAMPLE 1

Charles is a 45-year-old biologist who comes in for consultation with a psychologist at the urging of his girlfriend. He looks pale and tense, and he speaks fast and with bitterness. Charles has worked for 10 years for a travel agency that organizes special ecological trips. Until a year ago, he was able to be pretty much his own boss and always enjoyed his work. Especially the interaction with customers and the preparation and guiding of tours appealed to him, and he wholeheartedly devoted himself to these things. In the last year and a half, however, after the company was taken over by a larger organization with a more business-like and efficient approach, there has been a lot of unrest, discord and change.

For Charles this has meant fitting himself into a strictly managed department supervised by a young boss with whom he often disagrees. His coworkers, too, feel uncertain about their positions. While there used to be an easygoing atmosphere at work, now everyone is tense and irritated. An increasing number of employees have quit or have become sick. Despite all of this, Charles tried to be loyal for a long time. In the beginning of the reorganization he worked extremely hard; he participated in endless meetings with colleagues to develop new plans. But to his great disappointment, management paid no attention to the experienced employees and nothing came of all the plans. His former manager supports Charles in private conversations, but can't do anything openly against the new boss. As it has worked out, he now has to do work he considers far beneath his capacities, and has to account for every little mistake he makes.

Three weeks ago Charles made a stupid mistake in the planning of a tour. When that became known, his new boss, justified or not, started to make demeaning comments in the presence of others. To his own horror, Charles then burst into tears and went home in a panic.

Since then he has been at home sick. He feels completely exhausted as if he has just finished a marathon. He sits around like a useless bum or stares at the television. Reading the newspaper or a book is impossible; he can't even manage some shopping or cooking. Charles regularly has violent heart palpitations that frighten him, and for months already he has had a headache that comes up from the neck and for which he takes painkillers almost daily. He is startled at every sudden sound and in the relationship with his girlfriend, he is irritated at every little thing and often explodes in rage.

Although Charles emphasizes that he really likes his work, after all that has happened he feels deeply undervalued. He is raging mad at both his old boss and his new boss. When he talks about them, he gets highly excited and gets red spots on his neck.

After several live-in relationships, Charles now lives alone. For about the past five years he has been in a relationship with a woman with a 12-year-old son with whom he doesn't get along well.

EXAMPLE 2

Rosanna is 36. Pale and sad, she slumps in a chair and drinks one cup of coffee after another. She is the mother of three children aged seven, five and two. She views her life as a disaster—it can't go on this way. In the past few months everything has been too much for her; the smallest things irritate her unreasonably, and she can suddenly explode in anger, which is not like her at all.

After the birth of her third child, now more than two years ago, she has been unable to get her life back on track. Even though she says she does not work much—just a weekend now and then—she still can't seem to give her children the attention they need.

Rosanna feels angry and frustrated. At a young age she had a lot of responsibility for the community where she lived and worked in the beginning of her marriage; she played a leading role there, and now she can't even manage a regular family!

Six years ago, after a difference of opinion on the management of the community regarding policies and compensation, she and her husband Dan left the community and settled in a house in another part of the country. Dan found a job in psychiatry and Rosanna a part-time job in a daycare for handicapped children. Shortly thereafter she became pregnant with their second child, and it proved impossible to carry out their earlier plan, which was for them both to work part-time and share the care of their children. Dan kept working full-time, and Rosanna gave up her job. She is determined to give her children a warmer childhood than she had herself. To help pay the mortgage she is still on call for a few evening and weekend shifts per month in childcare.

Rosanna thinks she is a very bad mother. She constantly has the nagging feeling that she is shortchanging her children, and she worries about them. She doesn't feel at home in the bare, brand-new development where they live and misses the social interaction with colleagues and friends that comes with living in a community. She has little contact with her own family, and, because Dan's parents live far away, they cannot come and help.

She can rarely sleep through the night, because her eldest son wakes up terrified several times a night and calls her. At school they say he is maladjusted; he flies into a rage and behaves aggressively toward other children. They are considering seeing a child psychiatrist because of possible autism. All of this makes Rosanna very fearful. She has the constant feeling that she is failing in her duties, but she doesn't know how she can change.

For months all she has been able to manage is cooking, doing laundry, caring for the children, and sometimes a weekend shift. No matter how hard she works, the list of things to do grows longer all the time; the children look tired and quarrel with each other. Rosanna has an almost constant stomachache. She forgets engagements with friends and sometimes has to go back to a store three times because she forgets to buy what she needs. In the evening she is restless and takes a few glasses of wine to be able to sleep. She is afraid that some day she will "do something" to hurt herself or a child.

Dan, who works irregular shifts, complains that he doesn't feel comfortable at home anymore because the house is so dreary and messy. He misses Rosanna's jokes and banter and would like to do fun things with her, the way they used to. Since then Rosanna has made extra efforts to keep things neat and tidy. She worries that if things are not nice at home, Dan might start a relationship with someone else.

Rosanna is ashamed of feeling unhappy and lonely in her new role. Because of the problems with her eldest child and her worries about herself, she feels less and less equal to the tasks that are demanded of her.

In the next chapter we will discuss typical burnout complaints such as those of Charles and Rosanna.

2 Exhaustion on different levels

Burnout hits you on different levels. You may have physical complaints and irregularities, your life forces are exhausted, and your emotions are disturbed. Managing your life gets harder and harder; your self-esteem crashes and you have growing doubts about your own capabilities. In this chapter these four levels of complaints are identified and elaborated:

– *1st level:* warning signs in the body
– *2nd level:* exhaustion
– *3rd level:* emotional upset
– *4th level:* loss of self-direction and motivation

2.1 Warning signs in the body

EXAMPLE 3

Charles's physical condition and resistance to illness have been declining for quite some time. He lies awake at night for a long time and cannot fall asleep again. Often he doesn't get out of bed half the weekend because he feels dead tired. He had the flu three times last year.

Negative stress worsens our physical condition, which shows up in a range of symptoms and decreasing immunity to illness. Although none of these warning signs specifically indicate burnout, they almost always occur—as they did with Charles and Rosanna—during the year or years preceding a total breakdown. Lack of immunity, greater susceptibility to catching the flu and colds, and recurring infections are often the first signs. But you may also be troubled by dizzy spells, migraines, lack of appetite, stomachaches, overeating or low blood sugar (hypoglycemia). Increased tension may lead to muscle and joint pains, tension headaches, stomachaches and back pain. Heart palpitations, hyperventilation and high blood pressure may also be signs of overload. A common reaction is to take more and more painkillers, muscle relaxers, heartburn remedies, blood pressure and other medications instead of taking care that you get enough rest, healthy movement and reflection. As shown by the examples of Liz and Chris (below), burnout may also start with an illness that never quite goes away.

EXAMPLE 4

Liz, a 43-year-old experienced secretary, has always been healthy and a hard worker. She lives alone and has many friends and relatives whom she likes to visit. Her complaints began when it appeared that her way of working did not correspond to that of her new boss. She always had to do things differently from the way she used to do them, with the result that her work was not completed. That led to irritated comments. Liz's coworker, whom she liked a lot, couldn't deal with the new situation and quit. The coworker's replacement was someone Liz did not like at all, but she tried to make the best of it.

Over the past year Liz had a lot of colds, which lasted longer than they used to. At night she would lie awake for hours worrying about the conflicts with her boss. In her mind she often had angry disputes with her colleague and her boss. During the day she kept a low profile, swallowed all frustration, but often had a headache when she went home. In the morning she would get up nauseous with the result that she could not eat a normal breakfast. She would feel exhausted and keep herself awake with coffee.

Finally Liz got a serious flu that turned into pneumonia. She took antibiotics and wanted to go back to work after a week, but instead of feeling better after a few days, she was hit by unbearable fatigue. Her body continued to feel heavy and weak; she often felt something like muscle ache although she did next to nothing. After a month Liz couldn't walk a hundred yards without being totally exhausted.

EXAMPLE 5

Chris is a 57-year-old lawyer. After he was given a new management position three years ago, he began having more and more headaches. He would wake up early and could not fall asleep again. His condition deteriorated; after a short bicycle ride he was dead tired. He constantly had little infected injuries and he caught every cold in his vicinity which all lasted much longer than before. Eventually he developed diarrhea, accompanied by constant nausea and little appetite.

None of this, however, led him to see a doctor or take life a bit easier. On the contrary, he was irritated at being less productive in his work and he often took work home to get it finished. One weekend in January, to please his son, Chris went skating with him. But he fell and tore a knee ligament, resulting in his having to stay home at length to recover. Then suddenly a crushing fatigue descended on him, and he realized that he was at the end of his rope.

2.2 Exhaustion

Fatigue

Most of the time, people will feel increasing fatigue for months, even years. The time available for relaxation and rest—whether it is the lunch break, the weekend or a vacation—is no longer enough. In the morning you get up tired, and you get used to starting the work week tired. Your condition gets worse and, after a short bike ride or walk, a person who used to be energetic may be dead tired. More and more you feel that you're dragging yourself around, until everything feels like too much and you can no longer find the time for anything relaxing or enjoyable. You only have energy left for what absolutely has to be done.

EXAMPLE 6

Rosanna continually feels tired. When she has a chance—which is seldom—she will sleep for 10 hours, but she still never wakes up rested. She has exhausting dreams, for instance that she is folding towels all night which then fall on a dirty floor so that she has to start from scratch. During the day she may sit staring into space for hours, as if sleeping with her eyes open—and then suddenly an hour has gone by without her noticing it. She never takes initiative any more; life feels like a treadmill.

EXAMPLE 7

Malika is a 31-year-old manager in a publishing house. She describes how her burnout started: "I not only felt like a stretched rubber band, but also like a dried-out rubber band, you know, that will break if you touch it. I woke up during the night, and I had furious nightmares on the theme of death and being torn to pieces. During the day I regularly dozed off. Once I was home I just liked to read trash novels or watch videos, but I had hardly enough concentration to follow the plots. Getting up in the morning, getting dressed, doing household chores, preparing meals and all the common tasks I used to do so easily besides work, all went slowly, laboriously and without structure. I no longer had the energy to visit friends or do something nice; I felt lonely and abandoned.

Sleep Disturbances

In burnout we almost always witness sleep problems and the resulting further deterioration of inner stability. The causes may be external, as in the case of Rosanna who is constantly awakened by her son, or internal, as in the case of Liz, who lies awake for hours worrying hopelessly about her work situation. You might also have no trouble falling asleep but, like Malika, wake up again after a short time or, like Chris, wake up very early and not be able to get back to sleep. Pain in the back, joints or muscles may also keep you from sleeping.

Frequently, as in the cases of Rosanna, Malika and Charles, you might experience violent nightmares or dreams depicting your exhaustion, for example the scorched foundations of a burned-down house, a sinking ship, getting lost in the forest, or falling into a deep abyss. Such dreams evoke great fear because they are images of the inner situation which is kept out of consciousness during the day. Because of sleeping badly and the resulting increased fatigue, a feeling may arise of living in a kind of twilight state between waking and sleeping in which such pictures may also arise during the daytime.

EXAMPLE 8

Charles sleeps very badly. He has constant nightmares of being chased by big dogs trying to bite off his hands. When he tries to escape, the road is full of potholes he falls into. He also dreams repeatedly that his childhood home is on fire. When he tries to put out the fire, he discovers that the bucket he's using has a hole and all the water has leaked out. He wakes up screaming with a pounding heart and doesn't dare fall asleep again.

Increased Irritation

Exhaustion also shows in over-sensitivity and irritation, "a short fuse." Loud noises will hurt the ear, small incidents may cause excessive fright. To the gentlest critical remark you respond in anger while normally you would have accepted it with more understanding. This process is often noticed by family members and colleagues before the person himself becomes aware of it. Because people who become burned out usually emphatically deny it, remarks like this increase their feeling of being stuck and lead to violent anger and continued vehement denials.

Forgetfulness and Problems Concentrating

Gradually it gets increasingly difficult to focus on something you're reading, on a conversation you're having, on your job, or even on traffic as you're driving. You forget important appointments. All this makes it even harder to pretend you're still in control and leads to an increased likelihood of misjudgments, mistakes and accidents. This is how Charles made a mistake at work and how Chris caught his skate in a crack in the ice and was badly injured.

Together with reduced concentration, efficiency and productivity, this results in the feeling of working harder and harder for less and less outcome. The automatic pilot then takes over more and more with its routine behavior and habits. This further aggravates the feeling of falling short and the fear of making mistakes. All remaining strength is used to keep control over the situation at all cost.

EXAMPLE 9

In the year before she became burned out, Johanna, a 34-year-old psychiatric social worker, had the feeling of never being sufficiently rested. In spite of great fatigue by day, she could not fall asleep and often didn't close her eyes all night long. She would lie there worrying about her work and other problems and was unable to set those aside. At the clinic, in direct contact with patients she could function all right, but when she had to write a report, she would sit at her desk at home for hours laboring without result. She forgot appointments, and when people reacted angrily, she became very anxious. At home her head was full of whirling thoughts: "I couldn't even read the newspaper anymore because I couldn't relate to what it said; the letters and words were merely little black things without meaning and connection."

Screens, Alcohol and Drugs as Life Support

In the period preceding burnout, people will use all kinds of artificial means to keep doing their work and relax a bit in their leisure time. When you can no longer concentrate enough to read, slumping in front of the television or surfing the internet can be a pleasant diversion. During the day, more and more coffee, candy and cigarettes can help you stay awake; in the evening you can slow down your racing motor with one drink after another, and you'll finally need pills to help you sleep.

EXAMPLE 10

Eric is a 49-year-old history teacher at a large high school. He feels dead tired. He doesn't feel rested after summer vacation, and is a couch potato watching TV in the evening. He doesn't manage to prepare his lessons for the next day; stacks of student reports are lying unread on his desk. To be able to sleep he needs a couple of glasses of wine, although he rarely used to drink. At four in the morning he wakes and lies there until seven, when he really should get up; but he's so tired and stiff and cold that he dawdles, resulting in a mad, last-minute rush with no time for breakfast. At school it takes a big cup of coffee to wake him up, followed by five more over the course of the day.

Exhausted, Malika zones out in front of the television, although she is usually interested in what is happening in the world and reads substantive books. It takes her ever more effort to accomplish the ordinary daily things in life and to keep going. At night she drinks half a bottle of wine before she can fall asleep. If that doesn't suffice, a few sleeping pills will help. In the morning she takes Tylenol and a big cup of coffee to fight the headache she always wakes up with.

The Breakdown

Though other people may have seen it coming for a long time, for the person in burnout, the final breakdown usually happens from one day to the next. As for Charles and Rosanna, the immediate cause is often some little thing, like criticism from a colleague or partner, or upon return to work after a period of illness or vacation.

EXAMPLE 12
Rosanna goes to see her doctor because of her recurring stomachaches. The doctor says Rosanna is overworked and prescribes antidepressants, massage and psychotherapy. Rosanne comes home in a panic because this makes her feel even worse. She wants no pills and can't imagine how, with all the other things she has to do, she can find time for her own therapy. Then Dan tells her that he won't be able to do as much in the family; because of the illness of a colleague, he will have to work more, also on weekends. At that moment Rosanna totally panics. She throws a stack of dirty dishes on the floor and runs out of the house. It is raining and cold. She hides in a barn and lies there crying for hours. Finally, Dan finds her and calls 911.

EXAMPLE 13
During the day Eric has little energy; he continually feels cold, as if the wind is blowing right through him. In his classes, things are disorderly; the children are restless and listen badly. Shortly before spring break he forgets an appointment with parents to plan a field trip and doesn't show up at an important meeting because he forgot about that too. He gets more and more angry comments from colleagues, and the children complain that he doesn't correct their work. In lieu of saying they are right, he flies into a rage, which doesn't improve the atmosphere in the classroom.

At home his wife upbraids him for doing nothing. She is worried about his sudden heavy drinking. When his daughter asks him to set up a lamp for her, he promises to do it but keeps putting it off.

After a vacation Eric drives to school and is suddenly overcome by a wave of disgust for everything having to do with the place. Having parked his car, he panics, gets back behind the wheel and drives away, not caring where he ends up.

2.3 Emotional upset

Dullness and Emptiness

Everything in life seems dull, and you feel drained and flat, as if your feelings were smothered under a heavy blanket. You first notice this at home, during your time off, on weekends or vacations: You're having trouble enjoying anything. Meanwhile in the structured workplace setting, you can still keep up the pace.

As the pressure increases, you start to skip the very things that could help you relax: sports, taking a rest, or going out for an evening. You are more and more dominated by the tense feeling that you don't even have time to do all your work, let alone relax. Anything that's not in the line of duty gets moved to the end of the list. What used to give you pleasure—a simple conversation, making plans or doing something nice together—is just too much work. What you used to do enthusiastically you now do indifferently, which undermines your relationships with your partner and your children.

More and more, life is dominated by negative thoughts in which feelings of bottomless emptiness, despair and failure stand out. It becomes more difficult to separate work from private life; thoughts about frustrations at work are pushing into your time at home.

EXAMPLE 14

Joan, mother of two adolescents, is 47 when she faces burnout. She has always been an enthusiastic high school teacher. Normally she feels at ease in front of the class and can identify with the situations of the students. But after last summer's vacation, she didn't feel rested and, to her surprise, wasn't looking forward to the new school year. Now it is November and she feels inwardly a dull, gray fog. Her husband and sons complain that she is always sullen and doesn't laugh anymore. She no longer takes any initiative. She doesn't feel like going out, having a good conversation or making love. Every day is like a treadmill; adjusting to any change takes a lot out of her.

Gloomy Feelings and Thoughts

Constant stress and fatigue, combined with the feeling that you're not getting anything done, lead to dark thoughts about yourself, your job, your life and your future, as they did for Charles and Rosanna. Particularly if conditions at work are not good, if you are criticized or harassed by colleagues and get no support, self-confidence will start eroding and you get more and more the feeling of being a victim of circumstances. For that reason, burnout is often considered as a work-related depression. Feelings of powerlessness vis-à-vis a supervisor, the organization or management, or the inability to change the situation are things we often witness in the year before someone burns out.

Workaholic and Inner Unrest

In spite of growing fatigue, your inner motor revs up faster and faster until it runs wild in a crazy dance of whirling thoughts and fruitless worrying. Inner monologues, dialogues, self-criticism and anger at coworkers and managers go round and round with no resolution. Your behavior is also out of control. "Why don't you sit down and take it easy? You are making me crazy," Joan's son tells her, as she keeps jumping up to take care of little things instead of just enjoying a quiet cup of tea. This is obsessive unrest; you simply can't sit still anymore. Criticism from family members, however, leads to irritation and anger. Strangely enough, out of unease with their situation, people on the way to burnout often undertake something new, for instance, a new study or renovating the house.

EXAMPLE 15

Liz, the secretary, says: "For months before I fell ill, I felt like a chicken without a head at home. I walked aimlessly back and forth and did five things at once, but at the same time the house was a mess. I couldn't manage to just sit down and center myself. I was worrying day and night. It felt like a fast revolving centrifuge of thoughts over which I had lost all control."

Alternating Violent Emotions

Besides the dull undertone in your feeling life, often there is also an excess of emotions flaring up at the least provocation; you lose your temper with every claim or request due to the idea that it will be one more thing you have to do. You feel that no one understands or appreciates you, and can't manage anymore to resolve irritations and conflicts in a sensible conversation. Things like sudden noises or an unexpected traffic jam cause unreasonable fear and fright. You are highly sensitive and burst into tears at the slightest provocation; a moment later you feel terrible about your overblown response and try to make up for it. But also the ability to set ordinary boundaries, at work or for growing children, becomes more difficult; giving in takes less energy than saying no.

This creates an unstable atmosphere that causes tension in partner and children which, in turn, further enhances the risk of conflicts. In your dealings with coworkers, too, your irritability makes misunderstandings and disagreements more likely. Reflection on your own behavior, which requires a certain measure of inner quiet, becomes next to impossible. This reinforces the feeling that everyone is against you and out to get you.

EXAMPLE 16

Joan exclaims to her husband: "Don't ask me for anything more or I am going to scream." She is easily irritated, particularly by her children at home, and flies into excessive rage at little irregularities at school. Afterward she feels empty and cold.

EXAMPLE 17

Rosanna finds the way she's been reacting to her children lately totally unacceptable. She screams at the least little thing and a few times she smacked her five-year-old because he just kept crying and she couldn't take it anymore. She feels terribly guilty about this.

Mad at the Whole World

Because of all the frustration and powerlessness, often there arises— as in the cases of Charles and Liz—a constant stream of angry thoughts in the direction of employer and associates. Initial idealism turns to cynicism, enthusiasm for work to resentment. In this way we witness a vicious cycle of angry thoughts, desperate resistance and increasing fury, which further raises the level of stress.

On the road to burnout, normal everyday inconveniences become major stressors, and you no longer have the ability to just let them go. Irritation at your partner and conflicts with your children, especially if they're teenagers, increase exponentially. Resentment at being unappreciated may even lead to suicidal thoughts.

Tony, a 55-year-old seventh grade teacher, has worked for years in grade school education. For about a week now, he has been receiving disability benefits. He is mad at everyone: the school, the government, the parents, the children. In Tony's view, the headmaster has been against him for years instead of making use of his experience. Tony is also deeply disappointed with his coworkers, who are much younger than he and have different values and beliefs. Due to the umpteenth new government regulation, which no one supported, there had recently been endless meetings that caused a lot of unrest. The work atmosphere was becoming worse and worse.

A week ago, due to a conflict with an impossibly spoiled girl, a complaint was lodged against Tony by the girl's father. Instead of questioning the father, the headmaster promised to investigate Tony's functioning in the class.

This was the last straw; Tony called in sick. Only then did he notice how tired he was. His mood is low, he sleeps badly and he worries a lot. He conducts long inner discussions with the headmaster and the girl's father, and he and dreams up all kinds of punishments for "that stupid girl." This morning he caught himself having thoughts of suicide: In revenge he would walk in front of an oncoming train and thus saddle the headmaster, the parents and his colleagues with lifelong feelings of guilt.

Feeling Guilty

Being unable to function, to handle normal tasks, or to keep up our side of relationships, whether as a partner, parent or coworker, often lead to feelings of tremendous guilt, which make us feel even worse.

Rosanna's husband would like to do the fun things they always used to do, but she can no longer imagine doing them. She feels terribly guilty because she is ruining Dan's life, and her children's, by being so weak and incapable of anything. Doing fun things? Where will she get the time and energy, and won't people think even worse of her as a mother? She used to love to sing and to go out, but it doesn't work anymore. The last choir performance she was going to participate in was when she was still nursing her youngest. But she had an infection and was lying in bed during the performance. Another mother then told her that she had to devote herself more to the care of her children.

EXAMPLE 20

Joan burst into tears on a visit to a girlfriend. She feels she is falling short in everything: her husband, children, school and friends. She feels guilty all the time and lies awake worrying and repeating things all the time.

Denial

Most of the time, someone in burnout has been systematically ignoring all signs of overload for a long time. Not wanting to fail, not letting them get you down, and fear of emptiness lead to working ever harder so that you no longer get a chance to rest and relax. The constant denial is striking: "I like my work and therefore there can't be anything wrong" and a dogged persistence: "I won't let that stupid boss get me down!" It is as if the whole world will collapse if you give in.

The greater the threat of breaking down, the more desperately you cling to the security of the known situation. In most cases people such as family members, friends and colleagues are the ones who (often for a long time in vain) implore the person to seek help.

EXAMPLE 21

Susanne, a 32-year-old ambitious reporter at a major newspaper, remains weak and terribly tired after a bout of a bad flu. She has stomachaches and rarely sleeps through the night. When she gets heart palpitations, a friend suggests she see a company doctor who, after a careful examination, sends her home with the recommendation to take a few weeks' rest. Susanne is enraged. She finds the doctor incompetent; she wants to have a blood test and see a cardiologist. She feels put off and violated in her autonomy. Her general physician examines her also and comes to the same conclusion as the company doctor and advises her to slow down.

Outraged, she goes home and furiously unloads on her boyfriend, complaining about how she's being treated. Only when he bursts into tears and says that he would love to support her but that he can't handle it in this way, does she realize the situation she is in, and calls in sick. It takes a year and a half before Susanne is herself again and can go back to work part-time.

Am I Worth Anything? A Bruised Self-Image

Suddenly someone who never had trouble with anything dreads everything he has to do and is assailed by doubt and terrible fear. He used to throw himself into his work with heart and soul, and now senses that this is no longer possible. People who get burned out are hard workers, they are persistent; giving up is viewed as weakness by them.

The self-image of the healthy, strong and motivated worker, devoted partner, capable parent collapses; everything that used to give certainty and security crumbles away. This puts an enormous dent in self-confidence. Your sense of responsibility and guilt feelings for falling short drive you to squeezing out your last bit of vitality. The overwhelming feeling of being out of control may lead to fear of losing your mind or even thoughts of suicide.

EXAMPLE 22
Susanne: "When I finally had to admit that I was burned out, my world collapsed and I became fearful and depressive. My inner picture was of a big, strong oak that was splintering and slowly falling over. I, who was always so enterprising and strong, who helped others, who wrote good articles ... I didn't want to see anyone anymore and I didn't go out. I always wore the same old gray sweater because for some reason it made me feel safe. I felt like a total failure, like standing in a dark tunnel that grew ever narrower. Thoughts of death were thrusting themselves on me as a solution to my hopeless failing."

EXAMPLE 23
Malika: "I felt guilty about the publishers, my family and friends, and the many canceled appointments. I had no control of anything. I didn't even know whether there was food in the house, and I didn't care. I was sinking lower and lower. I did feel responsibilities burdening me, but I didn't do anything anymore. At a certain point I just wanted to die."

2.4 Loss of self-direction and motivation

Excessive Goal Orientation
Energetic people firmly committed to striving toward their ideals are especially vulnerable to burnout if they fail to pace themselves. Keeping your eyes on the prize while losing sight of the path you're on can lead to a fall; placing unrealistically high demands on yourself can take its toll. And if obstinate reality then does not give, you become disappointed in the goal, but also in yourself and your colleagues. You no longer succeed in adjusting your ideals to your own forces and those of the organization.

EXAMPLE 24

When one of Joan's friends warned her a year before she burned out that she needed to take it a bit easier, she replied that it was impossible to slow down or work any less. A new education system had just been introduced, of which she was the coordinator, and she could not possibly leave her colleagues and the children in the lurch by quitting now. Moreover, there were already so many sick teachers. It would be a disaster for the school if she, too, called in sick.

EXAMPLE 25

It is Rosanna's ideal to be a good mother and have a close family. The more she loses control of her own life, the more desperately she fights for her ideals. Neither getting help nor putting her children in daycare fits in the picture she has of a good mother.

Loss of Motivation

Motivation is an inner power—one person is more motivated for daily tasks and challenges than another—but this power is also strongly influenced by the pleasure you experience in your work, the meaning it has for you and the appreciation shown by family, customers, colleagues and managers. A basic level of vitality is a prerequisite for motivation. If you are so tired that you can barely stand, your creativity suffers and automatic pilot takes over. You get into a rut that eventually kills all motivation. Also someone who likes his work and throws himself into it full of ideas may, by overload or disappointment, lose his motivation and in due course burn out.

EXAMPLE 26

Eighteen years ago, Lara, a 42-year-old woman, helped set up a Waldorf school where she became the kindergarten teacher, but also worked enormously hard for the school. Thanks to the incredible commitment of the teachers and parents, the school grew into a flourishing grade school. At a young age Lara had highly responsible positions and was the one who engaged new teachers.

Over the past five years, the school has been changing; the pioneers and founders have left, one by one. A headmaster was appointed, with the result that a team is no longer jointly responsible for the whole school, as it was before. Lara notices that she has less contact with her much younger colleagues. Most of all she misses her warm connection with a close colleague she'd worked with for years, who took early retirement.

In addition, due to a merger with another school and to new government regulations, Lara finds less and less satisfaction in her work. In her eyes, there is no longer a real kindergarten, but she still feels that it is her job to see to it that there is a beautiful atmosphere in her class. She feels guilty toward the children that she can no longer provide what she feels they need, but as one of the old guard she cannot abandon them. Reluctantly she does her work. At home she grumbles about her colleagues, about young, thoughtless parents, and even about children who nowadays are so noisy and aggressive. She feels so guilty for having all these negative thoughts that she can't sleep at night. She feels dead tired all the time. During Christmas break Lara got a bad case of pneumonia and spent the whole vacation in bed. She didn't recover totally, but calling in sick—absolutely not! Lara just takes up her work again. Three months later her doctor diagnoses her as burned out. Lara is unable to work for two years.

Frequently, problems at work begin when you disagree with changes that have been imposed top-down. This undermines your enjoyment of your job and makes it much harder to identify with it. Motivation turns into its opposite, aversion. For Charles, as for many others, a reorganization made it impossible to structure his work in his own way. He became increasingly frustrated because what he wanted and was capable of no longer corresponded with what he was told to do. Liz, after years of working well with her old boss, was bothered by her new boss's frequent criticism. She received no support from her new colleague, which aggravated the problem of finding motivation for the things she used to like doing. In the case of Chris, because he was able to handle so much, he was given more and more to do. The demands on him were gradually raised so high that in due course it became impossible to satisfy them all. Even the most enthusiastic workers will eventually lose motivation when faced with huge backlogs of work or constant criticism.

Fighting Losing Battles
Your motivation can be undermined not only by unwanted changes at work, but also by promised or hoped-for changes that never materialize.

EXAMPLE 27

Phil, 37, has worked for eight years as head of the workshop of a farm that is part of an organization for adults with mental disabilities. The farm was bought almost nine years ago from an elderly farmer who retired. Although the workshop spaces worked fine for a small family enterprise, they are far from ideal for working every day with a group of nine young people with intellectual disabilities. When Phil was hired to set up and lead this workshop, he mentioned that the spaces were too small and needed soundproofing; the sanitary facilities also left much to be desired. The manager at the time was planning to make the necessary changes within the next three years. Despite the fact that Phil regularly called attention to the space problem, nothing has changed in five years.

In the meantime a merger has taken place, and the new boss has different priorities. The remodeling is being postponed all the time. Phil has to cope with a lot of quarrels among the participants because they have to work too close to each other. He often has to finish the work that is intended to keep the residents occupied because they are constantly in each other's way. The residents' parents, too, continually complain about the bad working conditions.

One day two boys start a fight after one pushed the other into a pile of manure when they had to pass each other with full wheelbarrows in a narrow passage. For the umpteenth time Phil sounds the alarm. The new manager proposes that Phil first find out how other similar farms solve this kind of problem, and then produce a concrete plan for the necessary changes.

For six months Phil devotes his weekends to visits to other farms that work with people with disabilities and gathers extensive information about the advantages and disadvantages of different solutions. His absences from home and his increasingly frequent migraines (always on his days off) lead to quarrels with his wife, who says that he never has any time anymore for her and the children.

When Phil hands in his carefully arranged file with information and recommendations, it takes his manager four months to look through it. In the end he is told that because of other priorities, the money for the remodeling won't be available until the following year.

Two months later one of the residents totally loses control. Someone accidentally upset her cup of coffee; she begins to scream, breaks a window and threatens another resident with a piece of glass. Phil manages to defuse the situation, but gets hit in the process. Angry and upset he sees the manager and says that until there is appropriate space, he will not work with more than five participants. He receives no response, but is then quietly informed that insubordination is grounds for dismissal, and that ten other people would be happy to have his job. Phil's world collapses; totally upset he goes home and that same week his doctor diagnoses him with burnout.

Always on the Go and Can't Stop

Getting things done and starting something new are activities that require energy. But pacing yourself, knowing when to stop doing things or to demand decisiveness and self-direction—this capacity for self-direction becomes undermined when you get burned out. As a result you find it harder to say no to others and to control your own impulses.

A person in burnout is like the driver of a car whose engine, steering and brakes aren't working, but which has made it to the top of a mountain. Now the car races down the other side of the mountain as you hang on, unable to steer, slow down or stop. In the meantime there is a growing chorus of well-meaning family members, colleagues and helpers who try to make you shift down, brake and steer through the curves. Realizing that you've lost control over your life and have no idea what to do next can result in total panic.

EXAMPLE 28

> Our secretary friend Liz has already heard from many of her friends that they are concerned about her. They suggest she take a few weeks off to reflect on her situation. But Liz waves it all off. She is just having bad luck with her new boss; everything will be all right. As a matter of fact, she is spending a lot of time at home to learn the new way of working that her new boss demands of her.

Symptoms of stress

Physical Complaints
- Deteriorating physical condition
- Diminished resistance, increased susceptibility to colds and flu, infections and inflammations
- More premenstrual complaints
- Decreased libido
- Headaches
- Dizziness
- Heart palpitations
- Hyperventilation
- High blood pressure
- Irritable bowel syndrome, digestion problems
- Stomachaches and/or nausea

- Muscle and joint aches, fibromyalgia
- Diabetes, high cholesterol, overactive thyroid

Energy Level
- Constant agitation; inability to relax
- Fatigue, despite getting sufficient sleep
- Sleep disturbances
- Difficulty concentrating and forgetfulness
- Problems taking in and retaining information
- Loss of interest
- No interest in sex
- Excessive sensitivity to impressions: sounds, light, smells, etc.
- Hyperactivity
- Increased use of aids such as coffee, nicotine, sweets, alcohol, sleeping pills, painkillers, etc.
- Turning into a couch potato in front of the TV
- Inability to accomplish anything unless pressed
- Total exhaustion after a workday

Soul Life and Emotions
- Apathy, inner emptiness, gloomy thoughts
- Complaining, inability to see the positive side
- Shakiness
- Increased anxiety and nightmares
- Frustration and anger
- Irritation at little things
- Fear of failure
- More frequent involvement in conflicts and quarrels
- Feelings of guilt
- Panic attacks
- Feelings of powerlessness and hopelessness
- Denial and avoidance of situations and people to avoid confrontation or questions
- Bruised self-image

Self-Direction and Motivation
- Loss of motivation and enthusiasm
- Loss of interest in doing nice things

- Unhappiness with work or life situation
- Desperate clinging to goals
- Lack of sense of humor
- Loss of ability to evaluate situations correctly
- Decreased ability to make plans and look ahead
- Loss of self-direction and creativity
- Loss of ability to adjust and slow down
- Grimly going forward until you collapse
- Loss of self-appreciation
- Cynicism and indifference
- Thoughts of suicide, death as a solution

2.5 Are you really burned out, or is something else going on?

None of the symptoms described above are unique to burnout. But it is the combination of chronic stress, physical exhaustion and the evident decrease in concentration and social functioning that lead to the diagnosis of burnout. However, there might also be something else going on.

Overexertion

Overexertion is burnout's next-door neighbor. Symptoms of over-exertion appear primarily on the soul level, rather than the physical or energy level. When you suffer from overexertion, it helps to take clear measures to restore the balance between rest and activity, in both your work and private life, as well as to reflect on possible tensions in your work situation and your motivation for the work as such. Overexertion may cause a brief sick leave, but in most cases, with the help of a therapist and deliberate changes in work habits, it is possible to restore your capacity to work in a short time.

Physical Illnesses

A variety of physical complaints is usually one of the symptoms of burnout, so it's a good idea to get a complete physical exam, including a blood test. Anemia, hepatitis, diabetes, mononucleosis or thyroid malfunction are but a few of the physical illnesses that can cause serious fatigue and despondency.

Burnout and Chronic Fatigue Syndrome

Burnout may look much like chronic fatigue syndrome, especially if the principal complaint is physical exhaustion and the person, even after a longer time, remains incapable of performing ordinary tasks such as the household chores and cooking. In burnout there is usually a long lead time of increasing complaints with an initial emphasis on the inability to do your work properly and on psychological fatigue and excessive irritation. Physical exhaustion appears only later and is usually the first symptom to recover from somewhat. It takes much longer for psychological equilibrium to return.

Chronic fatigue, on the other hand, often begins with an infection, such as mononucleosis or an intestinal infection. From the beginning, the emphasis is on extreme physical fatigue due to which sleep disturbance, digestion problems and muscle aches often occur. Varying intensity of symptoms is typical of chronic fatigue: Everything is better for a while, then suddenly you are completely incapacitated. Also typical is delayed fatigue, appearing the day after the overexertion. Sometimes burnout can develop into chronic fatigue.

Burnout and Depression

Burnout is not a static condition, but a process of increasing exhaustion. The boundary with depression, where the clearest symptom is a gloomy mood, is hard to determine. We could say that true burnout always goes together with depressed feelings and anxiety. Dark moods, guilt, resentment, anxiety, physical symptoms and sleep disturbances can also occur in depression, but exhaustion is not as common.

Depression may also occur independent of one's work situation and without any stress factors. It may not have a clear cause. It may be a family trait. The symptoms and complaints often recur. Events such as a deep life crisis or a chronic disease of partner or child may lead to burnout, with the result that you can't handle all your work and family duties anymore. In such a case there is not much difference between burnout and a reactive depression.

To help you decide whether you have the symptoms of burnout, go to the *Self-Examination Questionnaire* (Section 17.1).

PART 2

Fuel for the Fire
Backgrounds of Burnout

"Good morning," said the little prince.

"Good morning," said the railway switchman.

"What do you do here?" the little prince asked.

"I sort out travelers, in bundles of a thousand," said the switchman. "I send off the trains that carry them: now to the right, now to the left."

And a brilliantly lighted express train shook the switchman's cabin as it rushed by with a roar like thunder.

"They are in a great hurry," said the little prince. "What are they looking for?"

"Not even the locomotive engineer knows that," said the switchman.

And a second brilliantly lighted express thundered by, in the opposite direction.

"Are they coming back already?" asked the little prince.

"These are not the same ones," said the switchman. "It is an exchange."

"Were they not satisfied where they were?" asked the little prince.

"No one is ever satisfied where he is," said the switchman.

And they heard the roaring thunder of a third brilliantly lighted express.

"Are they pursuing the first travelers?" asked the little prince.

"They are pursuing nothing at all," said the switchman. "They are asleep in there, or if they are not asleep they are yawning. Only the children are flattening their noses against the window panes."

"Only the children know what they are looking for," said the little prince. "They waste their time over a rag doll and it becomes very important to them; and if anybody takes it away from them, they cry..."

"They are lucky," the switchman said.[5]

---

5 Antoine de Saint-Exupéry, *The Little Prince*, New York, 1943.

Introduction

Just as the symptoms of burnout affect us at different levels, this is also true of their causes, which can be traced to various interacting factors. It is always a combination of factors in which circumstances (work and home) enter into interaction with personality factors, and this within the greater context of our culture as a whole.

In the following chapters we will discuss:
- Risk factors in the workplace
- Stress management and the interaction between brain and body
- Life processes and vitality, natural ability and vulnerability of the life body
- Soul life and different "selves"
- Setting your own course in life
- Differences between men and women
- Life circumstances
- Cultural factors

If you are too tired to read all this now, just choose the parts that interest you or seem to apply to you. You could also skip Part 2 for now and go on to Part 3, which describes the road to recovery, and then do some of the exercises in Part 4. Once you're feeling better, you can come back and read more about the preconditions for burnout.

3 Your work: Does it energize you or burn you out?

Most people are able to endure long-lasting stressful circumstances, provided there are possibilities for recovery, and provided that their efforts are rewarded. Burnout is the consequence of chronic, unremitting stress that can't be avoided and is uncompensated. [...] Burnout is therefore the result of giving too much and receiving too little in return, while stress is the result of doing too much (or in some cases too little).

– Jaap van der Stel[6]

In 1974 the American psychiatrist Herbert Freudenberg was the first person to use the term "burnout" to describe a condition of fatigue and exhaustion he observed in health care workers in an alternative clinic for psychiatric patients and drug addicts. These generally young and idealistic helpers had the feeling of being deluged by the problems of their patients. Instead of their former enthusiasm, they had become irritated and cynical. Freudenberg noted suspicion, concentration problems, psychosomatic complaints, depression and suicidal tendencies in these caregivers, who used to be so deeply engaged.[7]

Burnout is still viewed as a typically work-related disease. However, it is always the consequence of a combination of factors, in which individual capacity and character determine how a person experiences the organization and circumstances governing his work. Yet it is clear that there are certain work circumstances that undermine everyone and increase the risk of burnout:

- if your job requires maximum alertness and/or other major stressors at all times;
- if your job is mind-numbingly boring, with no challenges or prospects for change;

---

6 D. de Ridder, K. Schreurs & W. Schaufeli (eds.), *De psychologie van vermoeidheid* [The Psychology of Fatigue], Assen 2000.
7 H.J. Freudenberg, "Staff Burnout," in: *Journal of Social Issues* 60, 1974.

- if your work conditions have been confusing or chaotic, or constantly changing, for a long time;
- if you are uncertain about keeping your job and cannot easily find another one;
- if there is little support and a lot of criticism;
- if you lose too much of your individual character and autonomy and cannot use your creativity.

In what follows we examine factors that affect stress levels at work.

3.1 Professions with increased risk

Initially, burnout was viewed as a disease that occurred exclusively in professions specializing in human interactions, such as caregiving, personal services and education. Caregiving professions (general physicians, psychotherapists, social workers) continue to create more risk of burnout, as does working in education. In all these professions we often see idealistic, hard-working people in work that, due to a structural lack of manpower and the vulnerable client group, makes extreme demands on the employees, while at the same time offering minimal chances of advancement.

Similarly, people whose work involves dealing with aggression or traumatic situations, such as police, paramedics, firefighters, or social workers, are at greater risk of burning out. Moreover, these professions have seen their chronic worker shortages increase in recent years, which puts even more pressure on current practitioners. However, burnout now occurs ever more frequently among administrators, journalists and other professionals whose work involves constant performance pressure, high stress levels and the need to be available at all times.

One striking fact is that in the traditional trades, for instance farmers, furniture makers and artists, for whom handwork is more in balance with headwork, there are far fewer cases of burnout than in professions that require mostly mental work, or where workers deal professionally with other people. Apparently the trades offer more potential for recharging while working, for example by daydreaming or thinking about other things, without feeling guilty or getting off track. When working with our hands, we have more control over our own pace and can get into our own regular rhythm. Finally, handwork produces a result that is concrete and immediately visible. The final product stands outside the maker and because of this the maker can more easily let it go.

3.2 (Un)healthy work/rest rhythm

A regular rhythm forms a firm grounding for the life forces (see Chapters 5 and 12). Fixed working hours and clear breaks support the work. For this reason, everyone should have the opportunity to take time for lunch and have time for a little walk or take a little distance from the work in some other way. Uninterrupted work with no respite leads to increased risk of burnout.

Work that is so structured that it leaves too little time for relaxation and rest constitutes an attack on the life forces. Coffee and tea breaks create brief moments of relaxation, which are important for handling stress and enhance concentration for the rest of the workday. Similarly, to really let go of work during lunch by taking a walk or eating quietly away from the workplace is an important factor in reducing and offsetting stress. Preferably the conversation during breaks should not be about business or irritations. Although the law may prescribe time off for lunch, this often does not happen, for example in schools where teachers have to keep the peace on the playground or for physicians who use their lunch breaks for phone calls and consultations with colleagues, or in companies where lunch breaks are used for mandatory meetings or training.

EXAMPLE 29

Joan has worked at a high school for twenty years. During breaks there are often conflicts among students, and Joan keeps an eye on those and mediates when needed. Sometimes the tension mounts to a pretty high pitch, particularly between children of different ethnic backgrounds. Joan hates that; though she does not consider herself a racist, she has noticed the school atmosphere hardening and has heard colleagues arguing heatedly about students who are children of immigrants.

Our hectic lifestyle is a burden for our stress management system and, moreover, leads to an increased risk of becoming overweight and developing other prosperity-induced illnesses. [Since the writing of this book, the global lockdown was instituted to cope with the Corona Virus Pandemic in 2020. Perhaps this abrupt change in lifestyle, of keeping everyone home to avoid infection, will bear fruit once the pandemic ends. A simpler, less hectic lifestyle might be one positive outcome of an unfortunate situation. – Ed.] During active mental or physical work we have to be awake and alert; our stress management system then sees to it that the body devotes its energy to the work in progress instead of, say, digesting your last meal. For this reason, meals that are gobbled down in haste, while you are doing other things at the same time, are poorly digested and deliver less energy and more fat tissue (see also Chapter 4).

Living for a long time with an irregular routine, such as working rotating shifts or unpredictable weekends or nights, takes its toll on our internal clock, which is often unable to reset, especially if you're over 40. A chronic sleep shortage can gradually accumulate when we never get enough sequential hours of sleep. Social life also suffers when our work hours are irregular, making it harder to keep up with family life, stay in touch with friends, or schedule time to play sports or simply unwind.

Our biological clock is also thrown off if we frequently travel to different time zones for several days or weeks at a time. On business trips there is usually no time to acclimatize; right away we have to work full speed and participate in meetings in the life rhythm of the receiving city or country. For many people this leads in due course to serious sleeping problems and exhaustion of the life forces.

3.3 Organizational structure and quality of management

The way work is structured in an organization can significantly affect employees' health, both positively and negatively. A chaotic and undefined structure in which exact functions and roles are not specified—just like an excessively rigid structure with inflexible rules and no space for individual initiative—can make it hard to define your particular responsibilities. This creates a feeling of dependence on bosses and rules, and undermines the autonomy of the workers. Both scenarios make it hard to see how you fit into the big picture, which can lead to passivity and indifference: "Whatever I do won't make a difference, so I'll just sit back."

Again and again people in difficult and stressful work situations indicate that support and acknowledgment by management and a good, well-ordered organization of the work are important factors in dealing with stress.

Burnout rates can be decreased if employer-employee relations are kept positive and if employees have a good overall understanding of the contribution and importance of their work. It is also important that the qualities of the employees are recognized and that people are actually able to devote their qualities to the work. Up-to-date managers therefore try to stimulate the inventiveness and creativity of their employees.

Contradictory and vague assignments, responsibilities that can be asked but not executed, and repeated reorganizations increase work-related stress and the risk of burnout.

EXAMPLE 30

Hank, 38, used to work in an administrative position, but after a period of unemployment, he became the janitor in a high school. He does his utmost to make his job a success. However, his tasks are not well-defined in the school, and everyone seems entitled to call on him, while it is also unclear who his boss is. After past "failures" he very much wants to do well in this job, and for that reason Hank is the first in school in the morning and the last to leave in the evening. He is always busy during breaks and never manages to take time for lunch.

Hank likes to be of service and assist other people, but he soon notices that, no matter how hard he tries, there is always someone who complains. He also has the feeling that the teachers look down on him, and the students are often rude and disrespectful. One day after an unpleasant remark from a student, Hank loses it and flies into a fury; he yells at the student and they get into a physical scuffle. Afterward, Hank receives no compassion or support from the teachers, only criticism. The headmaster says nothing at all. After 18 months in the job, Hank calls in sick with serious symptoms of burnout and an enormous dent in his self-confidence.

Position within the Organization

In larger companies the people in middle management run the greatest risk of burnout. They have to give guidance to those who do the actual work, while the creation of the means needed to succeed, such as sufficient resources and personnel, lies largely outside their influence. Obviously, motivated supervisors are going to try whatever they can to keep their departments going, with the encouragement of their colleagues and boss. If a department is not properly managed, however, if there is excessive pressure to perform or a generally negative work climate, the manager will likely receive blame from both the boss and the employees. This means that people in such positions are often criticized from all sides and put on the defensive, with little support and appreciation.

EXAMPLE 31

Chris, who had the skating accident, had functioned effectively for years as the manager of a small department in his company. After a merger with another company, he was made the manager of a much larger, combined department where there was still a lot of unrest and rivalry due to the reorganization. Everyone came to him with their anger and unrest while higher management expected of him that the new department would function smoothly and productively. In the meantime he wasn't able to get to the legal work anymore that really had his interest. Chris felt as though he were mopping up a floor while an open faucet kept flooding it. His relationships with former colleagues deteriorated.

Experiencing Autonomy at Work

The extent to which people experience autonomy in their workplace is important for the way they subjectively experience the tension and stress they have to deal with. Everyone longs for a certain measure of autonomy, namely control over your own situation, i.e., the ability to be creative and find your own solutions to problems you run into. Your unique abilities and creativity are called upon and your strengths can blossom, enhancing your feeling of self-worth. It makes a big difference whether you experience yourself as creative, mature and competent in your work, or whether you mostly have to perform assigned tasks while your own input and solutions are not appreciated. Especially in professions where knowledge and competence are prerequisites, such as education or personal and medical care, these aspects are often quashed to serve a standardized process that can be controlled by rules and regulations issued by higher authorities. This is demonstrated by many examples in which such factors are important causes for loss of motivation.

EXAMPLE 32

> Charles thinks the travel agency has become much too commercial. As a result they don't get any interesting clients anymore, and the trips have become superficial with a bit of obligatory ecological content thrown in. Moreover, he has lost his autonomy. He is no longer allowed to put trips together himself but has to follow all kinds of new rules in his plans and performance. Giving up is not in his nature; in his eyes that would make him a loser. In addition, he is carrying a big financial burden because of a new mortgage.

EXAMPLE 33

> For years, Liz had developed her own way of working that was effective and appreciated. But now, because her new boss wants everything done differently, and is nasty and critical as well, her motivation and creativity are rapidly declining. However, it is not in her nature to give up quickly. She keeps trying to make the boss happy.

The more an organization stimulates the employees' own creativity, and the more responsibility people are enabled to take for their own part in the greater whole, the better they will be motivated and the closer they will feel connected with their tasks and the organization as a whole. A teacher can then give expression in her own way to her commitment and efforts for a difficult student, and a caregiver can feel proud of an unexpected solution he has found. People who are free to work in this way experience that what counts is not just what they accomplish but also that they are appreciated for who they are.

If your work challenges and stimulates you as a unique person, it not only enhances your own satisfaction and motivation; it is a prerequisite for maintaining your commitment and continued development. With the constant possibility of mergers and the pressures of a production-oriented economy, companies tend to increase in size, with the people at the top knowing all about management and economics, but lacking any connection to the unique nature or identity of the company and what it produces. The result is a neutral, business-like approach directed from the top.

This happened to Charles, who enjoyed his personal contacts with travelers, but also to Tony who can't find his place in modern education. It means that a person has to adapt to the abstract rules and bureaucracy of the organization, and that personal responsibility and creativity are awkward rather than appreciated. This increases the anonymity and invisibility of the individual coworkers and decreases their feeling of autonomy; they feel rather like cogs on a wheel and no longer recognize themselves in the identity of the organization. Particularly for people who bring an ideal into their work, this is fatal for their motivation.

Working with Protocols

Health care and personal care are increasingly governed by standard protocols, written rules that prescribe the way clients are treated in each individual case. In this structure, a caregiver's own solutions that demand creativity and commitment, are no longer needed, nor are they appreciated. They are replaced by the pressure to act purely according to the rules, for if you don't follow the protocol, you can quickly get sued in court.

The satisfaction of finding a creative solution diminishes for the caregiver, while the client does not feel that he or she has been treated as a unique individual. While strict protocols may be necessary for the scientific study of certain treatment results, they tend to limit the diversity of ideas for treatments, as well as the unique encounter between caregiver and client.

As a result, reliance on a practitioner's own competence, insight and decision-making tends to decline ever further in therapeutic professions, despite the fact that most practitioners experience these qualities as strong motivators and sources of inner renewal and connectedness. Since the pressure to produce increases constantly— with an emphasis on a scientific approach and efficiency—and the uniqueness of each case is undervalued, it is to be expected that more and more workers in health care will face burnout.

EXAMPLE 34

Johanna is a 34-year-old experienced and well-functioning nurse in child psychiatry. When counseling young people she likes to enter into personal contact with them and to come up with creative solutions together with them. When a new insurance system is introduced, the clinic decides to begin working more according to protocols, and the departments are reorganized. The child psychiatrist and the new coordinator want to comply with the new rules, so the way Johanna's department works changes completely. She cannot find her place in this work style; it seems as if the rules are more important than the children.

3.4 Lack of positive feedback and support

The Importance of Support and Solidarity

An important factor in people's satisfaction at work is their relationships with colleagues and supervisors. A respectful and supportive mutual relationship, allowing for positive exchanges and joint solutions to mistakes, creates important protection against burnout of coworkers. If, on the other hand, there exists an authoritarian relationship with little mutual consultation and unreasonable demands, while assessments are always critical and discouraging, in the long run this will be a stress factor most people will be unable to deal with.

EXAMPLE 35

Johanna enjoyed her work in her previous department for years. She related how her new department structurally had too few employees with the result that those who were there were constantly overworked. She always had to work too many intense shifts in a row and also accompany a group of young people with too few coworkers. On top of this there were differences of opinion on the treatment of the young people, little time for review and discussion, and a lack of leadership because the child psychiatrist now had to devote so much time to paperwork. Although on paper the protocols were strictly followed, on a more hidden level everyone did his own thing, and different coworkers followed different practices. This was confusing to the young patients and caused increasing conflicts, often leading to aggression.

In addition, Johanna and her team coordinator did not get along. Johanna had the feeling that there was talk about her behind her back. The agreements in her contract were also not properly followed and she often had to do things for which she had not been hired, or shifts were suddenly changed. Performance reviews did not take place, not even when she repeatedly asked for them. When she finally did get a review, there was little understanding for her problems, but she was given a lot of criticism she had never heard before.

Johanna felt more and more isolated. Even at home her thoughts were always with her work. She was always busy dreaming up strategies that would make it better, but all her ideas were rejected. Finally one day she misjudged a situation and was assaulted by a patient, resulting in a black eye and a torn blouse. Even then she received no support from the management or her coworkers, who seemed to assume it was her own fault and that she had caused the incident. That was the last straw: She went home in tears, vowing never to return.

Mobbing

Most people remember bullying from their days in school. In almost every class there was a student who was the black sheep, as it were—the boy no one wanted to sit beside, who was not invited to birthday parties and found his backpack stuffed in a toilet; the girl who was ridiculed for her appearance, her way of speaking and her dress. At first sight, we would not expect this behavior among adults working together in an organization. Undesirable manners, however, have not so much to do with age as with group processes. Such dynamics are played out among adults just as much as among children.[8]

It becomes even worse when people are used as scapegoats and are harassed, humiliated or sexually intimidated, or when their work is deliberately made difficult by their colleagues or supervisors. It occurs much more frequently than most people think, and if it persists for a long time and the employee cannot leave, it often leads to burnout. These kinds of processes often begin surreptitiously and then have a way of progressing insidiously so that even people who used to function effectively are pushed more and more into isolation and are mentally broken.

Bullying and humiliating behavior at work is called *mobbing*. It has been studied since the 1990s. Mobbing is hostile, humiliating or intimidating behavior, always directed against the same person who is unable to defend himself or herself effectively against it. It may include pestering, excluding, ignoring, maligning, ridiculing, also gossip, verbal and physical threats, discrimination, and sexual intimidation. It may also include the assignment of senseless tasks, obfuscating documents, losing telephone messages and other things that make it impossible for the person to perform the work for which he or she is responsible. An even more insidious example is sexual harassment. Although such situations arise frequently in the workplace, they are usually kept hidden and are therefore hard to identify.

Mobbing victims are often too ashamed to report what's going on and may fear that doing so will just make matters worse. People who are harassed at work pretty soon start having doubts about themselves, and they suffer stress-related complaints such as sleeping

---

8 Adrienne Hubert: hubertconsult.nl.

badly, headaches, stomachaches and nervousness; about a quarter of people who are harassed end up staying at home with disability benefits, and for the rest, their performance declines. There can be many reasons why a person will remain stuck much too long in such a destructive situation and in the end leave burned out and embittered. These include needing the financial security of the job, fearing to admit failure to family and friends, or even fearing a repeat situation in another job.

3.5 Work-related trauma

In some professions you run a fair chance of being confronted with traumatic situations. Police officers, fire fighters and paramedics are sent to situations of acute emergency and danger, where every second counts and where they are themselves often verbally or physically threatened in dangerous situations in order to save someone. Sometimes they see someone who had called for help, or even a colleague, die or be injured right before their eyes. Fear and undermining of motivation are the result, whereas motivation and a feeling of being able to handle the demands of the job are especially important for preventing burnout.

Chronic stress and fear are specific factors that increase the risk of burnout. Biochemical research has shown that feeling powerless produces different stress reactions than those from feeling able to handle a situation (see Chapter 4). In the end this may lead to a lasting disturbance of the ability to deal with stress. The same is true for soldiers in war zones and reporters in crisis areas. In professions with a high level of physical or emotional pressure, which involve exposure to human suffering or aggression—such as in psychiatric or disability wards or prisons—a traumatic situation or a personal threat may be the last straw. Even though things may look fine for a long time and people—certainly those who choose such a profession—seem to be used to the danger and to witnessing the suffering, it may suddenly, or gradually, become too much. This is certainly true in big disasters or when several traumatic events occur close together, especially if colleagues are killed in violent situations. In all such events it is very important for support systems to be in place and for these workers to be given sufficient time to recover their equilibrium.

EXAMPLE 36

One day Joan hears the girls in her class screaming anxiously on the playground. She runs to them and sees that a strange boy has entered the playground, stabbed a student with a knife, and fled. The victim, Ahmed, is the strongest boy in the class and difficult to handle. Now he is slowly collapsing while his T-shirt turns red. Joan calls 911 and Ahmed is rushed to the emergency room where he survives, but Joan is now more on edge than ever and notices she is feeling anxiety on the playground. She regularly dreams of the stabbing and always being just too late to prevent it.

3.6 Reorganizations and conflicts

Reorganization often means drastic change, imposed from on high, in the organization of the work. Expectations and assignments change and, especially if there are also layoffs, the atmosphere among colleagues may turn grim. It becomes a case of bending or breaking— whoever does not cooperate loses his job. Charles's situation is a good example of this. The structure everyone was familiar with disappears, and with it vanishes the feeling of solidarity to get the job done together with trusted colleagues. Suddenly the old position is no longer secure and people have to fight for a new one, which leads to distrust and rivalry.

Especially when departments are merged, several supervisors or managers may change at once, and the new boss may have a very different style and set different standards from the previous one. This demands a capacity to adapt that is not natural to many people, and therefore results in increased unease, powerless grumbling and negative stress in the department.

The paradoxical aspect here is that it is the employees who are not particularly committed who won't easily become burned out, nor the ones who out of frustration look for another job. They are the ones who are fiercely loyal and hang on with everything they've got, even as their satisfaction and motivation dwindle. When there are several reorganizations in a row and workers barely have time to adjust, the situation can only get worse.

3.7 Stuck, and too little career potential

Too much repetitive work kills creativity and eventually undermines vitality. Human beings have an inherent need for development potential and challenges; these create possibilities for inner growth and for growing new capacities. "Forever learning" keeps people engaged and engenders fresh views of their work. This is why there is a higher risk of burnout in professions such as education and health care, which don't offer many possibilities for continuing education or job advancement but yet place great demands on workers.

3.8 When the demands are always a little too much

When you have a job with tasks and responsibilities that are just beyond your capacities, or where the pace of work is too fast, the job becomes a source of chronic stress. Moreover, what for one person may be agreeable and challenging may be a burden for another. If the pace of work of the boss is inherently faster than that of his subordinates, and he constantly spurs his team on to produce more, this will in due course undermine the life forces of the employees.

EXAMPLE 37

As the tension increases, Hank, the janitor, is less and less able to distinguish the essential from the non-essential. Thus it happens that, on the way to make a phone call for the headmaster, he runs into an overflowing trash bin and empties it; someone then asks him to make a quick copy, and at the end of the day he is upbraided for forgetting the phone call. Hank becomes more and more fearful and tries his hardest to avoid certain teachers and meetings, because he will end up having to do things for them. There is no one who discusses his performance with him. He increasingly loses his original enthusiasm and feels unhappy in a kind of isolation.

Particularly someone who does a good job can, by being promoted once too often, end up in a situation where the difference between the demands of the job and his own capacities is too great. It often happens that an employee functions well in a certain position and is then promoted, with the result that different capacities are then called for, such as managing others' work, which skill, as it turns out, he lacks. It may also happen that someone is placed in a management position but is not accepted by his colleagues; this may disturb the social relationships to such an extent that his successful management is made impossible.

> After a reorganization Chris, who studied law at night, has to supervise someone who was just one of his colleagues before. This colleague had wanted Chris's new position for himself and is mad that Chris got it instead. Whenever he can he tries to boycott Chris and undermine his authority. Chris has never had to deal with anything like this and doesn't know how to handle it. He feels that it has an impact on the atmosphere in the department, but for fear of discrediting his colleague, he doesn't dare broach the subject openly. He's afraid that would just make matters worse.

In such a situation the best solution might be for the person to be returned to his or her former position, or a comparable one, without losing face. But most of the time, with the support of higher management, he will try at all costs to satisfy the new demands put on him, and work harder and harder with a feeling that the things he has to do don't come off right. Since dealing with someone under stress usually doesn't get easier, interpersonal relationships become increasingly disrupted.

3.9 When the boundary between work and private life becomes blurred

Closing the door behind you and not taking your work home with you is an important factor that helps people overcome work-related stress. But many people live under constant pressure to produce, and all kinds of deadlines may force them to take work home. The internet and cell phones make us accessible 24 hours a day and it is increasingly customary to be available at all times. Add to this that overworked people work less effectively, which means that they often do not get their tasks finished in time, so they end up taking work home more often. The feeling of running behind and constantly being under pressure, while the quality of one's performance suffers, reinforces spiraling stress levels.

EXAMPLE 39

Chris does his utmost to live up to the demands of his new position. He takes ever more work home and during the day hardly allows himself a moment to eat. At home, his social life is minimal, and sports and formerly fun activities have fallen by the wayside. His wife is irritated and he feels she is always nagging him.

It is also hard to let go of mutual tensions among colleagues, conflicts, harassment and reorganizations when you are at home in the evening. That is brooding and worrying time. When you talk and think about unpleasant things all the time, when you fruitlessly try to come up with solutions and can't sleep, you are living with a chronic feeling of unease, tension and irritation. This soon leads to lowered life forces, and burnout may result in a matter of months.

People who are directly confronted with human suffering in their work, or who often experience aggression and rude behavior, may perhaps not take physical work home at night, but instead live with the emotional burden of what they went through during the day. The increase in aggressive relationships in society and the mentality that demands instant solutions to problems, preferably by someone else, also take their toll.

In addition to taking work home, women with children often also bring family problems with them to work. A mother who tries to bring up, support and direct her teenagers by phone from her work is always under pressure: "Is everything all right?" Similarly, for people with a chronically ill partner and who, on top of being the family provider, also carry the main responsibility for the household and the children, their concerns about the situation at home come through into their work life.

EXAMPLE 40

Lillian, a 39-year-old woman with two school-age children, happily works three days a week, and sometimes evenings, in a convalescent home. But when she sets the table there in the evening she often thinks of her husband Joe who has MS. "Are things OK at home? Is he managing even though he's so tired?" After the meal she quickly calls home, and though Joe says everything is fine, she can hear the boys fighting and yelling in the background. All evening she worries about it. She feels guilty for shortchanging her children, but she needs to earn money so she doesn't know what else do.

EXAMPLE 41

Jack is a 49-year-old clinical psychologist, but has worked for a number of years in management. He got married at a later age. His wife has a borderline personality disorder, but she was actually doing very well after the marriage. Her situation worsened after the birth of their daughter four years ago. Jack's wife was seriously traumatized in the past and now that she has a child herself, her moods go up and down, and she turns off when tension mounts. Then she doesn't know who she is and wanders around the house in a fog. Sometimes she hurts herself. She regularly calls Jack at work in a panic, so he has to hurry home to take over. Mockingly, his colleagues call him the firefighter, but fortunately they do accept it all. At work Jack constantly worries whether things are OK at home, whether his wife will remember to pick up their child from school, whether there have been any accidents. It is a big distraction from the work he should be doing.

In order to avoid burnout it is important to have a clear idea of how you stand in your work life. Are you able to set your own boundaries; do you always have to stretch? What is the impact on your vitality of the way the work is structured and of the atmosphere in your department? In Part 4 you will find exercises that can help you with these issues.

4 Stress management: Complex interactions between brain and body

When I am too busy I have to slow down and meditate more.
— Dalai Lama

Stress is what happens when we are confronted with a physical, psychological or social influence or situation which, objectively or purely subjectively, disturbs our state of balance in such a way that we cannot simply ignore it, nor can we handle it in a routine manner. — Theo Compernolle[9]

In the past twenty years there has been a great deal of research into the complex interactions between the brain and the body. In the process, the disastrous consequences of chronic stress on our well-being and health have become better understood. It was discovered that our nervous system is not, as was always thought, anchored only in the head. There are just as many nerve cells in the abdomen as in the head, and there are many extremely delicately regulated circuits and interactions in service of physical and emotional health. The brain influences the body and its organs, but conversely the body also influences the function, and even the anatomy, of the brain. Many complaints that used to be considered psychological in origin, such as fatigue, muscle aches and concentration disorders, can now be understood because the neurological processes underlying them are becoming ever better known.

This has brought traditional Oriental medicine and the more technological approach of Western medicine closer together. For it has been proved that all kinds of methods that the West used to view as vague and suggestive healing methods, such as acupuncture and

9 Theo Compernolle, *Stress: vriend en vijand. De aanpak van stress, thuis en op het werk* [Stress: Friend and Enemy. Dealing with Stress, at Home and at Work], Tielt, 2006.

meditation, have a demonstrable effect on the brain, the nervous system, the immune system and the heart. Also the placebo effect is visible in the brain. Apart from the search for the causes of illnesses and why they arise (*pathogenesis*), the question then arises how people's own healing forces may be so stimulated, preferably with natural remedies, that they become healthy and stay healthy (*salutogenesis*). In the West this is a relatively new way of looking at illness and health, but in the East it has been applied for thousands of years using herbs, meditation techniques, yoga and physical exercise.

Emotions are experienced in the psyche, but they have strong effects on the way the body functions. Conversely, physical processes also cause feelings and emotions. For instance, when certain substances such as adrenalin or Valium are injected, they can cause severe anxiety or calm indifference, respectively. Then again, strong emotion may have violent physical consequences, such as an acute heart attack. In recent years much research has been going into the complex balance among the various parts of the nervous system, the hormonal system, the immune system and the principal organs. In situations of chronic and acute stress, this balance is upset in the body, which causes both physical and psychological symptoms.

This will be discussed in more detail in the following sections. It is a complex subject that provides insight into the physical connections between body and psyche. (If you are too tired at the moment to concentrate on this part, you may want to read it another time.)

4.1 The brain

Roughly, the brain consists of three parts that, although they influence each other, work relatively independently.

1. The *vegetative brain*, which is located in the brain stem, is a system that works in profound unconsciousness to control and direct metabolic processes, growth and reproduction. It is always working, even during deep, dreamless sleep. The vegetative nervous system branches out through the entire body, receiving information and directing biological processes and automatic reflexes in the body. We have this system in common with reptiles and mammals.

2. *The emotional brain* is situated in the middle of the brain, in the limbic system. It is present in all mammals. In form and cell structure, in the way it functions and in its chemical processes, this system distinguishes itself from the neocortex (the conscious brain) and the brain stem (the vegetative brain). The limbic system lies in the border area between our conscious and unconscious soul life. It is involved in managing life processes, but also dreams and our immediate emotional reactions and behavior in social situations and in danger. The limbic system has its own memory that seems to be separate from our conscious memory. It works through direct physical experiences and reactions and functions in a delicate state of balance. It has great self-healing powers.

3. The *conscious brain* is located in the neocortex, which is folded around the middle brain and consists of evenly constructed layers of gray cells. Apes also have a neocortex, but in humans it is much more developed than in animals. The neocortex serves us in higher human functions such as language, thinking—abstract thinking and rational analysis as well as imaginative and intuitive thinking—looking ahead, planning, purposeful actions, impulse control, reflection, self-consciousness and morality.

The neocortex is divided into left and right halves that look identical but have different tasks. The left hemisphere serves our rational, analytical capacities and verbal intelligence; the right hemisphere serves our intuitive, creative, artistic, musical and non-verbal expression and proficiencies. The two hemispheres are connected and work together through a broad band of nerves, the corpus callosum.[10]

The emotional and vegetative brains are both always working, unconsciously and automatically, during waking and sleeping. For this reason, together they are called the autonomic nervous system. They pick up signals from our inner world—physical well-being, hunger and thirst, signs of fatigue, pain or illness and sexual feelings. They

---

10 This is wonderfully illustrated in a TEDtalk video presentation by neuroscientist Jill Taylor, who suffered a stroke: www.ted.com/index.php/talks/jill_bolte_taylor_s_powerful_stroke_of_insight.html.

The Physical Brain

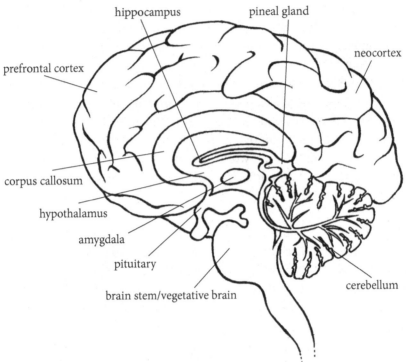

hippocampus

pineal gland

prefrontal cortex

neocortex

corpus callosum

hypothalamus

amygdala

pituitary

brain stem/vegetative brain

cerebellum

The Limbic System (Emotional Brain)

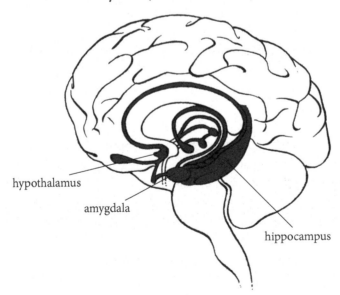

hypothalamus

amygdala

hippocampus

also help us survive in the world, for example by alerting us to danger with a fight-or-flight reaction to a fire or ensuring the continuation of the human species by causing sexual arousal based on something we see. Signs of danger are perceived in a flash by the emotional brain and cause physical action well before these signals penetrate to our consciousness.

The neocortex, and particularly the prefrontal cortex, is the instrument of our thinking, feeling and will. This system, which is highly developed in the human being, is a relative latecomer in evolution and works more slowly than the autonomic nervous system but can be consciously mobilized, directed, trained and developed.

Our cognitive capacities can be tested and expressed in an intelligence quotient (IQ). They depend on the layout of the brain cortex, but with schooling and training the intelligence can be developed further.[11] Collaboration of the conscious brain with the emotional brain generates emotional intelligence (EQ).[12] Our emotional intelligence enables us to perceive and recognize our own emotional state and the emotions of others, to understand the natural course of emotions, and to reflect on our own emotions and those of others. We are also able to learn to control our emotions consciously, for instance, by enduring frustration, postponing needs, or focusing consciously on the positive aspects of a situation.

The emotional brain can switch off our conscious thinking in situations of acute danger and fear, activating lightning-fast, automatic life-saving reactions that override the slower rational considerations of our conscious brain. In due course, however, we are also able to mitigate excessive emotions and automatic reactions using our powers of reason. This is a learning process that begins early in life and is supported by a safe bond with our parents and educators.[13]

---

11 Average intelligence as measured by the IQ has increased in each generation since World War II. Apparently this intelligence is trained and enhanced by our current educational and child-rearing methods.

12 J.D. Mayer, P. Salovey and A. Capuso, "Models of Emotional Intelligence," in: R.J. Steinberg (ed.), *Handbook of Intelligence*, Cambridge 2000.

13 People who lack such a secure bond generally experience more difficulty in maintaining relationships and in dealing with their emotions and strong feelings. As a result they run more risk of developing stress-related complaints.

If the stress reactions coming from the emotional brain get out of balance—for example by the experience of traumatic events or from chronic overload—the emotional brain issues alarm signals, although that is actually not necessary. The results are the psychological and physical signs we know as symptoms of stress, ranging from high blood pressure and heart palpitations to panic attacks, hyperventilation, digestive disorders and loss of libido.

If we are continually focused on our rational side and do not listen to our body and emotions, we run great risk of missing alarm signals and ending up with burnout. The conscious brain has only an indirect influence on the emotional brain. The knowledge that a phobia is irrational will not stop us from experiencing physical fright at the sight of a spider or mouse. However, certain therapeutic approaches, such as cognitive behavioral therapy and coaching, are based on the fact that the conscious brain is clearly, but indirectly, able to exert a favorable influence on unbalanced stress reactions of the emotional brain.

Research has shown that the EQ is more important for our success in the world than the IQ.[14] In other words, someone with a very high IQ who has little empathy (meaning little insight into his own emotions and those of others) and who, moreover, is not able to regulate these emotions sufficiently, has less potential of success in society than someone who does have such characteristics but a lower IQ. The one-sided training of and emphasis on rational, cognitive capacities in our culture may enhance our IQ but also diminish our sensitivity to signals from our emotional brain, with the result that our emotional intelligence declines. In recent years more and more therapeutic techniques are being developed—in part based on Oriental meditative practices—that have a direct influence on the equilibrium in the

---

14 This is true only for people of normal intelligence. For many situations in life and work, the rational thinking and analytical capacities measured by the IQ are absolutely essential for a degree of success. But if there is a one-sided very high IQ coupled with a low EQ (such as in forms of autism), the person in question will have difficulty maintaining himself in social situations. And since our entire society is based on social connections and on the ability to work together, the EQ is of decisive importance for success in society, healthy family life, and a feeling of happiness and belonging.

emotional brain. These techniques enhance the balance between our intellectual capacities, our feeling life, and our physical well-being.

In addition to the brain, organs and systems such as the heart, kidneys and endocrine system (for instance the thyroid and adrenal glands), as well as certain substances and cells in the blood, also play a role in stress regulation and in the maintenance of a healthy biophysical equilibrium. This is the subject of the following sections.

4.2 Messenger substances: hormones, neurotransmitters and cytokines

Many messenger substances circulate in the body and attune different types of cells, organs and organ systems to each other. We call them hormones, neurotransmitters and cytokines.
- Hormones are generated by endocrine glands in the body and brain and are transported by the blood; they affect a variety of organs.
- Neurotransmitters are produced by the nervous system and stay there. They affect the transfer of stimuli between nerve cells.
- Cytokines are the messengers of the immune system.
  Some substances, such as adrenalin, are both hormone and neurotransmitter or cytokine.

Hormones

Hormones are chemical substances produced by endocrine glands and have a restraining or stimulating influence in another place in the body. They are transported by the blood and work directly or indirectly on their target organs which possess receptors for this purpose. As messengers between metabolism and nervous system, hormones play an important role in stress reactions. Both the brain and the endocrine glands in the body—such as the pituitary gland, thyroid, adrenal glands, gonads—produce hormones and are sensitive to the effect of hormones. One hormone may be generated in more than one location. Adrenalin, for instance, is produced both in the adrenal gland and in the brain. Multiple organs may be sensitive to one hormone; for example, CRH works both on the brain stem and on the pituitary gland, while adrenalin works on the heart, the vascular walls, breathing, pupils, etc. Hormones that are produced in the body are, among others, the sexual hormones estrogen and testosterone, oxytocin, adrenalin and noradrenalin, the "stress hormone" cortisol, thyroid hormones, growth hormones and many others. The brain cells also produce hormones, including adrenalin and cortisol.

Neurotransmitters

The nervous system consists of millions of nerve cells that are able to transfer messages to each other with incredible speed. Neurotransmitters are substances that are generated in the cell body of nerve cells and transmit stimuli from one cell to another. They are important in the regulation of our moods, fear and aggression. Examples are serotonin, dopamine, adrenalin and acetylcholine.

-   Serotonin affects moods, control of fear and chronic pain.
-   Dopamine is involved in maintaining psychological balance, which is disturbed in many psychiatric disorders.
-   Adrenalin activates the body, and acetylcholine supports the state of relaxation and rest.

Cytokines

Cytokines are chemical messenger substances produced in the brain and in cells of the immune system. They regulate immune reactions and thus provide resistance against infections, but also against foreign substances and internal illnesses such as cancer. Just like hormones, cytokines are transported by the blood. Some of them stimulate inflammation reactions, while others suppress them. Some cytokines cause a feeling of being sick and having a fever. Examples of two interleukins, a type of cytokine, are IL-2 (defense against infections) and IL-6 (stimulant of inflammation reactions).

Important Messenger Substances in Stress Management

In dealing with stress a number of hormones are especially important, namely adrenalin, noradrenalin, cortisol, corticotropin-releasing hormone (CRH), and adrenocorticotropic hormone (ACTH). In addition, sex hormones are important (see Section 9.2).

Adrenalin and Noradrenalin

Adrenalin and noradrenalin (together called catecholamines) are produced both in the adrenal gland and in the cells of the sympathetic nervous system. These are hormones that work at a distance via the blood as well as neurotransmitters that work in the nervous system. Both substances lead to action when we are fully conscious. Noradrenalin increases blood pressure, narrows blood vessels (the face turns pale) and increases perspiration. Adrenalin increases the heart rate and raises blood pressure and blood sugar levels. We breathe more deeply and our blood flows more rapidly; the brain also receives more blood. Our senses work better, concentration is enhanced, we think more quickly. We feel energetic and ready for battle. Muscles contract, ready for fight or flight.

When we face a psychological challenge, such as an exam or concert performance, more adrenalin is generated. In the case of a physical challenge, for example if one is assaulted, the body produces more noradrenaline.

Corticotropin-Releasing Hormone (CRH) and
Adrenocorticotropic Hormone (ACTH)

CRH is produced in the hypothalamus, part of the emotional brain, when we are in tension or danger. It puts a brake on conscious processes, stimulates the sympathetic nervous system and the pituitary gland and also has stimulating effects in the body. CRH works as a neurotransmitter in the cerebral cortex and limbic system; it works in the body like a hormone and also stimulates other hormonal glands such as the thyroid. Moreover, CRH decreases appetite, libido and fear.

CRH stimulates the pituitary gland to produce ACTH, a hormone that in turn stimulates the adrenal cortex to generate the stress hormone cortisol (see Section 4.4).

Cortisol

Cortisol is a hormone produced by the adrenal cortex and is spread throughout the body by the blood. It can easily be measured in saliva. It has a biorhythm: In the morning cortisol concentration is highest, and in the course of the day it declines. Cortisol functions to maintain enough glucose in the blood and to replenish our energy reserves in the form of fat so that efforts can be sustained longer. It slows infections and regulates blood pressure.

Cortisol is produced in situations of danger, threat and psychological or physical stress, such as an injury. In the first instance it has an activating effect on immunity; it enhances concentration and memory while it diminishes sensitivity to pain. Cortisol slows the effect of the sexual and growth hormones. In higher concentrations, however, it also slows the production of CRH and ACTH, and in so doing puts a brake on the activating effect of the sympathetic nervous system, and on the production of more cortisol itself. Cortisol thus slows itself. This is part of the homeostasis of the body: the reactions that enable the organism as a whole, including stress reactions, to remain in balance.

A cortisol level raised by stress suppresses our normal immune reaction, resulting in a disturbed immune system. Resistance to colds and flu declines and the healing of wounds slows down. The production of infection-enhancing prostaglandins and cytokines (such as IL-6) increases, resulting in higher sensitivity to infections and allergies. This increases fatigue and causes flu-like symptoms. Cytokines activate stress reactions via the LHPA axis (Section 4.4) which causes further exhaustion.

Cortisol and Chronic Stress
If the cortisol level is too high for a long time, it will damage the limbic system, the center of our emotional brain (the amygdala, hippocampus, hypothalamus and pituitary gland), which, as we shall see, is important for the regulation of sleep, vitality, our emotional life and sexual functions. We witness all kinds of negative effects that we also often see in a person on the way to developing burnout, such as moods (depression, anxiety, unease, insecurity) and sleeping problems.

This brain cell damage results in a lower cortisol level and interferes with the work of neurotransmitters such as serotonin, dopamine and acetylcholine. The brain cells then also absorb less glucose, resulting in diminished powers of concentration, memory lapses and reduced capacity to oversee a situation and react adequately. The immune system then works less effectively and injuries heal more slowly.

Blood pressure rises. Bone- and muscle building decline. The working of the thyroid is slowed down, which leads to fatigue, a slower heart rate and other disturbances of the body's biorhythm. The regulation of blood glucose and cholesterol are upset so that people may develop hypoglycemia (low blood sugar), and symptoms of fatigue worsen.

In some cases of chronic fatigue and post-traumatic stress, cortisol levels and systems for restoring equilibrium appear permanently disrupted. Damage to the hippocampus causes a sort of allergic reaction to stress.[15] Even a little stimulus will propel the system into activity, and then doesn't slow down properly; the stress reactions in the body fail to stop. In due course the adrenal glands can no longer keep producing enough cortisol and other hormones. The cortisol level in the saliva is then permanently lowered. Cortisol's contributions to replenishing energy reserves, regulating blood pressure and reactions to infection, activating the immune system and enhancing the ability to concentrate are all greatly reduced, resulting in a lasting disruption of equilibrium in the whole body.

4.3 The autonomic nervous system, the autopilot

The autonomic nervous system (the emotional and vegetative brains together) influences the mutual relationships of the metabolic processes in our organs but, through messenger substances, also plays an important role in the regulation of our emotions. All physical reactions that take place unconsciously, such as digestion, muscle contraction, blood pressure, the biorhythms of organs and reproduction, are directed by the autonomic nervous system. Two neuronal systems, the sympathetic and the parasympathetic system, are each other's complement, and as such manage the balance between action and reaction, buildup and breakdown. In situations of stress the sympathetic nervous system slows the parasympathetic nervous system so that breakdown reactions dominate. In states of introspection and rest, the parasympathetic system dominates so that buildup takes place. In addition, the autonomic nervous system

---

15 See also Section 4.4, the LHPA axis, which maintains its full activity.

possesses a number of structures, hormone glands and nerve nuclei that have specific roles in dealing with stress and relaxation and in the regulation of emotions.

The Sympathetic and Parasympathetic Nervous Systems— Serving Action and Relaxation

The sympathetic system is the "watcher." It makes the body active and the spirit alert, focused on the outside world. It consists of a nucleus in the brain stem, the *locus cerulus,* which produces noradrenalin, and much sympathetic nerve tissue that has connections both with the cerebral cortex and the limbic system in the midbrain. The sympathetic system stimulates the adrenal gland to release adrenalin and has an activating and stimulating effect in the entire body, resulting in alertness, purposeful concentration and a body that is ready to spring into action. Breathing and heart rate increase, blood pressure rises, and the energy reserves of the body (glucose, fat) are consumed while, by contrast, the activity of the metabolism and sexual organs declines.

The parasympathetic system is the "relaxer" and the counterpart of the sympathetic system. It consists of an extensive nervous system that transports information from the brain to all parts of the body, as well as from the organs to the brain.[16] It slows the sympathetic system and stress reactions, and becomes active during periods of rest and relaxation. This system fosters recovery, buildup and growth; it relaxes us, makes us lethargic, and dulls our alertness. It causes restoration of life energy, slows the heart rate, strengthens metabolic processes and enhances sleep. The parasympathetic system fosters the secretion of acetylcholine, a hormone that supports the state of relaxation and rest.

In people who suffer from stress, who tend toward aggression or losing their temper, the parasympathetic brake on stress reactions functions inadequately. This may be a question of character or a condition made worse by life circumstances. Living under stressful conditions for a long time may increasingly undermine the parasympathetic system. In such cases, rather than high tension levels or interpersonal conflicts, it is the individual's reaction to the

---

16 The vagus nerve, the tenth cranial nerve, is essential for this.

stressful situation that activates the sympathetic system, causing it to overwhelm the constructive processes of the parasympathetic system.

The Autonomic Nervous System

sympathetic	*parasympathetic*
adrenalin	acetylcholine
action	relaxation
watcher	sleeper
alertness	dull consciousness
fight or flight	recover and restore
	digestion/recovery/growth
nervous, flustered	sickness response

The Limbic System

The limbic system is a complex structure of nerve nuclei and connections in the center of the brain. It forms part of the autonomic nervous system and represents our emotional brain. It plays a role in the management of all life processes, but also in our direct, emotional reactions and behavior in social situations, and in rapid reactions to danger.

Two structures in the limbic system are important for stress management: the amygdala and the hippocampus, both of which are active in the recognition of danger. They give us the "automatic pilot" that enables us to behave adequately without thinking—fight or flight—and to learn from earlier experiences. The amygdala are small nuclei in the limbic system that recognize danger directly through the senses but without the intervention of consciousness, and then direct the body's corresponding reactions. For example: You are hiking in the mountains and out of the corner of your eye you notice a shadow. Before you realize it you jump aside and a rock crashes to the ground just beside you.

The amygdala also conserve memories of unpleasant, traumatic events and—similarly via a quick and unconscious process—sound the alarm in situations that resemble the original trauma. One day in the past, for example, you escaped from a burning house; now an innocent smell of smoke tickles your nose and, before you realize that anything is happening, your body is ready for action. There are also nerve paths from the amygdala to the cerebral cortex so that a little later we do become conscious of the danger and, by thinking, can analyze things and react appropriately.

The hippocampus, another nucleus in the limbic system, preserves the memory of the context of events and stress situations, the circumstances in which something happened. Via an associative path, danger signals are generated unconsciously for something that to our consciousness is innocent or insignificant. For instance, a woman may become anxious every time she hears a key turned in a particular lock. It turns out that long ago she was abused by her brother who always first locked the door to her room by turning the key. The woman was not conscious of this memory, but the memory was unconsciously preserved via the limbic system, and now she always tenses up in a similar situation.

Thus when acute threats or danger are perceived, the stress systems of the autonomic nervous system are immediately activated via the limbic system, while at the same time the consciousness functions of the cerebral cortex are dimmed. This is the reason why in situations of acute threats and danger we can be alert and react fast and adequately, but not quietly consider things.[17] As was described earlier, chronic and great acute stress can lead to damage to the hippocampus from a high production of cortisol, resulting in inadequate behavior under threat.

Hypothalamus and Pituitary Gland: Regulators between Brain and Body

Hypothalamus

The hypothalamus is a central organ in the midbrain and consists of several small nuclei that each have their own anatomy and function. This organ plays a coordinating role in tuning our life processes, in quick, coordinated reactions to stress and danger, and in resistance

---

17 The two systems of the autonomic nervous system that are activated are the sympathetic nervous system and the LHPA axis (see Sections 4.3 and 4.4).

to illness and infection. The hypothalamus directs the autonomic nervous system, hormone production and the immune system. Information reaches it via our senses and the cerebral cortex, but also from the limbic system and the vegetative nervous system that is spread throughout the body. Conversely, signals also go from the hypothalamus to other parts of the brain and to the entire body. Thus the hypothalamus stimulates the sympathetic nervous system and the LHPA axis (Section 4.4), and also influences all kinds of immune reactions.

The hypothalamus itself produces hormones, such as CRH, which stimulate other glands, including the pituitary, thyroid and adrenal glands, to generate hormones. The hypothalamus is important for our sexual identity. It plays a role in concentration and attention and harbors a laugh-center. It also regulates body temperature and can cause fever, which helps kill harmful viruses and bacteria. But it can also raise the production of substances, for instance, certain cytokines that lead to feelings of general depression and fatigue.

Pituitary Gland

The pituitary is a small gland at the base of the skull. Together with the hypothalamus it stimulates and supports general vegetative processes and biorhythms, such as waking and sleeping, hunger and thirst. It also produces several hormones and stimulates other endocrine glands with those.

The anterior lobe of the pituitary gland is part of the autonomic nervous system and is closely connected with the limbic system and the hypothalamus. It directs the thyroid, the adrenal cortex and the sexual glands. Among other things, it produces ACTH, growth hormones and prolactin, the hormone that stimulates milk secretion.

The posterior lobe produces two hormones: the antidiuretic hormone, vasopressin, that regulates the secretion of urine, and oxytocin that stimulates feelings of bonding. Women produce large quantities of oxytocin when in pain or under stress. This helps stimulate the birth process and the production of milk, and also helps the mother bond with the baby. In both men and women it diminishes feelings of detachment and stimulates bonding (see also Section 9.2).

4.4 The LHPA axis

Hormone Circuits between Brain and Body

An important connection between brain and body is formed by the LHPA axis (see diagram). The acronym stands for limbic system, hypothalamus, pituitary gland and adrenal cortex. When in the limbic system (the emotional brain), the unconscious decision is made that a situation is threatening or dangerous, the hypothalamus is prompted to produce CRH. One of the consequences is that the anterior lobe of the pituitary starts to produce (besides other corticosteroids) ACTH, a hormone that prompts the adrenal cortex to generate the stress hormone cortisol. CRH puts the sympathetic system into operation and in so doing causes a general arousal of the body; together with cortisol it stimulates the body but, at the same time, puts a brake on the limbic system and the hypothalamus. The LHPA axis thus decreases its own activity, which helps restore a state of balance. In this way the stress system slows itself down via cortisol in response to the system of negative feedback, just like a thermostat in a heating system: When the temperature in a space drops, the heating system is turned on through the thermostat, so that the space becomes warmer. At a set higher temperature the system slows down and the thermostat turns the heating system off again so that the space does not become too hot. Such a feedback system serves to preserve a state of balance.

As we have seen in Section 4.2, chronic stress in due course diminishes cortisol production via the LHPA axis. This means that stress reactions are not as effectively controlled and more and more lead a life of their own. Vitality is permanently undermined. Both overreaction and sluggishness of the LHPA axis and the sympathetic nervous system are inimical to a healthy state of balance.

The assessment of a situation—whether it is stressful or not, dangerous or safe—is of course an individual question. We make this assessment both consciously and unconsciously, with different circuits activated in either case. Not the situation itself, but our personal evaluation of it, therefore, determines the quality of the hormonal reaction. The nature and quantity of the hormones released

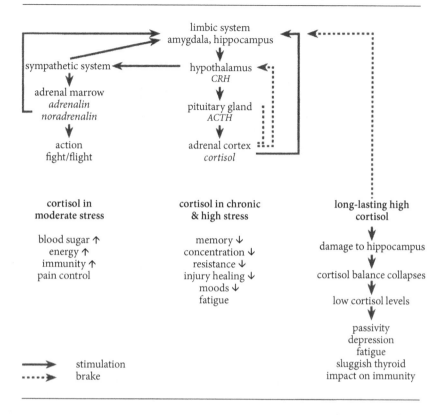

in the process in turn determine the quality and strength of our accompanying feelings.

An example from neuropsychology: When people are facing an assignment they think they can handle, the adrenal gland will, stimulated by the sympathetic nervous system, produce adrenalin and noradrenalin, which bring the body into a state of active alertness (positive stress). The corresponding feeling is: "I can handle this challenge, I am going for it." However, when people do not feel equal to an assigned task, the adrenal cortex will, via the LHPA axis, produce cortisol, which leads to a less aggressive or passive reaction (just as a little dog that is threatened by a big dog will lie on its back in surrender). The corresponding feelings are powerlessness and gloominess (negative stress). In these cases the body reacts to an assessment of the task made by the person. In their turn, the hormones influence the assessment. When test subjects are given an injection of adrenalin and a task at the same time, they cheerfully take up the task with the feeling they can do it. But when they get an injection of cortisol and a simultaneous task, they will feel powerless before the task and think they can't handle it.[18]

4.5 Regulation via the higher human functions of consciousness

Even though many of our physical reactions to threats and stress occur with lightning speed, directed by the automatic pilot of the autonomic nervous system, in most instances the capacity for human beings to evaluate and consciously make judgments and assessments of events is at least equally important. The capability to reflect, think and interpret both our inner condition and situations in the outside world is specifically human.

This capacity of reflection is physically supported by the cerebral cortex, the neocortex, and more particularly the prefrontal neocortex. Our capability to evaluate and judge raises us above the instinctive reactions of animals, enables us to react adequately in many (social) situations, and adapt our behavior as we deem appropriate in the moment. This also means that different people will assess a situation differently, and what for one person causes a feeling of irritation and stress may be a welcome challenge for another.

In recent years it has become increasingly evident that our interpretation of a situation, our habits such as complaining and criticizing or, conversely, viewing the world with optimism, have great influence on our health. Our feelings and thoughts about ourselves, others and the world, our worrying, negative thoughts and anxieties therefore form an important source of stress, which we ourselves can influence. Thus it has been shown that people with an optimistic view of life have a better functioning immune system and a better chance of

---

18 Carien Karsten, *Omgaan met burnout. Preventie, hulp en reïntegratie* [Burnout: Prevention, Help and Reintegration], Rijswijk 2008 (13); Boudewijn van Houdenhove, *In wankel evenwicht. Over stress, levensstijl en welvaartsziekten* [In Shaky Balance. Stress, Life Style and Prosperity Ailments], Tielt 2006.

surviving cancer than the pessimists among us. This research shows that inner development and certain forms of meditation have great influence, not only on our psychological well-being but even on the physiology of the brain.[19]

In situations of acute danger, the automatic pilot takes over with its quick, instinctive reactions. The autonomic nervous system then controls the conscious but slower functions of the human brain. That is why we can act quickly and effectively in such situations, but we can't quietly and deliberately reflect. Conversely, with our thoughts and interpretations of reality we can also direct the autonomic nervous system in various ways.

If we always assume that others think badly of us, if we have low self-esteem and expect to fail, if we constantly deprecate ourselves and interpret innocent signals from the outside world as life-threatening—such as a spider or heart palpitations—we precipitate an internal threat that is perceived by the limbic system as a real danger. Via the sympathetic nervous system and the LHPA axis, the body is put on alert and stress hormones are immediately produced. In this way the level of stress in our body mounts, and if this happens repeatedly without periods of rest and relaxation, the stress balance changes and is, one could say, set too high. The level of rest is no longer true rest, and every little disturbance raises the tension to excess.

We may also fool ourselves by consistently ignoring signals of stress, fatigue and danger, and suppressing normal biological reactions such as taking a break or pulling back. People who do this for a long time run a big risk of suddenly being felled, for instance, by a heart attack.

4.6   The immune system in times of stress

The Immune System

The immune system works via a variety of substances and cells and defends the body against invaders from outside, such as foreign cells, bacteria, viruses and poison. In addition, it fosters healing from

---

19 See Jon Kabat-Zinn, *Mindfulness for Beginners*, Boulder, CO, 2012.

injuries and illnesses. In case of an injury, for example, dead tissue is cleared away so that new tissue can grow.

The immune system is spread throughout the body. Important organs for the generation of immune cells are the lymph nodes, the thymus gland, bone marrow and the spleen. These white blood cells are then transported by the blood to the places where they are needed. Certain white blood cells, the macrofages and T-lymphocytes, attack invaders such as bacteria and viruses, while the so-called natural killer cells kill deviant cells so that malignant cancer cells can be removed at an early stage. Other cells, the B-lymphocytes, produce antibodies that render strange cells and proteins harmless.

These cells appear to have a memory for substances or organisms that cause illness or damage, and the result is immunity to certain diseases we once went through; this is the principle on which vaccinations are based. But it is also possible that over-reactions of the immune system cause allergic reactions.

In addition, both the cells of the immune system and the brain produce cytokines, substances that are important in the processes of tuning different immune reactions (see *Messenger Substances* in Section 4.2). The immune system is closely interwoven with both the autonomic nervous system and the hormonal system.

The immune system therefore shows that there are extremely complex interactions between brain and body; our thoughts and feelings, as well as our autonomic, unconscious reactions influence our immunity. Our immune system thus reacts both to physical stress and to psychological factors such as pessimism or confidence in a situation. Brief, acute danger and positive stress stimulate the immune system and make us briefly less susceptible to infections and inflammations. Chronic and negative stress, however, undermine the immune system, which makes us more susceptible to diseases "from outside," such as infections, and for illnesses "from inside," such as cancer and auto-immune diseases. For this reason we get sick more readily during burnout (see also *Cortisol* in Section 4.2).

The immune system, therefore, is directed from the brain, both via the sympathetic nervous system and the LHPA axis. The sympathetic nervous system is, via the nerves, directly connected with immune cells in the blood, the bone marrow and the spleen. In addition, adrenalin and noradrenalin, the messenger substances of the sympathetic nervous system, stimulate immune reactions. There are also more general reactions of the immune system, coordinated via the brain, both in infections and in injuries or surgery, when we witness a rise in temperature and the occurrence of sickness response.

Resistance and Stress

Everyone knows that in times of fatigue, grief or great tension we more easily catch a cold or the flu. In the run-up to burnout, when people are living in stressful circumstances for a long time, they are already more susceptible to bacterial infections and viral diseases such as the flu and mononucleosis. People who lose their partner run a greater risk of dying of cancer in the succeeding year. People who, in youth or adulthood, have lived for a long time in very stressful, traumatic conditions, for instance in a war or with domestic violence, are more likely later to develop cancer and auto-immune diseases such as rheumatism and multiple sclerosis.[20]

During recovery from illness an optimistic attitude with confidence creates a better chance to get better than gloomy pessimism in which the person seems to have given up. Also the placebo effect demonstrates that our expectations have a clear influence on healing processes. This is true in a positive sense (furthering healing) as well as in a negative sense (counteracting healing), for side effects also occur due to placebo pills.[21] Fear and negative stress have a unfavorable influence on healing. People who anxiously go into surgery run more risk of complications and on average stay in the hospital longer than those who look forward to the operation without much fear.

Long-term care of family members with dementia accelerates aging in the caregivers. There are more and more indications that stress can cause an aberrant reaction to vaccinations. In lieu of being strengthened by the vaccine, the immune system "goes berserk" and reacts vehemently, resulting in all kinds of symptoms of illness and

---

20 Annejet Rümke, *Verkenningen in de psychiatrie. Een holistische benadering* [Explorations in Psychiatry. A Holistic Approach], Zeist 2007.
21 Robert Bosnak, *Embodiment: Creative Imagination in Medicine, Art, and Travel*, London and New York 2008.

allergy. Possibly this contributes to increasing allergies in young children and to the "veteran syndrome" we regularly see in former soldiers—an unexplained, crippling illness that resembles chronic fatigue syndrome—with a lot of vague complaints such as extreme fatigue, allergies and pain.[22] By contrast, positive expectations and relaxation promote recovery. Mindfulness and other forms of meditation effectively help control chronic pain.

The Sickness Response

Sickness response occurs due to prolonged excessive activity of the immune system: a feeling of depression, muscle aches, weakness, diminished appetite, lack of concentration, and the urge to withdraw and get some sleep. Pro-inflammatory cytokines, the messenger substances of the immune system, contribute to this condition (see *Cytokines* in Section 4.2) and also to the activation of the vagus nerve, part of the parasympathetic nervous system. In normal circumstances this general feeling of being sick occurs in cases of flu or over-taxation, and alerts us to the need to go to bed and take time to recover. But in all kinds of modern, stress-related conditions such as chronic fatigue, fibromyalgia and post-traumatic stress, sickness response happens without any demonstrable cause. A day after normal activity or during a slight cold, people feel seriously ill and are forced to stay in bed. This inappropriate sickness response becomes an enormous obstacle to normal daily functioning.

In these conditions the stress system has probably been overloaded for a long time and has therefore become increasingly upset. As a result, the delicate balance between endocrine system (hormones), immune system and nervous system has become so disturbed that some parts of the immune system react excessively and others inadequately. In addition, the stress reactions of the sympathetic nervous system and the LHPA axis are constantly challenged. This leads to feelings of fatigue, general depression, greater susceptibility to infections, and all kinds of allergies to food and other external substances, such as we also witness in serious burnout cases.

---

22 See Boudewijn van Houdenhove, *In wankel evenwicht. Over stress, levensstijl en wel-vaartsziekten* [In Shaky Balance. Stress, Life Style and Prosperity Ailments], Tielt 2006.

4.7   The heart as mediator

A change of heart, from the bottom of my heart, to his heart's content, she has her health at heart, in one's heart of hearts, he puts his heart into his work, with heart and soul, etc. Our language has lots of expressions referring to the heart as an organ of feeling. The heart is known as the universal symbol of love and bonding, connectedness. It has been known for a long time that great stress increases the risk of cardiovascular disease. It has been shown that people in an impatient, hostile and aggressive mood run a higher risk of developing high blood pressure. That acute stress and anxiety may cause cardiac arrest has also been known for a long time. But chronic stress also affects the heart. People who are fearful and depressed after a heart attack run a much greater risk of a second attack than those who are optimistic about their future. Not only love and danger may affect our heart, an irregularly beating heart may also make us anxious.

In recent years, modern Western medicine has been coming around to the recognition, known in Oriental medicine for centuries, that the heart has additional, very different, functions than just being a pump for blood circulation. It plays an important role especially in the maintenance of our psychological balance, the perception of stress, and the preservation of a healthy equilibrium between our own inner world and the world outside. For this function, the heart is equipped with a finely tuned nervous system that is closely linked with our emotional brain.

Moreover, the heart generates hormones that are important in keeping our emotional reactions in balance. For instance, in times of stress the heart produces its own supply of adrenalin, the activating hormone, and in situations of connectedness it generates oxytocin, which supports feelings of love and bonding. Prompted by our autonomic nervous system in cases of tension and relaxation, our heart will beat faster or slower. But with practice, we are also able to observe what our heart is up to, and by doing that more and more carefully, we can better tune our inner state of balance and stress reactions. It has been shown, for example, that age-old practices of meditation, which have been cultivated in all religions and cultures, are balm for our heart and health.

Variability in Heart Rhythm

Our heart rhythm reacts directly to subtle changes in our inner mood and thoughts, even if we are not conscious of it. Emotions such as rage and fear immediately lead to a chaotic heartbeat and inner unease. Conversely, a general feeling of well-being, inner harmony and relaxation of the stress system will generate a quiet, coherent heartbeat. The important thing is not a faster or slower beat of the heart, but the variability, the interval between two heartbeats, which may be longer in one situation and shorter in another. Harmonious deceleration and acceleration of the heart rhythm is called a coherent rhythm; it gives a feeling of concentration and well-being. In young children this heart variability is most pronounced, and usually it declines as we age. Shortly before death, the heart loses this ability to change its rhythms and then it beats mechanically, like a metronome.

This variability of heart rhythm is not easy to feel directly, but it can be demonstrated through a computer program that measures the interval between two heartbeats. When the time between two beats becomes shorter the line on the screen goes up, when it lengthens the line goes down. A coherent heart rhythm of regular accelerations and decelerations shows a harmonious, waving line and predictable curve. As soon as we feel tense, however, the pattern becomes increasingly chaotic; the line then looks like an irregular mountain ridge.

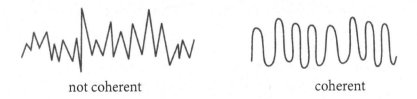

not coherent   coherent

Situations in which we feel safe, in harmony with ourselves and our surroundings, in which we have nice, positive memories and loving feelings, right away lead to a coherent heart rhythm and so strengthen our health.

Because of these subtle reactions of the heart, in daily life we see a more or less chaotic pattern that most people wouldn't be aware of without technical aids. But there are little gadgets we can clip to our ear or finger that tell us in which situations our heart beats coherently or chaotically. We can thus explore in what situations we experience physical stress, of which we may be completely unconscious, and when we are in harmony. We can then more deliberately create situations that foster coherence, such as in nature, meditation, or just musing with the cat on your lap. And in this way it also becomes possible to train ourselves to stay more in harmony and in a coherent heart rhythm in stressful situations, such as a meeting at work, in a traffic jam or in a conflict with our partner. (See also the exercises in Section 21.5.)

4.8   Stress management: a finely tuned state of balance

In summary: Positive stress, such as in brief, manageable tension, gives the body a pleasant, exciting feeling and focused concentration to accomplish a task. When chronic stress develops, the finely tuned neuronal and hormonal mechanisms are upset. During chronic stress or excessive anxiety, too much cortisol is produced, which may eventually lead to damage to the limbic and immune systems. The sympathetic nervous system and LHPA axis are activated, resulting in production of adrenalin and noradrenalin which put the body on active alert. Stress causes adrenalin to remain in the blood for a long time. When stress becomes chronic without periods of relaxation, the original natural level can no longer be restored. The adrenalin content remains permanently too high, which means the body no longer calms down and is always in a state of activity.

In addition, the cortisol level also becomes permanently too high, which diminishes concentration and memory. The immune system is impacted, and symptoms of chronic fatigue and feelings of depression occur. Muscles and bones may also develop damage caused by fatigue, which may lead to illnesses such as fibromyalgia. By contrast, by the time we witness a state of exhaustion such as in burnout, the cortisol level will be lowered. A condition of passivity, despair and, finally, apathy will then set in (see *Cortisol* in Section 4.2).

5 Failing vitality

Vitality is of critical importance for our functioning in life. If we sleep poorly, have to be alert too often, or give too little attention to the restoration of our physical and psychological forces and of our life energy, we will eventually burn ourselves out. For this reason the life body and the management of life forces lie at the core of most non-Western healing methods, including those from the Chinese and Tibetan traditions and also of shamanistic medicine as it has been practiced for centuries from Siberia to America.

Western medicine is focused primarily on the physical human being, and life and psyche are viewed as its result. In Oriental medicine things are precisely the other way around. In recent years, however, awareness of quality of life and life forces has been growing in the West. After the discovery a little over a hundred years ago of the psyche, and its importance in medicine, in recent decades the medical profession in the West has begun to pay more attention to life energy and the self-healing principle in our body, *salutogenesis*. Therapies based on Oriental meditation techniques and therapies, such as mindfulness and body-oriented consciousness therapies, are becoming more integrated into conventional medicine.

This chapter is about the life body, its qualities, and the ways in which we are able to care for it or damage it.

5.1 Vital energy

The Life Body
All physical processes are manifestations of non-material or energy forces hiding behind them. We can distinguish three areas in our non-physical being:
- the realm of *life energy*: growth, regeneration and reproduction;
- the realm of *the soul*: feeling and emotional life, likes and dislikes, talents and incapacities;
- the realm of *spiritual* impulses: as expressed in our "I," the director of our biography.

The life body permeates and looks after each cell and each organ in our body. It manages constructive forces, growth and repair throughout our life. Our physical body disintegrates as soon as death takes place. During our life, our life body prevents physical destructive forces from having the upper hand. All bodily structures and organs are nourished and maintained from moment to moment. The object is not just growth as such, but also growth into a particular form. A function of the life body is also to begin growth and recovery processes at the right moment, as well as to slow them down. We can observe such processes in the healing of injuries.

In children, the life forces during the first few years are still dependent on their surroundings, and are directly connected with those of their caregivers, first of all, of course, the parents. During the first seven years these life forces are individualized. Most people preserve in their vitality a certain dependence on their surroundings and the people around them.

However, what nourishes the life forces and what acts too destructively on them are factors that differ for each person. One person needs a lonely spot in nature to come to herself, another prefers a town in a warm, southern country with busy marketplaces and sidewalk cafés. One likes to go the same place year after year, another is always looking for something new. One feels nourished in an art museum, another can't stand it. Constant haste, situations of anxiety, criticism and cynicism work destructively on everyone's life forces.

Life forces express themselves in our vital energy and in fatigue. They strongly influence our moods and our feeling life. Life energy can be observed in all rhythmic daily processes that support buildup and balance in the body, such as the biorhythms of organs, absorption, digestion and secretion of foodstuffs, the formation from these of our own unique substances, and growth and reproductive processes. In the first years of life, our life forces are almost completely used for the growth and building up of our body, but with the change of teeth a differentiation takes place within the life body. Part of the life forces remains in service of our metabolism, maintenance and repair, but another part is freed to serve the soul and is expressed in psychological forces. It is not without justification that we speak of lively thoughts, lively imagination or memories, for these are fed by our life forces.

This is also the reason why, when the life body is exhausted as happens in burnout, thinking, imagination and memory are all affected.

By choosing a lifestyle that takes into account our natural biorhythms of sleeping and waking, rest and activity, and by choosing healthy food and good-quality clothing, we nourish and care for our life body. When our life forces suffice for an active life and its tasks, we feel energetic and rested and we are eager to do the things we have to do. We don't easily become sick because our resistance is good and our mood in balance. However, if we work the life body too hard and don't allow it time to recover between efforts, we will notice that our vitality and resistance decline, that we are always tired and often sick, and that our inner life becomes static and less lively.

This exhaustion may be physical when for years we don't sleep enough or live in a bad environment with constant noise and other excessive sensory stimuli, such as bright unnatural light, noisy traffic, bad air quality and a lack of nature around us. There may also be psychological processes set in motion by constant critical, negative and self-deprecating thoughts, demotivation due to boring work or being caught in a disintegrating relationship. The younger you are, the longer your natural life forces will be able to deal with these kinds of destructive circumstances, but eventually they will come home to roost, and in a situation of burnout, the life forces will completely collapse in the end.

"Structural" Differences between Life Bodies

There are major individual differences in vitality and in the quality of life energy. Of course the circumstances in which a child is born and cared for are important for the vitality of the life forces, but all of us also have innate differences. One child is born filled with energy; without the parents having to do much for it, the child eats, grows and sleeps well, is rarely sick, is full of confidence and enjoys life. When such a child is occasionally brought into a busy place or goes to bed late, it doesn't make much difference; a healthy child is not quickly thrown off balance.

Another child, sometimes in the same family, is like a frizzled little plant. It looks pale, is often cold, fearful and easily frightened, has trouble sleeping and grows too little. When you take such a child to a busy store or party, it is quickly overstimulated and has even more trouble sleeping at night. For such children the daily rhythms of eating, getting up and going to bed have to be observed much more strictly. The amount of sleep a child needs is very different from one to another, but it does remain constant throughout life. If you need a lot of sleep as a toddler, chances are that in adulthood this will stay the same.

There are dreamy children who like to observe the world or quietly read a book in a corner. They are often considered too slow and are then stimulated, whereas the quick, lively ones with their inborn inexhaustible energy are easily bored and always looking for a fresh adventure. They usually sleep well, but it is a big job for the parents to steer all that energy in the right directions.

This does not change in adulthood. One person is like a strong tree, deeply rooted in the earth with a large, healthy crown, and capable of living through periods of drought, storm or cold; another is by nature more like a vulnerable little plant that always needs to be nurtured, protected and taken care of for its development.

As long as our life circumstances are adapted to our innate life force, we will lead a healthy life no matter how we are constituted. But if by nature we have limited life forces and live in a modern city or in exhausting circumstances, for instance as a single parent, if there are big financial problems or the neighbors are noisy day and night, the risk is great that life itself becomes a battle for survival for the life body. Normal daily life may then already exhaust us, but this often happens before we realize it. Noise, constant sensory stimuli, television, computers and cell phones, pollution, noisy traffic and throngs of people—they are all integral parts of our culture, and people do not realize how much energy it all takes.

Great Openness—People Who Are Sensitive

The life body, life energy, called *chi* by the Chinese, mediates between the body and the soul. It is much less closed off than the physical body and is therefore not only the source of our own vital energy but also a sensitive organ of perception with which we are, mostly unconsciously, in close contact with our surroundings, as well as with the life forces and souls of people around us. In this openness there are also great differences in different people.

A large number of people possess great innate openness and sensitivity in the life body. These are the children and adults who subtly perceive a mood, who will bring you a cup of tea before you ask for it, who sense when someone is grieving even if the subject never comes up, or that something is brewing in the department although it seems that everyone is all right. As children, they surprise their parents by voicing the latter's thoughts aloud, or by answering a question before it was asked. They soon turn pale with shadows under their eyes and are often tired or listless, even though their parents say they get enough sleep. When there is a tense atmosphere in their class at school, or when their parents are having a conflict, they get a stomach- or headache, although they can't put their finger on what's actually happening. They refuse to visit certain of their friends, and when the teacher is angry with other children they are upset.

Often they need more regularity and sleep than their brothers and sisters. Sometimes they become caregivers for others at a young age and they may surprise people by their unexpected observations and wise remarks. These are children who ask profound questions and often have a natural spiritual or religious orientation. They visibly brighten up in nature and like camping in a quiet place or hiking in the mountains, where they may bubble over with energy.

Also as adults, such people are quickly thrown off balance when there are quarrels or disharmony in their vicinity. More than others they are bothered by sounds, smells or fast-changing images, and they may get upset by a TV program, movie or newspaper article. Also in places where there are throngs of people, such as a big store, market, swimming pool or sport center, they quickly feel their energy evaporate. They often react more strongly than others to certain foods and other things such as sugar, dyes, coffee, alcohol and cigarette smoke. Sometimes they are bothered by things others never even notice, like the sound of the refrigerator, a magnetic or electrical field around an appliance, cell phones or transmission towers, and computer and television screens. For these people actually all impressions in daily life in modern Western culture add up to chronic overload, and they run more risk than others of burning out or developing chronic fatigue syndrome.

EXAMPLE 42

Johanna, the nurse, is very sensitive to moods, sounds, smells and certain images. She bought a special refrigerator that doesn't hum, and she never has background music. When she has watched TV for an hour she feels inwardly empty which she finds unpleasant, and "all those images of violence" stay with her. Therefore she rarely watches TV and always avoids the news. Already as a child she had nightmares after scary stories. She says: "I always see in my mind what I read or hear. Strangely enough I can handle it when I hear bad things at work, as if the connection with the person I am talking with enables me to bear it better." She feels best in nature, when she is alone, and when life is not too hectic.

Interference in Life Energy

Generally speaking there are two areas that will interfere with our life energy. One concerns the life body that is connected with the physical body, the other, the life forces that express themselves in the soul.

Interference in the life forces connected with the body:
- insufficient sleep, irregular day-and-night rhythm
- excessive sensory stimuli of unnatural sounds, smells or visual impressions
- stress, hectic pace of life
- prolonged physical overload
- unnatural food
- overeating, especially refined and chemically processed foods
- unhealthy fats, overly sweet or salty food, food with unnatural dyes or chemical taste enhancers
- coffee, black tea, alcohol, nicotine, drugs
- chemical medications and chemical food supplements
- strong magnetic and electrical fields
- lack of fresh air, breathing polluted air.

Interference in the life forces connected with the soul:
- one-sided lifestyle oriented toward performance and goals for the future to the exclusion of the quality of experience in the here and now
- excessive sensory stimuli from artificial sounds or visual impressions
- unhealthy caricatures and violent images

- cynicism
- preprogrammed, performance-oriented, and unimaginative education oriented toward reproducing knowledge, not toward creative thinking and doing
- work that allows little space for personal input and creativity
- monotonous work, the pace and quality of which are determined by technology and not by the worker, such as at a conveyor belt or in front of a screen
- bad atmosphere in a social environment (school, work, family).

As we have seen, many of these producers of interference are normal, unquestioned parts of our daily lives, and if we want to nourish and care for our life forces, we must make conscious choices about the food we eat, about our lifestyle and work, and about learning to listen to our inner images. For if the interference is strong enough and goes on long enough, and the processes of restoration are not strong enough, the body-connected part of the life body that governs growth and well-being becomes overloaded and ends up exhausted. This can be observed in symptoms such as pallor, weight change (either way), fatigue, sleep disturbances, digestive problems, loss of libido and slow recovery from injuries and infections.

Also the free part of the life body, which works in the soul, becomes exhausted. Our thinking loses precision, becomes sluggish and associative, and lacks concentration. Our feeling becomes flat and heavy while, at the same time, the soul is naked and oversensitive to impressions. Willpower and persistence decline, as do creativity and imagination. Life then becomes a rut, like the horse that walks in a treadmill, always the same round, with hanging head and sluggish step.

The life body often observes this process of exhaustion already, long before we are conscious of it. It expresses this in symbolic pictures, the language of the life body: It warns us in our dreams at night and in semi-conscious images by day. Charles's dream, about falling into potholes and dogs biting his hands off, was his life body warning him, "You can't go on like this (potholes); you'll be unable to accomplish anything meaningful (hands)."

EXAMPLE 43

In the year before she burned out, Lara had the same dream three times: She's in her class in school and is taking care of a little baby. But when she takes a good look, the child turns out to be dead. Later she realized that her dreams had tried to tell her for a long time what she did not want to admit, namely that her inner child, her creativity and lust for life, were dying in this school.

Nourishment for the Life Body

The life body nourishes and takes care of us throughout our life, and for this reason it is of great importance for our health that we learn to nourish and take care of our life body. For children this is the task of the parents, daycare providers and teachers in school. Adults have to do it themselves. A variety of healthy, preferably organic foods provide good substances the life body can use for building up the physical body. Fast food and food with a lot of chemical additives may perhaps produce sufficient calories but no positive contribution to the quality of the life forces. The same holds true for substances such as sugar, coffee, alcohol and nicotine.

The life body thrives in a state of balance between rest and activity, regularity in daily occupations and alternating rhythms in time, such as in the course of the week, the seasons and festivals of the year. Concentrated, inwardly oriented attention, as in meditation, also nourishes the life body.

For most people sufficient challenge and variation in work and activity, as well as in their surroundings, are important; boredom and routine undermine the life forces The amount of variation and change needed differs for each person; one person needs more rest and another thrives on movement and activity. In our busy daily lives we usually do not devote much time to inwardly directed attention and therefore we notice too late that we are becoming overfed with impressions that tend to lead to excessive fatigue.

For questions and exercises related to vitality and the life body, see Part 4, Chapter 18.

6 Soul life

Our personality encompasses many different facets or selves, each with its own specific quality and energy. Consciously or unconsciously, we show those or put them into action in different situations. As chairperson in a meeting, we feel and behave differently than when we are taking a walk on a deserted beach or when sitting around the table with the family. As a teacher before a class or during a meeting with a customer, we are not the same as at a party with friends or in a hurry in line at a checkout counter. Yet in all those situations we say that it was me, myself. Apparently our self contains several, and sometimes contradictory, parts.

We are perfectly familiar with some of these selves, and we experience them repeatedly in all kinds of situations in our lives, intended or not. For instance, an ambitious self that operates ruthlessly, or a self that always has the tendency to help others but does not notice what we need ourselves. There are also selves that lead a more hidden existence, such as a rejected rebel, or an indolent lazy-bones, or a blunt, hot-tempered boss—selves we try to hide or deny or, if that doesn't work, at least ignore. But still, both the dominant and the more repressed selves have great influence on our actions, our feeling life, patterns of thinking and body language.

Whether we experience them as pleasant or unpleasant, helpful or problematic, we have developed these parts of our souls ourselves for certain reasons, and each of them has its own specific task in the whole of our personality. By learning to listen to their voices we can come to know much about ourselves and become able to more consciously direct our behavior.

6.1 Interaction between inner life and environment

Burnout is a complex process that slowly grows over the course of years. What counts is not so much the objective quantity of work as the manner in which both work and life are experienced. Although there are certainly work circumstances and professions in which virtually everyone at some point burns out, we also need to recognize the interaction between the assigned burden of work and the carrying capacity of the one who has to perform the work. In addition to work circumstances and life tasks, therefore, burnout also has much to do with the carrying capacity of the person in question. Finally, things may go on in private life that put great demands on life energy and carrying capacity, so that someone whose work is satisfying may still become burned out.

People differ greatly in their ability to handle prolonged stress. This is connected with differences in the constitution of the life body and with the quality of the life forces. One person is by nature more open and sensitive, while another is more self-enclosed and therefore less susceptible to outside pressure. In addition, however, personality and character traits we have developed as a result of earlier life experiences influence our way of dealing with work assignments and stress. All kinds of standards, views and contradictory inner voices determine our behavior and feelings in these situations.

Together, all these factors determine the way in which you experience your work at a particular time and the possibility or impossibility of finding a state of balance between exertion and relaxation. At the same time, this also opens the door to finding methods of prevention and recovery. If, because of a natural tendency or character trait, you are at risk for burnout, you can still manage to stay on top of things by taking certain measures, practicing certain exercises or changing the way you work. You don't need to wait until *after* burnout to change your ways.

In this chapter the emphasis is on character traits, contradictory inner voices and survival strategies as these appear or develop in the course of a person's biography.

6.2 Prior experiences as unconscious script for life

By their way of life, parents set an example that a child will unconsciously pick up as a guideline or, by contrast, as something he or she will resist for the rest of their lives. The relationships with parents, brothers and sisters, as well as the atmosphere in the family, leave lasting impressions in our soul. Certain parts of our personality are formed and reinforced by experiences from our youth.

The social-economic circumstances of the family in which you grew up, family culture, your place among the other children, and youth experiences with other relatives, at school, with friends and enemies—all of these contribute to your strategies in life and to your later work mentality. If you come from a large family, where it was hard to make ends meet and everyone had to work hard yet something was still always missing, it is very likely that working hard and earning a good income will become a way to create security in life. Thus grows the worker bee, while the bon vivant, the hermit and the complainer are definitely unwelcome guests in such a family.

EXAMPLE 44

Rosanna, the overworked mother, grew up as the eldest of two daughters of parents who ran a store together. From her earliest days she learned that working hard and giving service were praiseworthy traits. Her parents were always working, and as a child she already helped stocking shelves. Later she had few friends because she always had to help after school, and her parents were afraid of thieves and burglars, and did not want Tom, Dick and Harry to come into the store.

Because she was bright she skipped a grade when she was nine, and ended up in a different school with older children with whom she was unable to connect. The other children were able to do things Rosanna had not yet learned. She used to be the best in her class; now she was at the bottom and had to work very hard to keep up. On top of that she was bullied by the other children. Much of her self-confidence was now gone. The feeling that everyone understands something she doesn't know about has pursued her ever since, and she is convinced that her own accomplishments don't amount to much.

In (auto)biographical literature we can often recognize how different personalities develop. There is the story of how two brothers, sons of a deeply religious, hard-working market gardener, each choose a different role.[23] The eldest identifies with the mother and becomes a caring, responsible son. The youngest picks up the repressed parts of the father; he likes to hang out, drink and do things strictly forbidden in the family. In the biography of Annie M.G. Schmidt[24] you can see how, as the daughter of a rural minister and an obedient but unhappy housewife, she chose to develop a strong and humorous rebel, who stands by her all her life and empowers her in many creations and in writing wonderful children's books.

EXAMPLE 45

Chris, who became burned out after a difficult reorganization after which he had to manage a new department, grew up as the eldest son in a family with eight children. The father owned a small shipyard next to the house, where work was done also in evenings and weekends. In the family reigned the unspoken message that you must never become dependent on others, and that you can only make it in life by unceasing hard work. Moreover, the customer is always king, and therefore more important than you. The parents did not pay much attention to what Chris did in school as long as his grades were good. To help bring in some more family income, he already worked at the shipyard at a young age even though he wasn't interested in it. In this way he learned to put his interests in second place behind those of others and pay no attention to fatigue, let alone not feeling like working.

In some families the command to be available to others lives strongly; it is then almost obligatory to be the savior. Guarding your boundaries and making time for yourself is experienced in such families as selfish and undesirable.

---

23 Jan Siebelink, *Knielen op een bed violen* [Kneeling on a Bed of Violets]. Amsterdam 2009.
24 Annie M.G. Schmidt (1911–1995), celebrated Dutch author of children's books.

EXAMPLE 46

Bert is a 51-year-old burned out family physician. He is always ready to help everyone, but isn't able to take care of himself very well. He is the eldest of four children. His sister, who is two years younger than he, was slightly mentally disabled and Bert always had to protect her in grade school. If she was bullied or came home with a black and blue mark, the parents held Bert responsible. His parents were always ready to help anyone and simply expected the same of their children. Bert's father was a minister in a small congregation, and the interests of the congregation were always more important than those of the family. The family had to move several times when the father was transferred. Even though the children didn't want to change schools and leave their familiar surroundings, the family had no input in the decision. The mother was 100% committed to support the father. The parents never disagreed on anything. The children always had to behave correctly and quarrels were not allowed.

The eldest child in a poor family, where the mother is a single parent, or where a business is run from the home, often identifies already at a young age with the role of an adult. Such children will feel responsible for family life, including the income, and learn to put their own interests in second place.

EXAMPLE 47

Liz is the eldest daughter in a fundamentalist Protestant family with five children. Her father suddenly died when she was eleven, and since then poverty was always just around the corner. Her mother worked in other houses to keep body and soul together. As the eldest child, Liz had to make sure that the house was kept clean, and she had to take care of her younger siblings. "Whenever we were doing nothing or were bored, my mother always said: 'The devil finds work for idle hands,' and then she had us do something in the house or the garden." Liz was always afraid that she would also lose her mother, who looked so tired and exhausted. Therefore she always worked very hard and was proud to do things better than others.

After high school Liz trained as a secretary and worked evenings to contribute to the family income. She did not marry. She kept helping her mother for a long time, and afterward she liked to be alone and not have another family. For her, when she still had her former boss and colleague, the workplace was very important, like a kind of family. Even when she had a new, unpleasant boss, Liz still felt responsible for her. It didn't occur to her to protest openly or to refuse something.

In such ways the family may become a breeding ground for worker bees, where children learn that when you don't work you don't eat, and that the interests of the group are more important than individual wishes and needs. On the one hand this may foster great willpower and perseverance; on the other hand there is the risk that duty becomes the dominant motive for action, and there is insufficient appreciation for signals of overload and running on empty. It may also be that the adult is still in conflict with his parents as in his childhood.

EXAMPLE 48

Charles is the youngest, and the only son, in a family with four children. Father was a foreman in construction and brought his son up like a Spartan. For instance, Charles had to take swimming lessons before school in an ice-cold outdoor pool. If he did not get good grades in school, his father would not speak to him for days. He rarely received a compliment. His sisters left the home when he was still young. As an adolescent he had to find a job because he got no allowance and had to pay for the bicycle he needed to get to school. Mother was a sweet woman who totally submitted to her husband, but now and then she secretly gave Charles something. She was very proud that he was doing so well in school and supported his plans to go to university. Father had no use for that and refused to give his son any financial support.

Just before Charles graduated his father suddenly died of a heart attack. He is ashamed to say it, but Charles was actually relieved that his father had died. For about the last five years his mother has lived in a home for the elderly. He has a good relationship with her, as well as with his three sisters.

In Charles's life his Spartan upbringing shows. He works hard, never complains, and looks for solutions when he runs into a problem. But he also keeps trying to prove to his disdainful father, even though he died long ago, that biologists are no pansies. In addition, due to the style of his new boss, an old pattern reappears. He is overbearing and forces Charles to do things his way. No matter how hard Charles tries, he never gets a compliment or a thank-you. The woman who used to be his boss plays the role of his mother. She secretly supports Charles, but she can't do anything in the open. When Charles then does make a mistake and is humiliated in front of his colleagues, the picture is complete and the wounded child in him bursts into tears.

Another important factor is your birth order. Are you the eldest who from a young age had responsibility for younger siblings, had little freedom to play or go out, and soon had to contribute to the family income, or are you the youngest who was always cared for and who could always count on someone's help when needed? In the first case the capacity to carry responsibility and stand on your own two feet grows early on, but the ability to listen to your own needs may be lacking to some extent. In the second case, things are exactly reversed; such people may have trouble as adults making their own decisions and taking responsibility for their own lives, including their inevitable mistakes.

Also in families where the parents fight a lot and there is a violent atmosphere, the children often have to assume responsibility at a young age. They try to protect themselves and others by always being sweet and good and doing their best. Or, by contrast, they may develop into a rebel or a hermit who withdraws and wants nothing to do with the family. Or they may become fearful and dependent, letting others make the decisions.

EXAMPLE 49

When Rosanna was twelve her little sister, whom she loved very much, fell seriously ill and died six months later. The store was closed for two days and then life went on. Her sister, the loss and grief, her own fear and longing for death were forbidden subjects. To her father life seemed to have lost all meaning, and pleasure was forbidden. Mother worked with grim determination and never laughed. Rosanna concluded that it would have been easier for her parents to do without her than without her sister. She did what she could to make life bearable for them and functioned as mediator in their deteriorating marriage. At school she did her best because that was important to her parents.

Rosanna graduated from high school with good grades. To her parents' surprise, however, she decided against going to college, but chose to train in a community for disabled people with the intention to work there. When Rosanna also fell in love with a man her parents did not approve of, and moved in with him when she was nineteen, they broke all contact. Although her mother tried to restore contact when Rosanna's first child was born, things never were the same. When her father died, it had been his wish that Rosanna would not attend the funeral. She did go, but felt estranged and unwelcome. Later she had nightmares about her little sister.

With an effort, Rosanna only recently mustered the courage to express to her physician that she continually lives in fear that something will happen to Dan or one of her children. She is particularly worried about her youngest son, that he will suddenly fall ill and die, or have an accident. When Dan or one of the children goes somewhere without her, she says a quick prayer every few minutes for their safety. She is afraid something terrible will happen if she does not hold them constantly in her consciousness.

The Post-WW II Generation

People whose parents survived World War II but lived in fear, collaborated with the enemy, were imprisoned or lost family members are often subject to problems of a particular nature. The wartime history of these parents often forms a hidden, dark undertone in their family life. For those who were traumatized by the war, all later grief or inconvenience was as nothing compared with the great suffering they had gone through in the war. The children who were born during or after the war lived in the midst of often suppressed but omnipresent anxiety; they learned in many different ways to bear the feelings of their parents in mind and to offer consolation for their grief. Thus they grew up in families where unspoken fear and grief reigned while, at the same time, they were put under great pressure to see to it that life would still be worth living. Because of this they did not learn to become aware of their own needs and assert them in a healthy manner.

Many people in this generation became hard workers who tried to improve the world through their choice of profession, or else tried to achieve financial security for themselves. Especially when there are such secrets hidden in the lives of the parents, insecurity forms an unconscious threat to the basis of existence: fear of losing a loved one, fear of losing security and material well-being, fear of treason, anxiety that the secret will be revealed. For these reasons, many of these people, middle-aged by now, will get stuck in burnout at some point in their lives. However, this opens the door to developing greater clarity regarding the destiny they share with their parents, so that they become able to separate themselves from it and can perhaps make other choices that correspond better with their own inner needs and capacities.

EXAMPLE 50

Tony, the embittered teacher, was born in Rotterdam during the "hunger winter" of 1945.[25] The whole city was in ruins after successive bombings. He was the youngest of five children. An older brother had died before Tony was born, and Tony was named after his mother's twin brother who had been shot by a firing squad in reprisal for some act of resistance. As a

---

25 Translator's note: The last, very cold, winter of the war, when in Holland all production of food, coal, electricity and everything else came to a complete stop and people died of hunger in the streets, has ever after been called the "hunger winter."

child, Tony often had nightmares about the war, but he didn't dare tell his parents, because he hadn't really experienced the war. His father was a taciturn, gruff man; if you weren't careful you got hit or kicked.

His mother's life was governed by grief for the loss of her son and brother, as well as by fear. She was always afraid that something would happen to her other children. When an airplane flew over the house or there was a bad thunderstorm, she would shake with fear and call the children around her. When Tony had a stomachache, his mother would immediately think he was seriously ill and panic. Thus already as a child Tony learned not to make his mother even more anxious and not to say anything about pain or discomfort. He thought his parents' burdens were heavy enough, and always felt responsible for his mother.

Double Identity—Second-Generation Immigrants

Young immigrants of the second generation, particularly women, although they may be quite well educated and integrated, may yet be uncertain about their true identity. The need to adapt from a young age to the totally different demands of two cultures requires great flexibility and tactical skill. At the same time, however, it fosters rebels who set their own course in life.

EXAMPLE 51

Malika is the eldest daughter of Iranian parents. They fled in 1980 to escape from the new regime and were admitted to Holland as political refugees. Malika was five when she arrived and her little brother one. Later there were three more daughters. Malika did not adjust easily to Holland. What her parents had represented as paradise turned out to be a cold, wet place with children she could not understand. For the first two years, the family lived in a refugee camp. Her father, who in Iran had been kind and caring, was always tired and cross. He regularly hit Malika, something that never used to happen. Her mother spent much time in bed and was terribly homesick. Malika missed her grandmother and her beautiful garden with orange trees.

In high school Malika was not allowed to do things that other girls of her age were doing. Her parents were very proud of her and came to the graduation ceremony. But they wanted her to get married right away, to a distant cousin of her father, who was much older, had also escaped and was living in Germany. Malika resolutely refused and for the first time put up resistance. Her father became enraged, beat her to a pulp and locked her up. Malika escaped with the secret help of one of her sisters, just before the planned marriage. Via a home for immigrant girls she ended up in a big city. She found a place to live and entered university with a scholarship. She studied philology and soon found a job with a publisher to make some extra money.

Malika often felt lonely and outside everything; she missed her parents and siblings very much. The publishing house she worked for was growing; she liked her job and worked her way up to managing the translation department. It felt a little like family, although she never told anyone what her life was really like. She didn't see her parents for years; news came through the grapevine. But when five years after her escape her father got cancer, she mustered all her courage and went home. Her mother shed tears of joy, and Malika also became reconciled with her father before he died.

That was an enormous relief, but at the same time she felt estranged from the family; she had become too Dutch. Malika continued to live alone. She regularly has Dutch boyfriends, but she never mentions them at home. Her mother also never mentions marriage. A year before her burnout, her youngest sister came to live with her when the sister began her studies at the university.

6.3   Personality parts in dialogue—who is in charge?

People who become burned out often have a personality that is strongly focused on performance and accomplishment. Working hard is a source of self-respect and earns them esteem from others. Navel-gazing and whining about illness and adversity are foreign to them; "get on with it" is their motto. It is striking that the personality traits of people who become burned out are highly valued in our culture and usually stimulated and reinforced in the family from a young age. And precisely these idealistic, hard workers who commit themselves to a goal with great perseverance and loyalty are the ones who run the risk of overestimating themselves and burning out. If you have never learned to listen to your body, if you attach no importance to how you feel in a particular situation, if you always see merely the goal and not the way to it, you run a big risk of burning out sooner or later.

Someone's profession, of course, has to do with his or her character. People who choose a profession that engages them with other people are usually socially oriented and like to do things for others. If you are good at organizing things and naturally exude authority, you might well choose to become a teacher or a manager. But qualities like that can also become a trap if they push you in a one-sided direction.

Typical character traits for people who become burned out are the following:

- great ideals and lofty goals,
- perfectionism and perseverance in the execution of tasks,
- profound sense of responsibility and therefore difficulty with refusing or delegating tasks,
- tendency to become deeply touched by the suffering of others and to want to solve their problems.

We can look at the personality as built up out of many part-personalities or "selves." What we experience in a certain moment as *self*, such as "this is how I act" or "this is me" differs from one situation to another. We consciously, or unconsciously, adopt various roles. Character traits are then expressions of the stronger, dominant personality parts; they reflect inner energy which, as an internal personality, helps form the life tasks we set for ourselves and our ideas about the ways these tasks have to be accomplished, as well as our feelings about ourselves. Different personality parts may agree with each other and cooperate, but often there are also inner parts that criticize and fight each other. Some of our selves are so explicit in their opinions that we completely identify with them; others are taboo, repressed and starved in our inner world. Learning to recognize both these primary and rejected personality parts can give us insight into the ways we generate stress for ourselves.

It is therefore a good idea to discover which personality parts in our soul are more developed or less developed, which are always piping up and which are hiding in a corner. In this way we can gain insight into the selves that usually direct our will, as well as into internal contradictions that may demand much life energy. What we have rejected will often start to wriggle into view, for in the end it does want to be heard. Traits that are too dominant are often the first to clash with our surroundings, though we aren't really aware of them or we might even be proud of them. When important primary selves are hard workers and have high work standards, they may in their one-sidedness well lead us to exhaustion.

Personality parts as such are not autonomous, complete personalities with their own biography and development. Rather, they are forms of energy that in certain situations in our life arose, were formed or reinforced. Their outer purpose is to let us function better in the world, to defend us from injustice, to get ahead. They also have an inward function to protect us from soul injuries. In those cases they are often connected with painful life experiences. Even an aggressive or destructive self needs to be listened to; it tells us something about what we want or have to inwardly protect. In the end it is the task of our "I" to hear all those inner voices and learn to work with them more consciously.

Different Kinds

Some of our inner selves are archetypal; they live in each one of us. Thus there is, for instance, the inner child, the wise, good mother or father, and the hero or heroine. There are also selves many people will recognize, such as the perfectionist or the savior, but which have developed a personal color because they were formed by our life experiences. Finally there are very individual personality parts that you can give their own names, for instance, Little Anne, Fearful Frank, or Bully Bob; or you may find a mythological name that has significance for your own myth, your life story, such as Valiant Harold or Catherine the Fair. A woman may also have a Harold in her, and a man a Catherine. When you discover a self, you can always wonder whether it has a masculine or feminine energy; it may also be neutral or both masculine and feminine.

Dominant and Rejected Personality Parts

Our selves may work against each other or reinforce each other, and we may identify with each of them to a greater or lesser extent. The parts we completely identify with and that give us a feeling of "I am that" are called primary or dominant parts. We can experience them as positive and be proud of them, and secretly look down on people who have not developed the qualities represented by these parts. But we may also experience them as interfering characters that repeatedly cause social problems or keep us from doing the right thing.

There are also selves in our inner world that we do not know or recognize at all. We may have put them away long ago—in our childhood or in a prior relationship—and be so ashamed of them that whenever they raise their heads we shut them down. We often discover these rejected or repressed selves when we notice we are irritated by another person's speech or behavior.

Below are lists of personality parts often seen in people with burnout to help you recognize their effects, strengths and weaknesses, even when they are lying dormant. I have given them names that speak to me. You may recognize yourself in some of the personality parts described here, but you may give them different names. The more personal the names are that you give to your selves, the better you will be able to listen to their voices and thus also come to know yourself better.

Common dominant archetypes in people who become burned out:

- the worker bee
- the idealist
- the perfectionist
- the critic
- the organizer
- the slave driver
- the adapter

- the terrier
- the armored introvert
- Atlas
- the savior
- the pleaser
- the guilty one

Commonly rejected archetypes:

- the bon vivant
- the contented one
- the dreamer
- the jester
- the hermit
- the sensitive one

- the doubter
- the complainer
- the dependent one
- the rebel
- the border guard
- the victim

I have characterized these selves in the descriptions that follow. Keep in mind that these are not complete personalities, but personality parts that, working with others, affect us from our inner being. If a description jumps out at you, for instance that of the perfectionist or the terrier, that does not mean that you *are* a perfectionist or a terrier, but that these two personality parts are strongly represented in you, so that you identify with them. Finally, please note that I am using masculine pronouns to describe these selves, but as was mentioned before, personality parts may be masculine or feminine, independent of your gender. You may have a feminine energy that is your organizer, or a masculine one. This is also true for all other selves.

6.4 Dominant or primary selves in people with burnout

People who become burned out usually feel highly responsible for their tasks and often find it difficult to delegate, let go and draw boundaries regarding their work and other responsibilities. Their primary selves have high ideals, like to work hard and abhor laziness and weakness. For some of them it is also important to be appreciated and not to seem negative. Of course, not all the primary selves discussed here are dominant in everyone who burns out. But a number of them are often witnessed, and these tend to work closely together and reinforce each other.

Types of dominant selves are characterized below in a somewhat pictorial manner, like caricatures, so you can recognize and experience them better. Try to live into each of them, and pay attention to your reactions as you are reading. If you recognize yourself in one of them, or if it feels as if I am speaking to you, that says something about your primary selves, while if you get irritated it may be one of your rejected personality parts.

The Worker Bee: "If I perform, I exist."
The worker bee feels at home in our culture where hard work is valued and the customer is king. Social advancement and getting ahead in work and career are the most important factors in life. His views are strict and focused on accomplishment: "He who does not work does not eat." The worker bee brings great commitment and energy and does not easily say no, whatever he may be asked to do. His self-image depends on his accomplishments. His survival strategy is to work hard. Therefore, when he is tired or has physical complaints or feelings of unease, the motto is always: Work harder.

Worker bees find it very difficult to sit at home and do nothing. They don't want to be concerned about themselves. Even a vacation or an excursion with the family is not their greatest joy. People harboring a strong worker bee therefore manage to keep going for an extremely long time, and they fall into a very deep pit when they are finally so burned out that they really can't take another step. Their whole world image collapses. For this reason, a true worker bee goes back to work too soon, without having truly recovered, and without any change in the daily pattern of his life and work. In the course of years, people with a strong inner worker bee often develop a pattern of repeated illness, burnout, and going back to work too soon, without any basic change in their way of life.

EXAMPLE 52

Once Chris was married and had a family, he studied law in the evening, and when he was 32 he found a job as in-house attorney in a small steel trading firm. Chris took into his entire working life the mentality which he had grown up with. He was irritated by colleagues who called in sick for every little thing, and he had no problem working extra hours or weekends. When his children became adolescents, there were many conflicts at home because he couldn't stand it when they just hung out in front of the TV or went out gallivanting all weekend and spent half the next day in bed. When Chris was 53 there was a big reorganization at work in which he was forced to take a job he didn't have his heart in, but which he accepted without a murmur. However, he totally burned out at age 57, and even after several years he has been unable to find work again.

The Idealist: "Improve the world and start with yourself."

People who become burned out often have a strong idealistic streak in their character. Full of ideals, they set about working toward a higher goal. The idealist has a distinct vision and lives toward it. He is moved by social ideals, and has a hard time accepting a compromise. But the goal is always just beyond his reach. If his ideals collide with obstinate reality, if what he wants turns out to be impossible, he is likely to be deeply and bitterly disappointed. Examples of people with a strong inner idealist are the pioneer who founds an alternative school, the single-minded politician who wants everything to be different, the social worker who wants to give wayward youths a better chance, the whistleblower who reports injustice even though he puts himself at risk.

EXAMPLE 53

Joan works full of ideals in education. She is eager to work with children of disadvantaged parents to give them a chance. She is deeply committed to developing new educational methods that are more effective with such children. Joan herself comes from a blue-collar family; her parents worked hard to improve themselves and encouraged her to keep studying. She stands for honesty and equality and hates discrimination, bullying and crude behavior.

The Perfectionist: "Nothing but the best"

High ideals often go together with high standards; the perfectionist in us likes to work together with the idealist and sets his demands high. He does not overlook a mistake, be it his own or those of others. The perfectionist is unable to enjoy success, but always feels frustrated and is never happy with an accomplishment. He always sees just that one imperfection that nullifies everything that was achieved. The effect on achievement can be paralyzing; he keeps on changing a report or the minutes of a meeting, and in the end he either submits it late or not at all, for not-at-all is better than done badly.

Especially in cooperation with a strong critic, a strong perfectionist leads to chronic feelings of falling short and kills any joy in the work. The perfectionist also has never-ending criticism and moral judgments of others. Colleagues experience him as a know-it-all and get increasingly annoyed, but the perfectionist doesn't care. Someone who has a strong inner perfectionist may therefore become isolated or the butt of jokes and mockery. If the perfectionist reigns in us one-sidedly, we run the risk of getting hurt and disillusioned, and ending up quitting.

EXAMPLE 54

Eric, the history teacher, spends a lot of time preparing his lessons. He likes order in the class and a good working atmosphere. He likes telling good stories about history. But because the classes have grown in size, because cell phones are ringing all the time and children are rude, it is becoming ever more difficult to satisfy his own standards. He thinks his classes are too noisy and disorderly, and children are no longer able to listen. He feels old because of his views.

When he has to prepare a field trip to Rome, Eric has great plans, but in the end he can't get it together. This irritates his colleagues who have to pick up the pieces.

To his great frustration, Eric also notices that it takes him more and more time to correct the work of the students and to give them feedback on their reports and projects. He wants to give them an accurate, balanced picture in which the strong and weak sides of their work are illustrated. A system of just grades is meaningless to him. Eric always gives a lot of time to the final reports to make them beautiful, but last year he didn't finish, and the final result was far short of his expectations.

The Critic: "You are not doing it right. You never do it right!"

The inner critic judges everything we do and accomplish, and compares us with others who do things much better. He is always dissatisfied. Many people have not just one critic but a whole host of them that let them know in every possible manner that what they do, feel or are is no good. This chorus of inner voices is continually shouting at us: "You are bad, you are stupid, you are ugly. See, you are a failure! Others are much better. Stand up for yourself! Don't whine," etc. Just like other selves, the critic can often be traced back to our childhood years. Voices of parents and other adults, but also those of siblings and classmates, can morph into inner critics that consistently disapprove of everything we do, feel or think.

EXAMPLE 55

Mae is 24 years old and works in a daycare center. She feels very insecure in her job. She has a strong inner critic. She sees all her mistakes and it causes her to feel ashamed of them for days. There is always something that could have been better, and Mae keeps fussing about it. Her critic says that her colleagues are doing everything much better and that she can't even come close. When parents criticize something at the daycare center, her critic says: "See, I told you so!" And when Mae's supervisor gives her a compliment, the critic exclaims: "She may say that, but that is because she doesn't know how stupid you really are. If she would look more closely, she would withdraw all her compliments and fire you on the spot."

On the street, the critic keeps telling Mae that she's behaving weirdly and that everyone can see that she's strange. She doesn't even dare go to a party because the critic constantly tells her that her behavior is wrong, that she looks stupid, just sits in a corner, dull and boring; and when she is asked a question, she gives silly answers.

The Organizer: "I'd rather do it myself."

The organizer is always organizing everything in his vicinity at work, at home and in the family; he likes to work together with the worker bee, the perfectionist, and the pleaser. He organizes everything, also for others, and often changes things others have organized. He cannot delegate, he wants to be in control. He thinks: "Others don't do it my way. It is too much of a risk to let them do things. I can do it better and faster myself." He can't stand it when others work, cook or bring the children to school in a different manner. He is convinced that his way is the best way. But he has to work ever harder to keep things under his control, and he often works late. He is irritated when colleagues or family members interfere by doing things differently. At the same time, he has the feeling that everything depends on him and that he gets little support and cooperation from others.

EXAMPLE 56

Malika, who works for the publisher, has a strong feminine organizer. Malika is proud of her organizing talent and her ability to keep an eye on everything. At work she managed the contacts with translators and kept them on their toes so they would submit their manuscripts on time. She also preferred to maintain contacts with bookstores herself, because she was the one with the most experience and people knew her. She liked to visit book fairs abroad to find new talent to do translation work. She would quickly get her own flight and hotel reservations, and while there she would call the office every day to check that everything was all right. If someone was at home sick, she would send flowers, even from abroad. Her organizer told her to be fully informed always and leave nothing to her colleagues. For this reason she took a lot of work home in the evenings and weekends. The organizer made Malika very successful. She owes it to him that she was able to do this work and have a good career.

The Slave Driver: "We can always do one more."

The slave driver keeps us going. He thinks we can always work just a little harder, achieve a little more. His biggest fear is laziness. He is not impressed by physical discomfort or fatigue. He wants to scrape the bottom of the barrel and tells us we must always be reachable, no matter where or when. He pushes us to an ever-faster pace and tells us to skip lunch or come back early from vacation to finish a project. The slave driver tells us not to whine, that the work is fun, and if it is not fun then it is duty or necessity, and he stimulates us to take the next training course. "Complaining and idleness are for dumb people."

EXAMPLE 57

A year before Liz fell ill, she already felt exhausted. Nevertheless, just before she got sick, she enrolled in a new training course on her own time. She relates: "When I literally could no longer stand on my own two feet, I was not worried as much as angry, because I couldn't stand it that my body was not doing what I wanted, that it was weak and limited me in my work. I hated that weakness and tried to overrule it and tell myself I could do it."

**The Adapter: "You? You are really not important.
Others come first."**

The adapter says that you have to be flexible. He has no end of
understanding for the problems of others and does not complain when
he has to cancel his own plans because others are more important.
Unexpected things happen; it makes no sense to get excited when an
important meeting, for which you had to cancel dinner with your in-
laws, is suddenly canceled as well. The adapter says you must not be
a spoilsport when you miss an appointment because your colleagues
showed up late for a meeting which then took longer than expected.
When your boss swaps your day off with that of someone else without
consulting you, you don't complain.

While some people get very upset by such little things, the adapter
doesn't understand why they take themselves so seriously; they are
really not that important! He focuses on more important things. In
the meantime, he is terribly afraid of conflict; he tries at all costs to
keep you from pulling rank on him or exercising your authority.

EXAMPLE 58

Jack has a strong adapter. He has understanding for everyone and does
not easily dig in his heels on an opinion. He supports his wife through
thick and thin, and does not complain about her unpredictable fits and
moods. Also at work he creates no problems when things go awry. When
his subordinates do not perform, he doesn't say anything but resolves the
situation himself. When a foreign trip he has looked forward to is suddenly
canceled because he can't get a visa, he swallows it without grumbling.
His colleagues wonder whether he really wanted to go, because he shows
so little emotion at the disappointment.

The Terrier: "In adversity, grit your teeth and keep at it."

The terrier in us is focuses on the goal above all else, not on the way to
it or on any pleasure along the way; for him the only thing that counts
is the result. He views the most impossible requests and assignments
as challenges. If others think there is something he can't do, he has to
prove them wrong, no matter the cost. He doesn't feel whole until he
is 100% involved, and he considers himself the best means to reach
every goal.

Persisting is always better than giving up. Perseverance without
complaining is for the terrier the best strategy for solving problems.

Signals of physical fatigue are shrugged off as weakness or ignored. He therefore has great disdain for "weaklings" who give in to pain or fatigue. The terrier is successful in setting up a business or initiative. He also gets a lot done with others, but sharing ideas or concerns with others, delegating and letting go are things he is incapable of. That is why a person with a strong inner terrier becomes ever busier. He likes working together with the slave driver, the organizer and the perfectionist.

EXAMPLE 59

With a lot of hard work, and after twelve years as a paid employee, John succeeded in setting up his own carpenter workshop, even in a time of adverse economic conditions. Everyone had discouraged him from giving up his safe, paid position with all its benefits in exchange for the uncertain existence of an independent entrepreneur. But John was fed up with working under a boss, and he has never avoided a challenge. He wanted his own business, and he made it. Three years later he has to hire workers in order to satisfy growing demand. John has a strong inner terrier.

He often travels to customers to get new orders, and the terrier in him has to keep track of his workers in the shop and check up on what they are doing, "and that is a good thing." He regularly discovers mistakes and work that is not up to standard. He does not trust others with orders and payments. John is constantly irritated with his coworkers and openly criticizes them. He is not good at solving problems with them and many workers quit after a short time, which is one more reason to view them as softies he can't count on, proving he should just do the work himself. The business takes all his time, energy and fun in life. He used to play in a little band and play soccer on Saturdays in his club, but because he is so busy, that went by the wayside. The business comes first. John is convinced that without his commitment and control everything will collapse.

Finally, John himself collapses and at age 48 suffers cardiac arrest; only because of the quick intervention of a customer is he saved at the last moment.

The Armored Introvert: "Only weaklings show their feelings."
The introvert bottles everything up inside. He does feel a lot, but he will not easily talk about his problems, for that means that he has to lay himself open and show his vulnerability. Others will view this as weakness, and that is not acceptable. He has to be strong. He can only lay himself open if he feels totally safe, and that is something he has never yet experienced. The introvert lets his bucket fill up until the last drop causes it to overflow.

EXAMPLE 60

From a young age, Tony learned to keep quiet about his pains. As he was growing up, it was dangerous to become emotional; his father would slap him and his mother would panic. For a very long time he has been used to hiding his feelings. The people around him find him gruff. They don't quite know how to handle him, and some parents in the school are actually a little afraid of him. The introvert in him says that it is better that way— "What use is friendliness if they can so easily betray you?" As long as Tony does his work well and doesn't get too involved with the problems of others, the introvert is happy.

Atlas: "I carry the whole world on my shoulders."

Atlas is a Greek god who carries the whole world on his shoulders. Atlas is faithful, he doesn't give up easily. He feels responsible for the whole world and is shocked by the carelessness and light-heartedness of others. Atlas always has to see to it that everything is all right. He will work harder as others make mistakes. He feels guilty and unhappy when something still goes awry, for that means that he didn't do his work right. When others exclaim, "Come on, Atlas, stop worrying. It'll be fine," Atlas is convinced that they don't see the gravity of things. Without him there would be total chaos.

EXAMPLE 61

Jack has a difficult family situation for which he often has to go home, or think of home, during work hours. He says: "I had the feeling that I never did it right. When I was at work, I was abandoning my wife and daughter, and when I had to go home, I was abandoning my colleagues. In the evening I tried to make up for lost work, but then my wife would get angry because I was working all the time. So I always felt guilty toward my boss and coworkers, who had to do extra work when I left, and also toward my wife and child when there were problems at home."

The Savior: "When I help others I feel strong."

The savior feels good and strong when he can help others. He bears the suffering of others and makes it his own. Offering help justifies the savior's existence and gives him his identity. His sense of self-worth depends greatly on the appreciation and respect he gets from others. The savior is therefore busy all the time solving other people's problems. As manager he feels responsible for the well-being of his coworkers and asks them about their home life. As a colleague he is always ready to listen, and in so doing is always current with his colleagues' problems and tries to assist them with advice. The savior never hesitates to sacrifice himself if in that way he can help another.

Masculine saviors are especially oriented toward things, for instance a political party or an organization that has to be rescued, but they can also make extreme efforts on behalf of wife and children. Feminine saviors are more concerned with their colleagues, problems on the team, their family and friends. Again and again they sacrifice themselves for others, while they do not notice that their own space in life is shriveling up.

EXAMPLE 62

Bert, the 47-year-old family physician, describes himself as a savior type because he makes excessive efforts for his patients and others—always a listening ear for the coworkers in the medical center, never hesitant to take on one more patient. A few years ago, he got a slipped disk by carrying heavy beams for a neighbor who had a bad back. Because he did not want to abandon his patients, and in spite of his fatigue and back pain, Bert soon went back to work, seeing patients, doing night and weekend shifts, taking continuing education courses—he never stopped. At home he hardly sat down with the newspaper before jumping up again to take his daughter to her horseback riding lesson or help his son with his homework. He also kept helping his old neighbor with big projects in the garden. Ultimately Bert had another slipped disk and became totally burned out.

The Pleaser: "If I say no, I'll disappoint you."

For the pleaser the most important thing is life is always to be nice and sweet, reacting with understanding and being attentive and helpful. He compliments others when they do something right or look pretty. He can't say no when asked to do something. Others have to like him, they must not have any negative feelings about him, and criticism has to be avoided at all costs. Hurting or disappointing others is therefore inconceivable for the pleaser.

As a result he is often asked to do something: "Can you take care of our dog this summer? Can you drive me, since my car is in the shop? May I borrow your new bicycle? Can you swap vacations with me, for I suddenly have a conflict? Can you type this report, because I really have to go?" That is how it goes day in day out, and the pleaser does it all. He thinks first of the other and puts himself in second place, but in the meantime he may well secretly feel left out in the cold. If he gets less appreciation than expected for all this sacrifice, he will never say so. But in the long run, the pleaser feels taken advantage of and offended.

EXAMPLE 63

Hank runs through the school. He tries to do everything well. It does not occur to him to say no or object when teachers treat him arrogantly and give him humiliating orders. He is afraid that he will fail in this job and, when tension develops, tries even harder to do it right. "Hank never says no," the teachers scoff, and they are always ready to abuse that by giving him silly little tasks they should have done themselves.

The Culprit: "It is your fault that things are going wrong again."

The culprit feels guilty for existing and always tries to compensate for that. He has the feeling he is always in people's way and tries hard to make himself at least somewhat useful. He feels guilty for lapses of your parents and mistakes of your children; guilty as soon as you refuse to do something for someone or aren't nice to them. He is quick with his judgment that you aren't nice. He feels guilty when someone steps on your toes, and exclaims "I'm sorry!" when someone spills coffee on your clothes. He jumps up for a latecomer and offers him your seat.

The culprit always thinks it is your fault when things go awry or the atmosphere is not good. Forgotten birthdays and unwritten letters are big burdens for him. At night the day passes through his mind; he worries endlessly about a wrong word, an unkind gesture, an inappropriate tone, and then observes precisely all the things that went wrong because of you, how you should have reacted, how you should have done something differently. When your partner is in a bad mood, when the children are having a bad day, or the boss stumbles—it is all your fault.

When you are burned out, the culprit has a field day. For in his eyes you are failing in all your tasks and assignments. He lets you worry for hours without coming to a solution. Simply accepting things as they are is impossible for him. The culprit likes to work together with the pleaser and listens closely to the critic and the perfectionist.

EXAMPLE 64

Lara has a strong culprit. Whenever something goes wrong, her culprit feels guilty for it. When a child is hurt in the class or when a parent is unhappy, the culprit always thinks she is responsible and that she has to make it right again. But the culprit also plays a big role in the family. She says that Lara is badly shortchanging her children by working so much, and sees to it that when she is at home she compensates for that by rarely saying no to them. As a result the children are asking for more and more, and when Lara says no, they know exactly how to get the culprit to the point that she gives in. It wears Lara out, but all the time the culprit shows her what her responsibilities are and spurs her on to be there for them.

6.5 Repressed or rejected selves in people with burnout

In people who have a tendency to develop burnout, certain characteristics tend to be pushed into the background. These are usually characteristics that indicate a person's own vulnerability. When we were young, admitting vulnerability even to yourself, let alone to others, was hazardous for many of us. We were told: "Boys don't cry" and "You are the eldest, pull yourself together!" Grief and pain were not talked about, and crying was viewed as whining, complaining and asking for attention. That is why we buried those vulnerable selves so deeply.

Among those repressed parts are also selves that relate to recognizing and respecting our own boundaries, and the simple, free and easy enjoyment of things. Whenever Liz was pondering something or quietly reading a book she was told, "The devil finds work for idle hands," and was given something useful to do. Doing nothing or letting others do the work was taboo. In many serious, hard-working people, selves that recognize the importance of feeling happy and carefree have been buried deep. Following are a number of personality parts that have often been repressed in people with burnout.

The Bon Vivant: "Enjoy life and don't fret."

The bon vivant never worries about anything, why should he? There are so many delicious things in life, why make difficulties when you can just enjoy all the good things? Best of all is daydreaming in the sun with a drink within easy reach. He can spend whole days like that, fantasizing about all kinds of things he might do someday (but never will because they require too much effort). Enjoying things— that is what counts in the life of the bon vivant. He can't understand why people always need to stay busy and get excited about things for nothing. Tomorrow is another day...

Eric blames himself for just driving away and not telling anyone that he was not coming back. He didn't come home until the afternoon and then went straight to bed. When he examines this he notices that, behind his exacting perfectionist, a repressed bon vivant is languishing, someone who loves to wander in the fields for hours and watch birds. As a child, instead of doing his homework, Eric liked to stretch out in the sun to listen to the humming of the bees and dream about ancient cultures. The bon vivant had a wonderful time when after high school Eric went traveling for a year. Especially in India, where no one is in a hurry and life goes the way it goes, the bon vivant came into his own. And later in college, the bon vivant could still wander through town and go to a pub for a beer. But when Eric went to work and had to make every effort to get a job and keep it, the bon vivant was completely snowed under.

The Contented One: "Things are fine as they are."

The contented one does not have very high ambitions. The bow can't always be stretched tight. When the contented one has done everything he reasonably could, he will with a clear conscience leave the rest for tomorrow. It is not finished, it is not perfect, but that's OK. It is what it is, and that's how it's supposed to be; there is more to life than rushing ahead. The contented one also likes to look back on what he has already accomplished, and he basks in that. He does what he now has to do quietly and with full attention; he never gets himself excited about other things that still have to be done—that doesn't make sense. One thing at a time, step by step. The contented one lives in the here and now and enjoys the little things in life.

EXAMPLE 66
Joan notices that behind her nervous idealist, a rejected, contented one is hiding, whom she at first disdainfully called Old Liza, and who reminded her of her grandmother who always sat quietly with her needlework and never interfered. Grandma Liza simply accepted things and never rebelled. And yet she seemed happy. Joan decided long ago that she would never be like that. Indeed, that was never very likely, for in their house everyone was

always busy doing something useful. Her mother volunteered in several organizations and her father was active in a local political party. Since Joan is now so tired and has begun to realize how she keeps trying to reach some goal, even when that is not realistic, she is learning to revive the Old Liza part in herself by consciously taking time in the evening to review what went well during the day, and to celebrate that for herself in some way.

The Dreamer: "Thinking about things is more fun than doing them."

The dreamer gazes into infinity. He is like a traveler without a goal; he revels in the process. The things he sees are mostly not nearby, but in a distant, golden haze. Sometimes his eyes are closed, and then he is gazing at even more tenuous pictures that have not yet taken on a fixed form, but perhaps … someday … ? Every object the dreamer meets may be like a door to another world: An old workbook takes him back to grade school; the scent of a rose evokes pictures of his first love. He loves to drift off in an ocean of rest while one picture after another passes before him.

The dreamer often gazes into the future. He can make endless plans: a long journey, all the things he will do when he wins the lottery, complete renovation of his house, the perfect reorganization at work, meeting the love of his life, writing that fascinating book. Sometimes his thoughts are in the past. Old precious moments or sorrows pass in front of him; he smells his grandmother's apple strudel as if it were yesterday. Time for the dreamer is different from our regular time; in daily life time flies while he is lost in his delicious dream. His imagination is boundless; the only place he has trouble reaching is the here and now.

EXAMPLE 67

Rosanna sometimes catches herself daydreaming away. She then gets angry at herself and calls herself a lazy bum. But it doesn't help; lately it has been happening more often and for longer periods. Sometimes she wakes up after an hour has gone by while she was in the middle of folding the laundry; and then she is late picking up the children from school.

When she was little her parents were always busy in the store, and Rosanna had few friends to play with, but she was never bored. She would make a secret little "nest" for herself behind the sofa or under a big bush in the garden. For hours she would lie there and make drawings and stories in a little world of her own. At school she always got A+ for the stories she wrote, and sometimes she had to read them to the class. When her sister died Rosanna stopped her imaginings; they felt too much like the hope she had nurtured during her sister's illness that she would recover. "The world is cold and cruel," her father had said. "The sooner you realize that the better."

The Jester: "Just laugh at yourself a little more."

With his mild humor that puts things in perspective, the jester shows us when we take ourselves too seriously. With faultless precision he hits on the core of what is going on and throws light on it from another angle. When we are worrying and brooding about something, he'll make a pun and let us laugh. When we are hurrying to make it to a meeting on time and arrive huffing and puffing as the first one, he lets us see the humor of it. If you think you are terrific and indispensable, he lets you stumble into a puddle so that you get to work dirty and limping. And should you be too assertive or serious, he always comes up with a healthy dose of self-mockery. With humor and wisdom he lets us put ourselves and the world in perspective. In this way he keeps us from viewing the world from just one angle.

EXAMPLE 68

Susanne noticed that in the past year she had lost all sense of humor. How long ago was it that she had really laughed? She used to get the giggles often with her colleague. At times like that she could look at her own behavior and mistakes with humor, but over the past few months the jester in Susanne had gotten lost. Ever more cramped and fanatic, she had tried to keep up with her colleagues, to give people what they wanted and, most of all, not to slip up. Wouldn't it have been much better to laugh at herself now and then, and to make a quick joke to take the sting out of their badgering?

The Hermit: "In rest the spirit thrives."

The hermit knows the value of silence and meditation. He withdraws from all daily unrest and seeks inner quiet. Gratefully he listens to the songs of the birds. The beauty of an autumn leaf, the color of a rose, the fresh scent of rain fill him with profound joy. He reflects on life and feels part of a greater whole. Full of wonder he watches the sunrise and sunset; he waits until the last color has faded before he walks on.

The hermit opens himself to the beauty of the earth and knows he is connected with all that lives. He need not hold on to anything for fear of losing it; he is taken care of. He need not worry about anything that is not; he is grateful for what is. He has no need to remember something for fear of forgetting it, for he is in tune with life, and life tells him what is needed. The hermit never needs to hurry to be on time, for time adjusts itself to his calm pace. He lives in the here and now in harmony with nature.

EXAMPLE 69

Malika was not often alone. She grew up as the eldest of five children in a small house in a city. She helped her mother with the younger ones and functioned as interpreter for her parents when they had to see a doctor or attend a parent evening at school. She did her homework in the midst of the family. Questions as to the reason for rules and customs were considered insolent; there was no time for reflection. Even now a younger sister shares her apartment with her, and she is rarely alone. Since she no longer works because of her burnout, she notices her deep longing for rest, solitude and silence—not needing to do anything for anyone, no goings-on around her, time to come to herself.

Pictures from long ago emerge, how she would sit musing as a little girl in the garden of her grandmother in Iran, enjoying the humming of the bees. Grandma wanted nothing of her, she was fine the way she was. In Holland this had become a distant dream and too painful to remember—she had never seen her grandmother again. She had deeply buried the hermit. He could emerge only when Malika was lying in bed with the flu for a few days.

The Sensitive One: "I sense everything."

The senses of the sensitive one are particularly tender, so his observations are much more intense than those of others. It is as if he has no skin, so that everything streams into him unhindered. In quiet surroundings this may be wonderful; the colors and scents of a flowery garden fill his soul with joy, the songs of the birds may deeply move him. The sensitive one feels at one with the life that streams through everything. But this openness may also be painful. For instance, he cannot bear to watch the news because of all the dismal pictures that show up unexpectedly at times; loud sounds pierce right through him; in a room full of bustling, noisy people he literally becomes nauseated. When he watches the bright red picture in the waiting room of his doctor too long, he feels it cutting through his soul like a sharp knife.

With his delicate senses the sensitive one perceives things others usually cannot see: Something in his neighbor's eyes tells him that she is pregnant; he knows right away whether someone is sincere and reliable. The fact that your last job wouldn't work out was something he knew already on the first day, when he sensed the atmosphere in the department. There are places where he gets a bad feeling because something is off there.

Taking in so many impressions is tiring. Little things that others have no trouble shrugging off enter deeply into him. The sensitive one therefore needs much time and rest to process them. He avoids busy places and prefers a quiet, rhythmical life. The hermit is a good friend of his. He is appalled that there is so little compassion in the world, that people have so little interest in each other. Sometimes the suffering is so great that he can't handle it any longer and just wants to hide in a safe place where no one can hurt him anymore.

EXAMPLE 70

Now that she's home, Johanna notices that she reacts with great sensitivity to all impressions, sounds, the news, and moods. She doesn't even think of going to a busy store, and even the farmers market, which she is fond of, is a place she can't stand anymore. When, together with her therapist, she takes a look at what she is experiencing, she becomes aware of a highly sensitive part of her that observes everything, absorbs everything and suffers when others are having a bad time. She realizes that she noticed long ago that she can pick up moods and sometimes even feel the physical pain that someone else is suffering.

Johanna pushed her sensitive self away at the time of her nursing training, when she saw a lot of horrid things during her internships. In her work she excelled in the way she understood younger people and always knew exactly what to ask or say. But she never wondered what all the misery she was confronted with was actually doing to herself. As it turns out, her sensitive self suffered greatly from those things and feels pushed away and denied.

The Doubter: "Choosing is losing."

The insecure doubter sees all possible (and often also a few impossible) angles of a situation. If he chooses one thing, he has to let something else go; but what if the other thing would turn out to be the better choice? He does not want to make a bad choice, but how do you make a good one? He looks at a situation from an ever-widening perspective, takes more and more factors into account, but the more he considers it, the less he knows what to do. So, he does nothing.

In reality, he is afraid of the consequences of his own deeds, scared of having to bear the responsibility of his own choices. The doubter doesn't dare take a single step; he wants to leave nothing to chance, wants to determine for himself what happens to him. He went through bad things in the past and doesn't want things like that to happen again. In this way, his future is strongly determined by his past. Actually he would love to be able to look into the future, in order to see where different possibilities would lead. That would give him the security he needs to make a decision and take a step.

EXAMPLE 71

Hank, the janitor, is actually very insecure. As a boy he was often ridiculed for it. He hid his doubting self long ago behind a façade of rules and does precisely what he is told. If he is unsure of something, which happens all the time, he does not admit it but sticks obstinately to his first opinion or choice. He does not allow for the possibility of another view and, therefore, is unable to take a flexible position; neither can he handle criticism. As a result he often gets into fruitless discussions with students and becomes the butt of their nagging and teasing.

The Complainer: "Don't swallow it, say it!"

The complainer wears his heart on his sleeve. When he doesn't like something he will immediately and clearly make it known, and it takes a while before he is finished with it. He doesn't care whether others like it or not, most of the time he doesn't even notice; he simply has to get it off his chest. He also finds fault with everything—the parking habits of the neighbors, lack of respect of his children, bad public transportation, politics, you name it. If the complainer has to bottle it all up, he gets all tensed up and can't sleep at night; much better to get it all out. He also likes to make his displeasure with badly functioning government agencies known by writing letters, and he doesn't accept any excuses from some official behind a window. He wants his opinion heard.

EXAMPLE 72

John never complains. No matter how hard he has to work, no matter the setbacks, John grits his teeth and perseveres. He does sometimes become pretty aggressive with coworkers over things that aren't working right, and over the whole world. When he examines his selves together with his coach, he realizes that under all that perseverance and aggression there lives a deeply hidden self that has had enough of it and would love a good bout of complaining and whining. That would get things off his chest. But this part never gets a chance with John. However, when in one session he gives voice to this part of him, he realizes what a relief that is.

The Dependent One: "Help me!"

The dependent one is no hero, and need not be one. He shows his pain and sorrow. He needs help. He feels small and ignorant; life is often complicated and troublesome. He can't keep track of it. He is convinced of his own incapacity and insufficiency. He quickly gives up, actually even before he has started. Fortunately there are usually others around whose minds are more quick and intelligent than his and who know what has to be done; he can then simply follow their instructions.

The dependent one likes a predictable life and no to-do with difficult decisions. Every year he wants his vacation in the same place where he knows the way and people know him. He dislikes being alone, for that makes him feel lonely and insecure. Making choices is not his strong point, which is why he postpones them for as long as possible. He is happy when there are other people he can trust who can help him with his choices. All he looks for in life is someone with a strong shoulder he can lean on, strong arms that can carry him—someone who helps and protects him and can be his tower of strength.

EXAMPLE 73

After he quits his job at the school, Tony is angry at everyone and everything. He feels misjudged and insulted. His whole life he has worked hard and now? Is he supposed to wait to go on disability? Become dependent on someone else's money? That is the worst thing that can happen to him. In the Depression before World War II, his parents had lived on welfare. Later they often mentioned how humiliating that had been for them. After the war they had worked very hard to get on their feet again. There was nothing worse than ending up on welfare. Tony had always avoided asking for help with little things; someone might think he was an incapable weakling!

The Rebel: "Whatever happens, I am going my own way."

The rebel doesn't worry about what others think of him; he goes his own way, preferably against the tide. If that means offending others he is all the more pleased. He likes to tease people and get a rise out of them. Blazing new trails, shaking up the established order, waking people up—that's what he came to do. He doesn't let anyone put him in a pigeonhole. He walks into the fussy director's office with dirty shoes in spite of your pleaser's efforts to be on good terms with him. The rebel doesn't easily accept someone else's opinion, but views the world entirely from his own standpoint. He always speaks the truth, but what is true for someone else is not necessarily his truth, and disguising his truth is the same as lying, which he despises.

EXAMPLE 74

Bert, the pastor's son, had to behave appropriately all his life—no open quarrels, no wild parties. Service to others was the motto of his parents. He is annoyed at the pigheadedness of his son. In therapy, Bert discovers a long-forgotten self: the rebel. When he was sixteen, he would climb out of his window at night with a secret girlfriend to go with her to a party in town. The rebel in him also made Bert, to the disgust of his parents, participate in demonstrations against the war in Vietnam and in anti-police riots. To Bert's astonishment the rebel makes no effort to save others, he enjoys life and does what he deems important for himself.

The Border Guard: "The only one who can look out for you is you."

The border guard isn't about to sacrifice himself for others. He doesn't mind helping others, but not at the cost of his own pleasure and health. He does take an interest in his fellow human beings, but never loses sight of his self-interest. He will never accept a situation as it is and make the best of it; he looks for what he needs in order to function properly. Before he goes to work he first orders a new desk chair and computer screen. The boss may be the boss, but his own welfare comes first. The border guard never takes work home. Everything at the proper time and in the proper measure. At home he also sets up a good division of labor. On Sundays the phone is off the hook, and vacations are sacred.

EXAMPLE 75

Phil, the group leader on the farm for disabled people, comes from a farmer's family. They all took care of each other, and helping with the work was normal. From a young age he learned that the family and the farm were number one and came before your own self-interest. He looks back with love on his youth, and as an adult he still easily adapts to every situation. It never occurs to him to say no when he is told to go and ask other similar farms how they set up their spaces, nor does it occur to him to declare these trips as time on the clock.

There is no question that the interests of the farm are more important than those of his family, but when his children ask him for something, he is always there for them. Deeply buried is the part of Phil that has to guard his own borders, that wants to shout no, and that wants him to do something nice for himself.

The Victim: "Will it never stop?"

The victim knows what it is like to be injured; he is the puppet in a cruel game and gets hit all the time. Life is hard; people don't understand. No matter how hard he works, others don't see it; they keep expecting more of him. It is never right! The more he tries to please, the more others take advantage of him. And if anything goes wrong, of course it is his fault. He thinks he has had bad luck with his partner, his job and his whole life. The victim does not feel equal to those difficulties. He feels that others have it much better; it is unfair that he has to face everything all alone. He feels he has a right to lean on someone. Sometimes it looks like someone is willing to help him, but before you know it, that person will walk away from him again.

EXAMPLE 76

Charles feels humiliated. His reaction is anger. The fact that he burst into tears is the worst that could have happened to him. Being pathetic—he despises that. When he examines why he has this strong feeling, and why he cannot feel injuries, he ends up back in his childhood. His mother was sweet but also a "victim" of his father. She just let everything happen and complained with Charles about her hard life, but she didn't do anything about it. Although his father was aggressive and surly, he too was a victim; his bosses were always worrying him, life was against him, they were always out to get him. No, Charles never wanted to be like that. Anything that felt like being a victim and pathetic he deeply, and successfully, buried.

6.6   Listening to your selves—striving for balance

If you recognize many of the dominant personality parts and are irritated by the suppressed ones, it becomes possible to start giving the latter a little space. Perhaps your inner bon vivant has an urgent longing to do nothing for once, but never had a chance; the jester laughs at all that serious business, and perhaps invites you to have some fun too and join him in his merriment; the inner hermit wants rest and silence for contemplation. And what is even worse for many "burnouters," the victim finally wants to be heard, and the sensitive one demands that you stop walking right over him.

By focusing your attention consciously on the more repressed selves, you can begin to hear what they are saying, and often it won't do any harm to follow their propositions. At the same time, this will evoke anxiety and anger in the primary selves, for they will want to maintain their positions and guard you from calamities they foresee. They try to protect you from the pain borne by the rejected parts.

Almost all our selves arose in answer to something in the past to help us bear our lives and overcome the obstacles life brings with it. They want to protect us from pain and powerlessness, but they have often been with us so long, and have sung the same song for so many years, that they fail to notice that our situation has changed, that the old patterns are no longer working, and that strict protection of our vulnerable parts is not needed anymore. Thus they overshoot their mark, and we may become completely exhausted by all those protecting selves.

The inner element that can listen to all inner selves and can make changes is the "I." That is the subject of the next chapter. In Part 4, Chapter 19, you will find many exercises relating to the soul life and to getting acquainted and dealing with the various inner selves.

7 The "I": Setting your course in life

We have our vitality, but we *are not* our vitality. Our personality parts often direct our feelings and behavior, but we *are not* fully any of them. Who is the owner, the director of this all? How do we keep ourselves on course and continue to develop? How can we be in tune with the whole and still realize our own individual ideals?

Besides our body, our life forces and the experiences that originate in our soul, we also possess a member that can reflect on this, our "I." Our "I" enables us to maintain perspective, look forward and make plans. The "I" can listen to our various inner voices; it can direct our behavior and make decisions. Through our "I" we experience inner motivation and are able to say yes or no with conviction. The "I" is thus the director of the various personality parts and forms our conscience based on moral considerations.

In this way the "I" is also the mediator between self-interest and the interests of others and of the community. We are able to express a different opinion, but we can also engage in loving relationships that transcend self-interest. Similarly, empathy and forgiveness are qualities of the "I." We can thus enter into relationships and tune into a social situation, while leaving others free to go their own way.

This capacity to reflect on a situation, and also on our own thinking, feeling and acting, on the basis of which we can direct or change our behavior, is specifically human. It is the foundation on which all inner learning processes are based that go beyond just memorizing or training for something. The "I" is the ground on which our development as human beings rests.

A number of the qualities of the "I" are highlighted below from the point of view of burnout.

7.1 Reflection, self-reflection and the capacity to change

Autonomy and setting a course of our own in life always have to be balanced with the needs of other people and the world around us. Our soul qualities tend to give us too much of a one-sided focus, for instance either to strive forcefully for our own interests and defend our positions or, alternatively, to take care of social needs and help others. In principle, both are good qualities, but only if they are in balance with each other. The tasks of the "I" encompass not only the ability to take initiative and say yes with enthusiasm, but also to say a well-founded no and control our impulses. The "I" enables us to process and actively deal inwardly with the things that happen to us. For instance, we may, on the basis of reflection and insight, consciously decide to change certain things in our life or work situation or, conversely, to bear them.

After a period of burnout, many people find it easier to plot their own course through life. They make fewer concessions to outside demands and to their inner personality parts that push for their own objectives in one-sided ways.

7.2 Motivation, an inner enlivener

Motivation is an inner driving and enlivening force in everything we do. Without motivation you don't feel involved in what you are doing, it is hard to concentrate, and the task you're facing proceeds sluggishly. Children and students literally fall asleep when the lessons are not interesting. A mountain hike becomes torture if you don't like hiking.

"You don't feel like it? Too bad!" many of us were taught as children. You can indeed create motivation because of an external stimulus, such as approval or love, monetary compensation, or to avoid disapproval or a penalty. It may also be something that comes completely out of yourself; in that case you have inner motivation for the task. Most of the time, inner motivation is more effective than external motivation. The two are often confused.

EXAMPLE 77

> We see this in the case of Malika, a hard-working young manager who
> burns out in her early thirties. Since graduating from college she has had
> a good career and is proud of her accomplishments. She does not realize
> that she is still busy wresting herself free from the sadness at home, and
> is still trying to prove herself to her mother who, even though she got a
> good education, was never allowed to work outside the home.

Motivation may take a variety of forms, from feeling good about something without wanting to make much effort for it and having ambivalent feelings, to being full of ideals and commitment to get going. Most people who become burned out are strongly motivated to succeed at work and to achieve things in general. They want to realize their goals and in the process lose perspective; as a result they don't notice that they are burning themselves out. Their managers or customers won't try to slow them down but, on the contrary, will demand ever more of them and put ever more tasks and responsibilities on their shoulders. It is the job of the "I" to distinguish between sources of motivation.

We can nourish inner motivation for our tasks by taking an interest in those tasks and in our connections with colleagues. Here it is important that we can recognize ourselves in the identity of the organization or company we work for, and that the norms and values in the work culture correspond at least to some degree with our own. When there is a threatening or negative atmosphere in a department and people do not mutually support each other, employee motivation usually declines rapidly. In case of an overly attractive external motivation, it may be a good idea to take a careful look inside and wonder about the effect on your more hidden inner wishes and longings. Are you allowing them to be heard, or do you have to suppress them under the influence of your environment or your own inner slave drivers and judges (moralists)?

No one can always and in all respects be motivated for everything he or she does, for unavoidably life is full of unpleasant chores and necessary work that isn't especially fun. But it is very important that every day there are moments in your daily work that mean something to you and give you a feeling of satisfaction, moments that make a difference and tell you that you have a place in the greater whole of the organization or community. Inner meaning, acknowledgment, and a bond with other people are prerequisites for continued motivated and meaningful work.[26]

Disappointment as Energy Destroyer

Disappointment in yourself occurs when you cannot realize your ideals and goals: You fall short of your own expectations. Disappointment in others occurs when they fall short of your expectations. Because people who burn out are usually loyal coworkers who dislike whining and often take little time for inner reflection, they are able to suppress feelings of disappointment and discontent for years. Instead of feeling and expressing anger, they put additional effort into being nice, accommodating people and maintaining friendly relationships with colleagues. Rather than discussing repeated sticking points with a person, they swallow them or solve them in their own ways. Feelings of unease then do not penetrate into consciousness, but cause inner tension that leads to all kinds of physical discomfort and complaints.

7.3   The capacities to steer and to slow down

You can look at the "I" as the helmsman in your biography. Steering in your biography means that you have a goal in view and are able to figure out how to get there, that you can deal with adversity and good fortune on the way, and that in all the everyday happenings you do not lose sight of the big picture. Steering means to continue to develop and actively give form to your life without exhausting yourself. In addition to the ability to take initiative and get things done, which is usually very well-developed in people who get burned out, it is of course also important to slow yourself down and attune your ideals and level of activity, within the context of the greater whole, with your own life energy.

This is also a function of the "I." We see that people in the run-up to burnout are less and less able to stop working and doing things, but also can't stop worrying and making plans. They keep on going in a

---

26 See also Part 3 and the exercises in Part 4.

vicious cycle of working harder, achieving less, and worrying without finding solutions. In the process, because they lose sight of the big picture and can't say no anymore, they often initiate new things, such as extra lessons in school, another training course, or taking someone into their home. Chaotic deeds and impulsive decisions, alternating with worrying and apathy, are common symptoms in people headed for burnout. All of this indicates that the "I" has withdrawn and no longer adequately directs the soul functions of thinking, feeling and the will.

7.4   Empathy versus cynicism and indifference

Empathy is the capacity to identify with others, even if they're in a situation that's unfamiliar to you or they react differently from the way you would. This requires an ability to take a little distance from yourself and put energy into understanding the standpoint or behavior of others. Feeling and expressing empathy forms the basis of loving relationships. You take a step back and try for a moment to see life through the eyes of others, to experience their problems and joys. People who develop burnout are so busy surviving that they have less and less space for connecting with others, sympathizing with them and showing interest in them.

Empathy helps to mitigate unease and judge others more mildly; it can also nourish our sense of humor. Empathy is important for entering into and maintaining all kinds of relationships, such as with your partner, children, friends and colleagues. When stress mounts there is ever less space for the ability to identify with others; the "I" pulls back more and more, and cynicism and indifference begin to dominate in relationships. This may express itself in rough language, blunt reactions and a refusal to have compassion for others.

If the person is, for instance, a social worker, this will have an impact on relationships with patients or clients. But in relationships with colleagues, partner, friends and relatives, too, there will be increasing conflicts, arguments and irritation if cynicism and indifference get the upper hand. It is often extremely difficult for people in the immediate environment of a person who becomes burned out to keep the relationship alive. This is especially true in cases of prolonged denial, and if they strongly project their own problems onto the outside world. We regularly see that when one of the partners recovers from burnout, the other, who until then has managed to keep the ship afloat, then also collapses.

In Part 4, Chapter 20 you will find exercises for the "I."

8 Personal circumstances influencing burnout

One of the circumstances influencing burnout is our life at home, which may either nurture or exhaust our energy. The quality of your marriage and family life, living alone or in a relationship, your living quarters, and financial worries are some of the factors that influence vitality. According to many researchers, critical events such as the birth of a child or living through traumatic experiences may create an increased risk of burnout in the following year. Similarly, certain phases in life as well as pre-existing personality problems may cause vulnerability to burnout.

8.1 Your home: happiness or burden

Your living conditions at home play an important role in the degree of stress you have to endure. Just as at work, recognition and support of colleagues and a good atmosphere are of essential importance for the vitality and satisfaction of the coworkers, at home, too, a good relationship and a social network of family, friends and good neighbors are equally important to how we handle the difficulties and hurdles of life and celebrate pleasant events. People who live alone not only lack support at home, they also have less diversion and have no one to call "Stop!" when they just keep on working. A partner or children who expect you to join in the family dinner and want to talk about things other than your work may be a help so that your bow is not always stretched tight. For this reason people who live alone run a bigger risk of burnout.

A good relationship with mutual support strengthens our vitality and psychological forces. In contrast, a bad marriage with much conflict or a messy divorce, chronic illness in the family or the death of a partner greatly increase the level of stress. In such situations people sleep badly and cannot truly relax. The same may happen to people who have to care for sick parents or in-laws, especially if they have to somehow fit it into their lives and receive little appreciation, or if there are frequent conflicts with neighbors. Although in such situations work is often experienced as an escape from daily worries, in the end it may become too much to combine the different functions.

Following is an example of a woman who could not work for a long time due to burnout, while the real cause lay in her life situation.

EXAMPLE 78

Lillian enjoyed her work with seniors. She had good relationships with her colleagues, and at home everything was going well, partly because her husband Joe was at home one day a week and her mother was always willing to come in to help with the children. But when Joe developed vague physical complaints and could do less, quarrels arose about that. After a year his ailment was diagnosed as multiple sclerosis and he soon became an invalid. Lillian's home life now required all her energy, yet now more than ever the family depended on her income. When her mother broke a hip and then needed help herself instead of regularly helping with the children, Lillian could no longer cope and, on her physician's advice, went on sick leave. She now sleeps badly, cannot concentrate, cries a lot and feels dead tired and desperate. And yet, she would love to go back to work tomorrow, for it is there that she finds diversion and satisfaction.

8.2   Typical challenges in certain phases of life

Burnout used to be called a midlife crisis, since it often happens to people between 40 and 50 years old. Today, although burnout occurs more and more at younger ages, most of the people who burn out are in the middle phase of their life, between ages 35 and 55.

Young and Burned Out

People in their twenties and thirties may burn out and become incapable of working for a long time. This is caused by a number of things, including the fact that children nowadays are more protected as they are growing up, young people live at home longer and bear little responsibility in family life, and university programs do not adequately prepare students for their professions in the real world. This means that young people start work sooner and with less life experience.

At the same time, there is increasing pressure from a young age to perform and achieve, both in school and in sports. Learning things, reading books, participating in sports thus become activities that are not pursued out of interest or pleasure, but to get high grades or achieve certain objectives. Increasingly, development and success in life are not measured by inner criteria, but exclusively in terms of performance expressed in numbers. However, autonomy, pleasure in what you do, creativity and motivation are at least as important in working life as measurable achievements.

With excessive value placed on being young, the pressure increases to be successful at a young age. When you graduate from college at age 22 and are offered a nice job, you may think that is terrific, but often the corresponding professional responsibility feels heavy and you find yourself in a conflict between the demands of the job and the longing to be free and enjoy life. Young employees, newly in the workplace and with little life wisdom as yet, react to tensions at work with stress symptoms sooner than older colleagues.

Young People with Personality Problems

Burnout in young people is often influenced by personality or constitutional problems due to which it takes extra energy to sustain normal life. If because of his inner make-up someone has to make extra efforts to adapt to prevailing social conditions, life and work will also demand extra energy in these cases. Burnout then indicates an inability to adapt to the demands of life as an adult, and a problem in tuning one's own capacities and needs to the demands of the environment.

For example, young adults with a mild form of autism may function well in a clearly structured, not overly demanding job or learning situation, but they run increased risks in case of job changes and reorganizations, since these always entail unexpected situations and require extra effort to adapt. For all people with a vulnerable constitution who just have to follow along with everyone else, the risk is great that they will become burned out at a young age if they do not receive some form of structural coaching. Some of these people prove unable to maintain themselves in the labor market and become permanently disabled.

Peter van der Heide coaches young people with such vulnerable constitutions. He says: "More and more people with autism spectrum disorder (ASD, a mild form of autism) and attention deficit-hyperactivity disorder (ADHD) drop out. This has to do with the fast pace of life in society which they cannot follow. There were of course always people with ASD and ADHD, but in former times they were not noticed as much because less was demanded of them. Modern educational methods expect one to be more and more independent and responsible for one's own study, planning and achievements."[27]

EXAMPLE 79

Mae, the shy young woman in the daycare center, has always had difficulties relating to people. She had a hard time in school, where she felt stupid and not accepted and was also bullied by classmates. In the end, by working very hard she managed to graduate with good grades, after which she decided to train for social-pedagogical work. Again she felt like an outsider in the group and tried to avoid her fellow students as much as possible. After great effort she found an internship in a daycare center. Although she liked the work with the children, she always had the feeling of being pushed to her limit and was afraid of failure. She looked up to the experienced coworkers and whenever she made a mistake she was deeply ashamed. Actually, the daycare center appreciated her work with the children and offered her a permanent job. Mae was very happy with this opportunity and did her utmost to satisfy the demands made on her.

One day a mother scolded her because her child's diaper wasn't put on right, and also started criticizing the daycare center for all kinds of other things. Mae was totally put out by this. Although the experienced leader of the center explained to her that she should not take the mother's anger so personally, Mae worried about it for weeks. The old feelings of not being accepted and not being equal to her task came back in full force. Due to this and other little incidents, she became more and more tense at work, and out of fear of making mistakes she functioned less and less well. Because she did not dare join in staff activities and made few contacts with her colleagues, she did not notice that other younger coworkers were going through the same kinds of things and handling them differently.

A year after she started on the job, her physician declared her burned out and sent her to a psychotherapist. It became clear that Mae had developed a social phobia and that normal contacts were already more than she could handle.

---

27 Peter van der Heide, *Nederlands Dagblad* (a Dutch newspaper), October 17, 2007.

Too Much Responsibility too Early

Some people go to work at a young age in an idealistic profession or in management and are very successful at it; for years they are strongly committed to their ideals. However, it may turn out that certain forces and capacities that weren't given time to mature were expended too early, sowing the seeds for a later burnout.

EXAMPLE 80

Together with Dan, Rosanna worked for years in a community for people with developmental disorders. They made very little money and were know as driven, committed, responsible coworkers who always stood ready to help someone in need. When she was 23 Rosanna carried all kinds of responsibilities, both with the residents and in the community. The ideal was more important than her own wishes and longings. The interests of the community always came first, and actually there wasn't much money for doing things for herself anyway. A degree of responsibility and stability was demanded of her that was not really appropriate for this phase of life, which is usually still characterized by experimenting and gaining experience. In the process, life forces were used up, and too little was built up for the succeeding life phases.

The Middle Phase of Life: Ages 35 to 50

Just as the first working years are characterized by gaining experience and the maturation of the personality, in the middle phase of life we witness a deepening and the development of a person's own style in her profession. In addition, people are tending to postpone marriage and family life longer. It demands great effort to keep family life, work and social life in harmony. When the children have become adolescents they may need less direct care, but then the organization of the family often takes even more time and energy. The children have to be guided in their school life and sports, experiments with alcohol and drugs have to be controlled, and friendships may need supervision. This requires first of all a good relationship with one's children, but finding quality time to be together isn't easy. Vacations during these years aren't really restful because everyone always wants something different.

The relationship between the parents, assuming it has survived, is under constant pressure because there remains so little time to be together. Moreover, in this phase of life old wounds from childhood often assert themselves and ask to be processed and transformed, which also takes energy. If the original marriage does not survive and a new relationship is entered into, there is the additional problem of the combining of two families. Negotiations with the ex and the organization of contacts with the other parent often take a great deal of energy, especially if the divorce involved a lot of pain, resentment and fighting.

Add to this possible financial burdens caused by the mortgage, vacations, school- and sports life. For many people these years may rightfully be called a war of attrition. Women especially suffer from this and, more often than not, become burned out somewhere along in the process.

If in the midst of all this a person is also unable to realize his or her ideals in their work life, a feeling of discontent will gradually creep in. Feelings of disappointment are repressed by working ever harder and by criticism and cynicism. This process may grow unconsciously for years, with the result that people hollow their life forces out more and more and in the end drop out, full of bitterness.

Many of the people discussed in this book as examples are in this phase of life.

Burnout Later in Life

Around age 53 to 57 there may be a crisis particular to this phase of life. The children have left the roost, established patterns are being broken. There may be a feeling of unrest around the question: Am I going to develop something new or is this it? There may also be power conflicts at work: Am I going to get that promotion? Am I going to be part of management or will I be bypassed by the younger generation?

A feeling that work has become a rut and the wish to do something new can be strong factors in this phase, especially if you have had the same job for years and have never paid much attention to retraining or working on your own development. But it is not easy to find a new job or challenge within the company. The younger generation often gets all the attention for new jobs and reorganizations. Disappointment at not being recognized, and also at not having achieved more, can lead to anger and resentment.

But even people who have been managers in large organizations, or people who have built up their own businesses, often develop problems in this phase. Natural vitality declines, you feel a greater need for more days off or vacations, and you can no longer manage to put in unlimited hours and late nights. People who work shifts notice that the changes in rhythm and weekend, evening and night shifts become increasingly difficult to bear. Problems falling asleep and sleeping sufficient hours, as well as chronic feelings of insufficient rest are the results.

Around this age it may be necessary, but difficult, to start sharing power and handling responsibilities over to a younger generation. If the competitiveness and assertiveness that earlier led to a good career continue to be strong, it will inevitably result in conflicts with coworkers and a bitter attitude about "things nowadays."

At home too a new state of balance has to be found, for the kids have gone to college or to work and have left the home, and new forms have to be developed in the relationship with your partner. Sometimes it looks like starting a new relationship could be a solution, or a sudden new beginning in another job or business of your own. Confronting the rut you're in and your unfulfilled ideals may lead to burnout, which at this age tends to result in prolonged, maybe permanent, unemployment. However, if people make it through such a crisis period, it may be the start of a new chapter in the last part of their working life, often with a change of jobs, perhaps even of their profession.

Burnout in the last years before retirement is often connected with the discrepancy between our declining forces and the need to slow down a bit on the one hand, and the performance and production demanded of the senior at work on the other. In reorganizations it is especially the older generation that can no longer muster the needed flexibility to adapt for the umpteenth time to new demands and structures. For this reason good workers like Tony and Chris, after many years of excellent work, drop out embittered and burned out. People who burn out after age 55 often can't find other work, but they're still too young to sit at home. If they don't succeed in finding a way to make some other positive contribution to society, they may develop feelings of uselessness and depression.

EXAMPLE 81

Chris, who grew up on a small shipyard, worked very hard all his life. His self-image and sense of identity are determined by the picture of "Chris the go-getter" and "Chris who did better than his parents." Laziness and hanging out and doing something just for fun are foreign to him. Once he is confined to his home because of burnout and his knee injury, he falls into a deep depression. He feels worthless and useless but he also regrets that he put so much of his energy into a business that didn't even really appreciate it.

A year later he is less tired, but he still can't find another job. When he applies somewhere he is repeatedly told that he is too old, and a younger, less experienced applicant is chosen. But Chris not working? That is unthinkable. As this fruitless job hunt takes longer and longer, he becomes more depressed. He manages less and less to find meaning in his life. Finally, after a suicide attempt, he is admitted to a psychiatric hospital.

Nodal Points in the Biography

Now and then there are periods in our biography when we come into closer contact with our inner motives and ideals in this life. In a way you stand nearer to your origin, which may open up an inner reference point. Is my life, my work, in harmony with my deepest intentions and ideals? What have I made of it so far? What is my relationship with my partner like, and my family life? Do I want to continue on this path, or do I need to change course? These are the kinds of questions that belong to these nodal points. It is actually a meaningful period of confrontation and introspection in which things are put into a new perspective, and which may result in a different line of work or lifestyle.

In our working life, such a period often happens around our 38th year; for women it may coincide with menopause. If you have deviated far from your own inner course, you may get into a violent crisis that often takes the form of an illness or burnout.

EXAMPLE 82

Rosanna is 36 when she breaks down. For some time she feels ill and miserable, and in psychotherapy she processes old wounds. Eventually, stimulated by the therapy, she takes up a former artistic impulse again and decides to go part-time to an art academy.

Also around age 57 there is a period when people may be looking for new inspiration for the last phase of their working life. If they don't succeed, such as in the cases of Tony and Chris, they often end up with serious burnout and permanent disability. Although this effectively puts an end to the question of whether or not they should go back to work, it sometimes proves possible to turn a page in life and still begin something new or take up a study. It may also happen that someone picks up long-forgotten ideals again and gets involved in volunteer work. Others are not able to make such a change, just stay home embittered, and are "written off."

EXAMPLE 83

Chris improves in the hospital and in the subsequent therapy. He gets his dominant worker bee, perfectionist and slave driver back in view. He finally comes to the realization that life is also about other things than just working for money. When he is 59 he is declared disabled. Although this used to seem like the worst thing that could happen to him, to his surprise it turns out to be a relief. The battle is over. He discovers a rejected part in him that is socially engaged and likes to sit and philosophize with people.

Chris makes inquiries into volunteer work and soon becomes a highly appreciated coworker in an organization for refugees. He can now engage his legal knowledge, idealism and perseverance in an entirely different way. His wife also becomes involved, and their life together takes on a wholly different color.

9 An emancipated woman is not a man

The diagnosis of chronic fatigue, often called neurasthenia at the time, was in the first decades of the 20th century still principally applied to men. In the middle of the century women with complaints of fatigue were already over-represented with their physicians. That has continued to be the case.

– Jaap van de Stel[28]

9.1 Women burn out more often than men

In Holland, more women than men have complaints about stress, fatigue and burnout. According to a Dutch study in 2003, 50% of women and 30% of men are troubled by fatigue. People living alone and single parents—more often women than men—are more tired than people in a relationship and parents who have a family together. About 15% of the population suffers from chronic sleeping problems—twice as many women as men.[29] Insufficient sleep leads to a higher load of stress, but is also often a sign of too much tension.

Biological, psychological, cultural and economic factors all play their roles in the differences between burnout in women and men. Of course what I am saying here does not apply to every man and every woman. The crucial point is to be aware of general tendencies that help form our identity in our culture, in our time, as man or woman. In this chapter some differences between women and men are discussed as they relate to burnout.

---

28 D. de Ridder, K. Schreurs & W. Schaufeli (eds.), *De psychologie van vermoeidheid* [The Psychology of Fatigue], Assen 2000.

29 Sleep problems occur more in older people and menopausal women. Parents of young children often get up at night, their sleep disrupted.

What Throws You Off?

Women become stressed by different things than men, and with different consequences for their physical and psychological equilibrium. Both from experience and from research, we know that for women it is generally important to feel part of a social community that extends beyond just their family. Women talk more with girlfriends about their lives and their successes and problems than most men with their friends. Women experience more stress than men if they have relationship problems, if the mood in their department at work isn't good, or if they feel excluded from a group.

This creates physical stress reactions such as production of adrenalin and cortisol. Moreover, because of women's higher estrogen levels, stress reactions are slower to reverse. Recovery time is therefore longer and varies with the monthly period. Women know from experience that just before and during menstruation they are less able to concentrate. However, study and work schedules don't take this into account; exams, night shifts and exhausting meetings continue as before.[30]

Women also deal with stress differently than men. They express their emotions more directly. Their facial expressions change much more rapidly than those of men, they are quicker to cry or laugh or scream, either in rage or in pleasure, and they seek more physical proximity. They actively seek support from girlfriends and try to deal with problems by talking instead of fighting, with the results that conflicts don't escalate as much. Talking about their problems tends to reduce stress for women, while for men it often increases it. Men soon consider all such talk as interminable whining and navel-gazing. Men benefit more from working off tension in physical action, such as sports and sex, which women may consider deficient or crude.

Because women stand more rationally in life, they frequently have a strong supportive network of neighbors, colleagues, girlfriends and sisters. This provides support in tough times, but may also turn into

---

30 In this connection psychotherapist and psychologist Martine Delfos sounds a warning about theories of women's liberation that ignore biological realities. In her books she repeatedly points to the great innate biological difference that exists between boys and girls even in the womb. Martine Delfos, *Verschil mag er zijn. Waarom er mannen en vrouwen zijn* [Differences Exist. Why There Are Men and Women], Amsterdam 2008.

a burden when there are emotional or distressing incidents in their family or social network. A woman will be sooner thrown off balance by the sickness of a friend, problems with the children, or a quarrel with her partner or close girlfriend. This means that for women the vicissitudes of their soul life and private affairs are more difficult to keep separate from their work than for men. When stress mounts, work functions as an escape and safety valve for a man, while women experience it as an extra load they have to carry.

Where all those differences come from has been a subject of vehement discussions in families and the media for many years. In the following sections I will deal with a number of researched differences between women and men that may clarify the subject.

9.2 Biological differences

There are major biological differences between men and women in genetics, in hormones, in the structure of the brain, and in the way they behave in situations that cause stress. Because as women and men we have very different bodies, our psychological functions are also supported and developed in different ways from childhood on, long before puberty. Until the 1990s scientific research into gender differences in dealing with stress and their biological causes was not considered politically correct. There was hardly any funding for such research, and it was hard to find reputable journals willing to publish articles on the subject.

Hormones and Their Effects

Because stress reactions are largely physical in nature and are governed by our autonomic nervous system, therefore not under our control, the hormonal differences between men and women have far-reaching consequences, notably the different ways women and men experience and deal with stress. It is interesting that in men the stress hormone cortisol is produced especially when facing stressful outward challenges, such as having to achieve something, taking an exam or participating in a contest. In women, cortisol is mostly produced during tense interpersonal situations or the experience of social exclusion.

Women make more estrogen, men more testosterone. Besides the development and function of the sexual organs, both of these hormones have a profound influence on the development of our brain, our stress management, our psyche and our behavior. For instance, testosterone supplies energy and decisiveness. Men produce much more testosterone than women. This has a pronounced influence on aggression, decisiveness and sexuality. Both men and women with high testosterone levels are more aggressive than those with low levels. In stress situations more testosterone is produced.

By nature women produce much less testosterone and also less adrenalin and noradrenalin, but more cortisol and estrogen. In situations of physical and psychological stress, they also generate prolactin and oxytocin,[31] hormones that quell anxiety and slow down the reactions of the sympathetic nervous system. Simultaneously, estrogen interferes with the feedback system that slows down the stress reaction. Initially therefore, the fight-or-flight reaction in women is suppressed, but their stress reactions last longer. For this reason, women are more sensitive to chronic stress.

Women produce oxytocin during sexual activity and while giving birth, but also in situations of stress. During childbirth, the greatest natural physical stress situation that exists, oxytocin encourages contractions and, with the aid of endorphins and dopamine, also causes a reduction of fear and an increase in sexual desire and emotional bonding.[32] In danger, women are stimulated not so much to fight or flight, but rather to connect with others, to protect and take care of each other and their children. This is called the tend-and-befriend reaction.

Differences in Brain Development and Empathy

Testosterone also stimulates the development of the left hemisphere of the brain and slows down that of the right hemisphere. Because of the dominance of the left brain, men have by nature a greater tendency toward abstractions, toward impersonal and creative thinking, while

---

31 S. Taylor, "Biobehavioral Responses to Stress in Females: Tend-and-Befriend, Not Fight-or-Flight," in: *Psychological Review*, 2000, vol. 107, nr. 3.

32 In men bonding is fostered more by adrenalin and noradrenalin, which are generated by energetic action, achievements and dangerous situations.

women think more logically and relationally and can voice their feelings better.

Another consequence of these innate differences is that women's bodies support them in having a clearer picture of themselves in relation to others, and that, based on their nature, they develop an introspective capacity more easily. Empathy with others is more natural for them, while men have to learn it more consciously. On the other hand, because of this, men do not naturally get themselves involved in the soul life of others and are therefore less troubled by it. According to Martine Delfos, women develop "a morality that is based on care for others and cooperation, while men by their biological nature are more oriented toward justice and competition."[33]

At work this means that women often have a different management style, but they are also more influenced by all kinds of subtle and unspoken tensions. By their nature, women are more tempted to adopt another's point of view and feel responsible for the whole, while men more easily stay within themselves and will less quickly become overwhelmed by conflicts and mutual tension in a work situation. Frequently this quality of empathy in women, although highly valued and used to build team spirit, ends up creating more stress rather than giving them an advantage.

Pregnancy and Childbirth

Pregnancy is a condition in which a woman's whole body functions entirely differently. All biological processes are focused first of all on the well-being of the unborn child. Through the entire pregnancy most women tire more easily and need more sleep and rest. In addition, during the first few months, and sometimes also later, they often feel nauseous in the morning and it takes more effort to get the day started. The body is asking for more sleep, more time to begin the day, more healthy food and more time to dream.

Stimulants such as cigarettes, coffee or alcohol are not good for the baby, so their use should become less frequent to not at all. If you normally practiced a sport you will have to slow down with

---

33 Martine Delfos, *Verschil mag er zijn. Waarom er mannen en vrouwen zijn* [Differences Exist. Why There Are Men and Women], Amsterdam 2008.

it. All of this makes dealing with everyday stress during pregnancy different than before. The body asks for "brooding," something our culture, and especially our work life, does not allow for. Many young women think when they become pregnant that they can simply go on as before until the delivery. When that turns out not to be the case, self-doubt and annoyance may result; tension in the relationship with the baby's father is also likely, especially if he is also unaware of the normal biological and psychological changes that occur during pregnancy. As we have seen, prolonged stress leads to an elevated cortisol level, which negatively influences metabolism, reduces resistance to infections and may lead to higher blood pressure, which is particularly dangerous in a pregnancy.

Consequences of Stress for the Unborn Child

For pregnant women there are additional reasons to be wary of the increased tension caused by working too hard or continuing to work full-time despite worrisome symptoms. The mother's stress has critical consequences for the unborn child. Prolonged high cortisol levels lead to a decline of growth hormones, resulting in a lower birth weight. But research has also shown that the nervous system of the child is vulnerable to stress in the mother. Even years later this may be the cause of a child's sleeping problems, or of the child's tendency to react more quickly to stressful situations by presenting with learning disabilities, anxieties and depression.

The sleeping-waking rhythm of young children is in part connected with the circumstances during the pregnancy. Children whose mother was anxious or depressed during her pregnancy have higher cortisol levels in their saliva after birth, as well as a 40% higher incidence of sleeping problems, such as lying awake late and waking up too early, than children of more relaxed mothers. This effect still exists around the age of 30 months. Behavioral problems and hyperactivity are also observed more frequently in children of tense mothers. The presumption is that the high stress level of the mother has a negative influence on the developing brain of the child.[34]

---

34 ALSPAC Study Team, "Prenatal Mood Disturbance Predicts Sleep Problems in Infancy and Toddlerhood," in: *Early Human Development*, July 2007; vol. 83.

Quickly Back to Work, Child to Daycare, as if Nothing Had Happened

Finally, the time available to recover from a pregnancy and childbirth, and to attune to the new role and the new family situation, is often extremely short. Some women are indeed ready to go back to work after a few weeks, but for most young mothers the amount of time off granted by their employers is too short. Physically and psychologically they are not yet ready to devote themselves fully to their tasks at work again, and they miss the proximity of the baby. Breast feeding too is more difficult when you are working again. For the babies to be separated so young from the mother, especially if they are brought into a strange environment, constitutes a big burden on their stress system, and it makes the bonding process more difficult. If babies can stay at home with father or grandmother taking care of them, the situation is more favorable.

9.3 The feminine psyche—does it exist?

The Feminine Psyche: More Socially Focused, Less Self-Involved

More difficult than outer emancipation is the need to adapt one's inner patterns of expectation, social behavior, and biological nature to the predominantly masculine climate of the (work) world. Women's sense of self seems to play an important role in this. Psychiatrist Nelleke Nicolai describes the sense of self as "the subjective experience of yourself, its evaluation in the eyes of others in your own mind, the experience of who you are and how this makes you feel."[35]

Among other causes, sense of self is built up from inner pictures of ourselves that have grown from examples of other people in our biography with whom we are able to identify. Many of those pictures result from mirroring people around us. A child whose parents radiate happiness that it is there with them, and positively stimulate and affirm it, will more likely develop a positive self-image than a child who gets negative comments all the time and is compared unfavorably with siblings.

---

35 N. Nicolai, *Vrouwenhulpverlening en psychiatrie* [Women's Assistance and Psychiatry], Amsterdam 1997.

Similarly, the feedback in grade school from teachers and classmates is most important for our sense of self. When parents, relatives, teachers or friends express positive or negative comments about us, especially when those comments are oft repeated or when we hear them in different situations, they become part of our sense of self. Other images of ourselves arise from the way our character and capacities interact with our ideals and our ability to achieve them. The feeling of success or failure in the tasks we find on our path forms an important part of our self-image.

In this regard there prove to be big differences in the life experiences of boys and girls. At a very early age boys already prefer to play with boys, and girls with girls. From about age 8, they tend to find the other "stupid." The kinds of games boys and girls play, and the group dynamics, have very different qualities.

From a young age, boys are more oriented to the outside world, to experiments and competition. They pit their strength against each other more than girls do, and they like that. They are also tougher on each other when one of them makes a mistake, and they tend to want to solve their own mistakes. From very early on boys learn from visible achievements, from competing openly with others and also by working together in teams—and this is all reinforced by adults. Little boys learn early on that mistakes are there to learn from, that survival demands a certain aggressiveness, and that a conflict is not the end of the world. By their experimental behavior they also gradually learn better to gauge what they can handle and to behave accordingly.

In their play and friendships, girls are more oriented toward maintaining a good atmosphere and harmony in the group. They suffer deeply if they are excluded from the group. The quality of their relationships with their girlfriends is primary. But within a class there can be, without the adults noticing it, a strong hierarchy. Girls do not so much get into open competition with each other, but they begin early on to adapt, to take care of each other and, by being nice and sweet, to make sure they maintain their place in the group. A girl who rejects help when she makes a mistake is soon seen as catty. While boys get together to handle conflict—they are going to fight it out— girls will more likely exclude each other from the group. Also in the family, girls are still held more responsible for a good atmosphere and harmony than boys. More often than their brothers, they have to babysit their younger siblings.

In their upbringing, in school, and among their girlfriends, therefore, they learn to mirror particularly being nice, sweet and responsible—and this is reinforced by adults—while rivalry and open aggressiveness are condemned. Perhaps this is one reason why women are less quick to express anger, and more often hide their irritations and enmity, expressing them only indirectly. From the point of view of stress management, however, this leads to the more harmful, chronic stress reactions, while working it off immediately causes a shorter stress reaction, which is healthier. More than for men, for women mistakes are something to be ashamed of and feel guilty for. Assertiveness and standing one's ground are capacities women often have to make a real effort to acquire, but in the more male-oriented work culture they are indispensable.

9.4 Social patterns

Building a Career with Young Children at Home— a Double Burden

For many women it is hard to satisfy the conflicting demands of our culture. It is ever more the norm (imposed both by themselves and others) for women to develop themselves and have a career. This enables them to earn a substantial part of the family income, but at the same time the traditional obligation of the care of the family continues to rest principally on their shoulders. Mothers of young children often suffer more than fathers from the double burden of work and family care. Particularly women with young children who work full-time run a risk of burnout.

Women in a Man's World

Socially and politically, women are increasingly pressured to perform in the economy. While thirty to fifty years ago it was barely acceptable for women with young children to work outside the home, there are now daycare centers that are open at night, and working has become a social obligation for all women, with or without children. For centuries, all work other than caring for the household, preparing food and taking care of the sick was done exclusively by men. Therefore, it is logical that in work life a culture reigns that is organized more along the lines of masculine principles, norms and traditions than feminine ones. This means that many women find themselves in a culture with not only unspoken expectations about performance, behavior in meetings and communication, but also standards that are primarily based on masculine ways of thinking and functioning. In many companies there also continues to be an underground expectation of women to be tactful, caring and discrete. The modern generation's working women are in a certain sense pioneers in this regard.

This means that most women between 30 and 60 grew up in traditional families with the father principally responsible for the family's income by working outside the home, and the mother—even if she had a job—for the well-being of the family. As young children these women had mothers who were mostly at home and whose specific task was bringing up the children. For many women, therefore, the "caring mother" was an important role model, for daughters learn much from their mothers about what it is like to be a woman in this world. For the caring mother, the family as a whole, the community, is more important than her own interests. It is her task to keep the peace and see to it that all family members are happy and can thrive. She is everyone's pillar of support and tends to moderate her own ambitions to harmonize with the interests of the whole. The daughters of these women were the first to step into the masculine world of work, where entirely different qualities were demanded. One could say that they entered the world of the father with the equipment of the mother.

Superficially speaking, most modern girls and women in our emancipated society seem to satisfy the demands of their new roles pretty well—they stand their ground. But with their feminine constitution, self-image and survival strategies, it often takes them more effort to adapt than they realize. At a deeper level an estrangement grows from their own soul and needs. As their inner make-up, soul structure and expectations diverge more, even modern working women will experience a measure of inner confusion and increasing insecurity about the way they function and about the value of their own qualities. Eventually, this will undermine not only their self-confidence and self-image, but also the quality of life.

It takes ever more life force to hold their own and persevere. This might contribute to the fact that even women who derive great satisfaction from their work and are good at separating their roles of caregiver and worker, still burn out sooner than men in similar situations.

EXAMPLE 84

Lois, a 35-year-old shopkeeper's daughter, has happily worked for years in the family business of her husband Ham. Besides her work Lois is involved with several other activities: a theater club and sports. She is also on the board of a daycare center for children. After the birth of her second child six years ago, she wanted to stop working temporarily, but Ham considered their business a joint project. He said that it would be impossible to find a good replacement, especially because the business was successful and they were planning to expand. Her women friends also advised her not to "mope at home."

When her parents-in-law promised to help, Lois decided to keep working. Shortly after, she became unintentionally pregnant again, now three years ago. After the sudden death of Ham's father, his mother has been needing more care; she can't help in Lois's family any longer. Lois has no time to reflect or mourn. When her sister-in-law got sick and her mother-in-law's care fell even more on Lois's shoulders, she broke down.

Working Women Often Get Little Support at Home

The most successful male managers in top executive positions, male medical specialists who frequently have to be on call, and men with their own businesses are often married to women who are home most of the time or do a little work outside the home. While he runs the business, she runs the family. His work is, as it were, their joint project. For these men their wives are usually their most important source of support, advice and care. The women identify with their husbands' work: In these situations the energy the men devote to their jobs is carried by both partners.

Women in prominent positions and female managers are much more likely to be unmarried than their male colleagues, and if they are married or live with a partner, the latter mostly works as hard as they do. The partners have their own lives at work and are not particularly focused on supporting and encouraging their wives. Women in management and responsible positions therefore end up facing their work challenges alone, despite the fact that, as women, social support is so important for them. Even in families in which both partners do support each other and the household tasks are equitably shared, there is more time pressure and stress in organizing and running the family than in more traditional families with one partner who works outside and one who takes care of house and hearth.

The organization of a family life—the demands and rhythms of two jobs, daycare, school, sport, music, extra lessons, needs and longings of all family members, as well as social involvement with relatives and friends, everything in its time and place—is therefore something that continues to generate much stress for women.

The "feminization" of the workplace is progressing very slowly, and it will be a while before traditionally feminine qualities and norms will become accepted in our work life. But in recent years there has been something of a turning of the tide. Management books and training seminars increasingly suggest to manage not only out of masculine principles such as hierarchy, competition and striving for individual autonomy, but also to create more space for the more feminine principles of development, solidarity and individual creativity in the business.

10 If you are not busy, you are not important: Burnout and culture

There are no indications that in the 21st century humanity will slow down its lifestyle. Ubiquitous complaints of fatigue show that performance and achievement expectations have lost none of their luster. At best we look for new approaches focused on bending working and living conditions even more to our objectives, and on experimenting even more with the adaptability of human beings. The possibility that the dynamics of modern society harbor great risks that fatigue will grow into a lasting health problem is therefore entirely conceivable. It is not so probable, in spite of the oft-mentioned desire, that humanity will for that reason slow down its lifestyle.

– Jaap van der Stel[36]

10.1 Brief history of a concept

Although burnout occurs more and more often and is viewed as a disease of our time, fatigue syndromes have been known for a very long time. In the 19th century people spoke of *neurasthenia*,[37] a condition that occurred mostly in men and which showed great similarity to chronic fatigue syndrome and also to today's concept of burnout. Until the 1960s terms such as "nervous exhaustion" and "mid-life crisis" were used for conditions of fatigue that we now call *burnout*, ever since Freudenberg[38] introduced this concept in the 1970s.

---

36 Jaap van der Stel, *Vermoeidheid: een blik terug en een blik vooruit. Een historisch perspectief op vermoeidheid en de wetenschap van vermoeidheid* [Fatigue: A Historical Perspective on Fatigue and the Science of Fatigue], in: D. de Ridder, K. Schreurs & W. Schaufeli (eds.), *De psychologie van vermoeidheid* [The Psychology of Fatigue], Assen 2000.

37 George Miller Beard, "Neurasthenia, or Nervous Exhaustion," in: *Boston Medical and Surgical Journal*, 1869.

38 H.J. Freudenberg, "Staff Burnout," in: *Journal of Social Issues* 60, 1974.

Meanwhile, burnout and symptoms of fatigue have grown into an epidemic that affects tens of thousands of people, and also the economy. Burnout occurs in increasing numbers of professions and at ever younger ages. Apparently because of cultural changes, people are not only subjected to more stress but are succumbing to it sooner. Since World War II the quantity of work hasn't increased drastically, but the pace of life certainly has: There are more requirements to meet and more impressions to process. Concurrently, life expectations regarding prosperity, gratification and happiness have consistently risen, and more than before, people have the feeling that it is their own fault if they do not satisfy the high demands they, and also the culture, set themselves. The following sections highlight some of the cultural factors that cause our level of stress to rise.

10.2 Expansion, mergers and the pressure to perform

Because we are seeing mergers and expansion at all layers of society—in companies, schools and neighborhoods—our social environment is becoming more impersonal. We are updated daily by the media and the internet on what is going on in the whole world. Especially in cities, life has become more anonymous, but at the same time, more importance is given to personal views and especially feelings. Every day much "anonymous" suffering and tension is brought into our lives and, whether we want it or not, becomes part of our personal concerns. This has made our social life more complex.

The security of the natural group to which you belong—family, faith, profession—and the feeling of "we" are disappearing into the background. The protection of a clearly structured social life with predictable relationships, firm and clear roles, and corresponding tasks has permanently been replaced by a life full of change and dynamics. This means that a capacity to adapt to change and a high degree of flexibility have become prerequisites for success in this environment. Much more than in prior times, we can develop as individuals and work on our personal growth; our well-being thus depends increasingly on our individual choices, qualities and capacities: *I* am responsible for *my* life.

But the other side of the coin is that, in a culture that is strongly oriented to success and achievement, this puts us under great pressure to succeed in life. In the lower grades and high schools standardized tests and grades are increasingly used as the decisive measure of development. And also later, our (social-economic) value is measured largely by outer achievements, a successful career and a high income. Every day, the media and advertising feed the myth that if we only want to, we can be successful, beautiful, sexy, rich and happy. The result is that the pressure to succeed and perform has increased enormously, as has the belief that if we don't manage to be successful and happy, it is our own fault. Self-worth and happiness are increasingly measured by outer results and depend less on inner motivation and feelings. As a result the pressure from a young age on every individual to perform and to satisfy a range of demands has increased dramatically.

10.3 Lifestyle

The myth of material happiness thus leads to a hectic lifestyle and an excessive focus on the outside world. That life has become more complex expresses itself already in such simple things as shopping. Instead of being able to leisurely pick up what we need at a local store, while chatting with the grocer or baker we know, we end a busy workday by racing to an anonymous supermarket, filling our cart and waiting in nervous irritation for our turn to check out. Instead of taking our time to cook, we put the ready-made meal in the microwave and gobble it up before the television, after which we quickly return to doing useful things, often at the computer. Instead of quietly watching our child play in the sandbox, we jog behind the stroller so as to make good use of the time the child needs to get some fresh air by getting our exercise. If we want to comply with the cultural norm, we all live under great time pressure, work pressure and life pressure.

In addition to what we expect of ourselves in our career, an interesting social life and happy family, we have to live in a beautiful house, own at least two cars, practice a sport, and regularly go on exotic vacations to see the world. Conceivably, all of this might produce happiness, but it certainly also creates chronic stress, not least because it usually requires that both partners have to work hard to make it possible. Not only is there a shortage of quiet and time for rest and reflection, the moments when you can sit down undisturbed and daydream a bit are more and more experienced as a useless waste of time. This begins already in childhood, when children are driven to daycare or school by car, often live in two different families, have a full schedule and, when they are at home, are busy with computer or television. There is no time left to let the overstimulated organism recover from all the impressions it has to take in. Research shows that having a family in itself does not aggravate stress, but the combination of tasks does. Mothers in intact families who work part-time are generally the least troubled by stress and fatigue.

10.4 Always awake, within reach and alert

Due to the 24-hour economy, in which our work rhythm is less and less determined by natural factors, and office hours and store opening times are no longer fixed, our biorhythms are increasingly upset. The waking workday keeps getting longer at the expense of the period of rest. Also in the evenings there is more entertainment, and through the television the whole world comes into the home. Many young people surf the internet or are on Facebook till all hours, and being unreachable is simply "not done." While in the 1960s adults still slept an average of eight hours a night, today this has been reduced to about six and a half hours, which for most people is too short.

It is not only adults who have to conform to this rhythm, which is imposed by the economy; children also have to adapt to their parents' work schedules, for example by going to daycare before and after school. Stressed parents often have stressed children. Because dinner is much later than it used to be, young children go to bed much later, and they have to get up earlier for daycare or school. This means that for many adults and children the recovery period every day is actually too short, which not only adds to fatigue but also results in their becoming accustomed to it.

10.5 Increased fear in our culture

The general level of stress in our culture as a whole has been growing due to an increase in fear. Not that the dangers and risks of life have increased so much—those have always existed—but our way of dealing with them has changed. Maybe it is because we lead much more luxurious lives than people fifty, a hundred, a thousand years ago, and because birth, death and social support systems are now more under our control, that our fear of losing it all has increased.

Fear of losing our job or possessions, fear of illness, fear of fellow humans (thieves, murderers, terrorists), fear of war, terror or natural disasters, to name but a few—they affect us all and we are constantly reminded of them through the media and insurance companies. In essence, this fear is about loss or damage to the physical ground of our existence, our body and our possessions—the fear of being helpless and losing control over our own life. The stronger the illusion that life is controllable, the greater the fear will be to lose it all and thus to fail in the unspoken task of making the myth come true.

Safety and security are fundamental needs, not only for children but for all people. As feelings of security disappear, alertness grows and, with it, the level of stress. The increase in violence and aggression in society are therefore not only a *cause* of fear and unease but also a *consequence* of increased stress and fear. Someone who is fearful feels threatened more quickly and will become aggressive and fight sooner than someone who feels at ease. In the United States it is perfectly evident that even as more and more people arm themselves for security reasons, safety does not increase at all. In daily social situations, such as in traffic, our increased fear and stress lead us to react more explosively, and aggressive confrontations arise more often—which in turn evoke even more fear and unease for the one who is being attacked. All of this undermines the life processes and contributes to burnout of the individual.

10.6 The screen culture

In our culture computers, cell phones and television are important sources of information, learning and entertainment. Many adults, but also children, watch television for hours every day and sit for additional hours at the computer and play with their phones. This means that every day we absorb many images that do not come to us in a direct and natural way, but indirectly and virtually. Be they images of war, nature or human encounters, as long as they come to us electronically, we are not personally involved with them, and we have hardly any choice on what we focus on. When watching a nature film I can be astounded at the grand picture of nature and fascinated by strange animals, plants and volcanoes; I do acquire knowledge, but I have no personal relationship with what enters into me.

When I walk out in nature in my own neighborhood, my eyes may wander through trees and hills, I may be surprised by dark clouds in a clear sky and the beauty of the sun reflected in the surf along the beach. I smell the scents of plants and hear the birds sing. I determine for myself where I look and what I let pass without giving it my attention. My eyes are not fixated on one definite point, my body is in active rest while I walk and enjoy what I experience. I feel connected with my surroundings and with myself. A state of balance grows between alertness and dreaminess, an interaction that is determined by the natural space around me and my inner constitution. If I succeed in avoiding brooding and worrying about things that have been or are to come, I find myself in an extensive spatial *now*, that brings quiet to the organism and the spirit. No matter that it is not a tropical jungle, a fascinating desert or spectacular ocean, I have a direct, personal experience of living nature close to home.

Even in a game of solitaire it makes a difference whether you play with real cards you have to shuffle, lay out and turn over, or whether you play with virtual cards on a computer screen that you only move with mouse clicks. While we are absorbed in that virtual world and play a computer game on high alert, only a very limited part of us is called into action. The computer demands minimal movements of our motor system, our eyes are focused straight ahead without much movement, our brain becomes passive. We do not practice any real motor skills, no real balance and dexterity, no true connection with anything and no responsibility for our actions.

While our motor system is thus inactive, a flood of images comes into us from outside, images that we have not formed ourselves and are in essence foreign to us and forced on us. When you read a book or listen to a story, you call up your own inner images with the aid of the world of images that lives in you based on experiences, memories and imagination. This is an active process that stimulates creativity and enriches the inner life. When you take in too many prefabricated images, the deadens your inner imagination and creativity. The inner life is not activated but rather overwhelmed and stifled under a flood of alien images. The possibility of recovering and regaining our balance out of our own inner capacities is diminished, and also our ability to be creative, at the cost of an overstimulated and stressed system and an inner world full of images that don't really belong there.

Violence on TV and in Games

A special source of stress is the violence portrayed on television and in games. This holds true for both real-life wartime violence and virtual violence in films and games. Children and young people are inundated by such violent TV programs, movies and video games. The more innocent people are abused and killed, the better or funnier it is; the perpetrators of course feel no shame or compassion. In the 1990s in Holland the average child before age 13 saw at least 90,000 violent acts and 6000 murders on TV, not counting video games.[39] This excessive amount of TV violence does not seem to have lessened in more recent years.

Continued research demonstrates that this is harmful to children's development and aggravates stress symptoms of fear and aggression. Dave Grossman, one of the experts in this field, was for a long time a lieutenant colonel and psychologist in the U.S. Army. Since 1998 he has been focused on *killology*,[40] the science that investigates the effects of murders and other violence on the way we function and on society. Deeply concerned about the effect of media violence on children and young adults, he wrote: "People today are bombarded with thousands of acts of aggression and violence on television. They laugh and romp and eat chips on the couch while on the screen the corpses accumulate. We are in the process of bringing up a generation that from their youngest ages has become used to associating the atrocious images of violence with merriment, excitement and relaxation."

Research into the learning processes of the human being has disclosed that watching how people behave and observing others'

---

39 Estimate made in 1997 by Patti Valkenburg, professor at the University of Amsterdam and founder/director of CcaM, an interdisciplinary research center on youth and media.
40 *Killology* is the study of the psychological and physiological effects of killing and combat on the human psyche, and the factors that enable and restrain a combatant's killing of others in these situations. The term and field of study was coined by Lt. Col. Dave Grossman (U.S. Army, Ret.) of the Killology Research Group in his 1996 book, *On Killing: The Psychological Cost of Learning to Kill in War and Society*. Source: Wikipedia.

reactions to that behavior are important sources of learning. This is especially so when the actor is attractive and impressive, when we identify with him and when there is a reward for the behavior. Repetition is also important. Violence on TV and in games satisfies all those criteria.

Research also shows that especially explicit violence that is consistently presented as cool and fun is very harmful. This is particularly true for violence with a lot of action and sensations, quick cuts and special effects, and when there is no evidence of compassion for victims or putting oneself in their shoes. The perpetrators are big and strong, have no regrets or shame and are never punished.

Watching so-called "sensible" violence is less harmful. Sensible violence is not pictured as cool and fun; as the viewer you are given the opportunity to imagine yourself in the victim's place. There is less action and more dialogue, and the consequences of violence are realistically represented.

According to many scientific studies, watching a lot of violence, particularly sensational violence on TV and playing violent games, has a number of negative effects especially on children, but also on adults:

— it aggravates feelings of fear,
— it increases aggressiveness,
— it dulls our reactions to violence,
— it damages our cognitive capacities.

Fear

Research has shown that repeated viewing of violence on TV and in movies increases people's feelings of fear. In children this is often evident; they may have nightmares, wet the bed, or keep their parents awake at night. The symptoms may last a long time, even after a single incident. In addition, as many parents know from experience, due to games and movies with a lot of violence, children will become hyperactive. This indicates that their stress system is being heavily taxed. In due course, children have less confidence in the world around them if they are consistently presented with a reality in which might makes right and people are tortured and killed for the fun of it.

Aggression

Research also shows that immediately after watching a program with a lot of violent action, children and adults behave more aggressively toward other people and objects. A study among Finnish toddlers showed that, after watching a violent film, the children had a greater tendency to hit other children, yell at them, threaten them and break their toys. And research in the U.S. indicates that, as children get to watch more violent acts in their lives, they continue to show more aggressive behavior, even into adulthood.[41]

Violence Becomes the Norm—So What?

Watching violence on TV and in games makes people less sensitive to real violence. Images of aggression and violence bring on feelings of excitement and sensation, particularly in boys. But if it is repeated, they become accustomed to it; the viewer then looks for ever more extreme versions to produce the same feeling. The U.S. Army makes use of this dulling effect by means of *killing simulators* that are much like violent games. Soldiers practice shooting people virtually as long as it takes for them to become sufficiently insensitive to it. Then they don't mind doing it for real and they become "good soldiers." Grossman warns that boys who at home or in game rooms practice killing people for hours on end with fake guns and joysticks eventually become just as insensitive to using violence as soldiers.[42]

10.7 Children and stress

Our culture is increasingly oriented toward results and achievements. Starting even in kindergarten children continually have to prove themselves in school and also in sports and other extracurricular activities. Whether it be in football or music making, dance or history, the object is less and less the pleasure of the activity and more and

---

41 There is a famous long-term study by Leonard Eron and Rowell Huesmann that shows that boys who watched a lot of violence in the media in 1982, when they were 8 years old, behaved on average more aggressively as adolescents than their peers, and when they were 30 had more often been arrested and prosecuted for criminal acts they committed as adults.

42 Dave Grossman, op. cit., note 39.

more, and at ever younger ages, how you perform and what you achieve. And the performance is constantly measured by tests. If you are not within the standards, you soon lose the support of the group and become an object of concern for your parents or teachers. Many children thus constantly experience that there is something not OK with them. And as we have seen, worries and negative thoughts about yourself immediately result in all kinds of physical stress reactions.

There is a disturbing trend of symptoms that indicate fatigue and stress are occurring at ever younger ages. Since children are still developing in every respect—in brain development, in stress management, in immunity, in the formation of habits and in their soul properties—it is extremely important to create optimal surroundings for them, in which biological rhythms can thrive, life forces can be used to build up the body, and the soul can unfold in a safe environment.

Because of the long lead times of burnout it is interesting to investigate to what extent the changing economic circumstances and family conditions in the past thirty to fifty years have influenced the increase in the number of children with problematic behavior, such as anxieties, sleeping disorders, hyperactivity, destructive behavior and learning problems. The manner in which we, as a culture, handle our children might well have a connection with the increase in complaints of stress in ever younger adults.

Bonding, Security and Stress

A secure bond forms the basis for our later ability to enter into relationships, but also to console ourselves and deal with frustration and stress. Very young children are capable of bonding successfully with up to five people. If they continually have to get used to different persons with different rules and rhythms at a young age, this leads to a less stable condition of the personality. For most very young children it is probably not good for the process of bonding and the development of the personality to be put in daycare, or to have a different babysitter every day.

I am not saying that all mothers should stay at home like in the olden days, but that 24-hour childcare or placing very young children in daycare is not in the children's best interest nor that of most young parents. It would be much better if society took more than purely economic factors into consideration and made room in people's work lives for new members of the community to be born. This would mean that money would have to be made available to give women a longer period of time to recover from pregnancy and childbirth, time during which both parents could adapt to their new roles. Or to give young parents encouragement and support to divide their tasks so as to benefit both their child and themselves, for example, if it could be made much easier for young parents to work part-time.

Dreaming and the Art of Boredom

Today children are under adult supervision much more than they used to be, and are on their own less than they were thirty or more years ago. They are more often kept busy in organized activities such as sports and clubs, as well as by television and social media. In kindergarten it is already noticeable how children have to be kept busy. They are more lively and noisy and have less concentration, imagination and initiative for games than in previous generations. Ever more children don't know the art of being bored, just as ever more parents don't allow their children to be bored, because right away they think they are falling short.

Being bored means not knowing right this minute what you want to do and then, out of yourself, out of your own imaginative and creative sources, you find something to do, like a game or something else.[43] In this way you learn to activate your own sources of inner activity; you activate the imagination and will to undertake something yourself. It is no accident that in prior generations boredom was primarily something that happened to children; young adults had learned how to keep themselves occupied.

Today we never get a chance to be bored anymore; even in the back seat of the car children watch videos, and whenever we don't know what to do, we turn on music or TV, play with our smart phone or get on Facebook or other social media. Dream time and time to sink down into ourselves thus evaporates. But the price we pay for all this passive entertainment is an overstimulated nervous system and possibly ever more and ever younger complaints of fatigue and stress.

---

43 Spoken by a kindergarten teacher with forty years of experience.

Children in Changing Families—Adaptation

While the home used to be a place of rest where you could be by yourself, or you could play with other children in the street, these days most children have two working parents, which means that they very quickly have to learn to take care of themselves outside the family. Much earlier than in previous generations, they have to learn to adapt to the rules, customs and surroundings of the various people who supervise them other than their parents.

More and more children live in blended families after their parents' divorce. Both for those parents and for the children this generates a lot of extra stress. They continually have to switch homes, often to a different city or neighborhood, and have to make friends and a place for themselves in two different environments. It is no longer quite clear where "home" is. And if you want something or are not allowed something, you can always play parent against parent.

Moreover, if the parents' divorce was full of conflicts and quarrels about money and visitation rights, this creates one more burden on the children. Especially in contested divorces or if the parties keep trying to harm each other, children end up in an unsafe no man's land. They learn to keep mum about what goes on in one or the other family and thus at a young age to stand emotionally on their own two feet. This often results in a fragmentation that has deep consequences in the life of the young child. Although many children seem to succeed pretty well in adapting to such situations, it takes a lot of life energy that then is not available for other developmental tasks such as playing and learning. The same holds true for the many children who grow up in two conflicting cultures and somehow have to find a way to adapt to both.

Feelings of security, wholeness and happiness are important prerequisites for thriving in life; they promote a stable heart rate and the physical relaxation we need as countermeasure to our excessively stressed way of life. Add to this that working off stress and tension in play, imagination and movement, especially in cities, is less and less possible, partly due to lack of space, but also because parents find it unsafe to let their children play out in the street and instead put them in front of the TV or a video game.

Stressed Children, Overstressed Parents

We have seen that women who are under pressure during their pregnancy run a greater risk of having a baby that cries a lot and sleeps poorly. Still, our cultural influences, stressed parents and the TV screen are not the only reasons that children are restless, get out of bed often during the night, and display unfocused and maladjusted behavior. Some children, such as those with ADHD, are by their own nature more restless and have more problems with controlled and appropriate behavior. Other children have, from birth on, a vulnerable stress system.

Also children who suffer from fear and anxieties, children with an autistic tendency, and over-sensitive children are more quickly thrown off balance. They can get very upset by things that don't bother other children at all, or suddenly become extremely angry for no apparent reason. Parents of such children have their hands full guiding and protecting their son or daughter and explaining to others how to handle them so that their child does not always get rejected. They have discussions with the school, or talk to other mothers to try to arrange playdates or a longed-for invitation to a party. But in most cases, despite their efforts, they cannot prevent their child from clashing with its surroundings at times.

Out of the blue, Johnnie who, a minute ago was quietly playing in the sandbox, attacks another child and hits him on its head with a little scoop. An hour into the birthday party, Mary has to be picked up by her father because she can't stop crying after watching an exciting video. Again and again Rachel's parents have to come to school because she is rude and doesn't listen. Kevin's neighbors called the cops for child abuse because he was screaming every evening.

With these kinds of behavior the first thing grandparents, neighbors, friends and other parents think is that the problem is with the way the child is being brought up. Whether these people express it aloud or not, the child's parents continually feel disapproval and unspoken judgment that it is all their fault. They should have been more strict, or perhaps more lenient; they should have protected the child better; they should have let the child figure things out for himself; they should have …

All of this causes a lot of tension and stress for the parents. Moreover, in such cases differences in upbringing between a child's two parents will often show up quite clearly, which makes it more difficult to agree on a consistent approach and not blame each other. I have seen many parents of unusual children become burned out, not so much because of work-related stress, but because they had insufficient diversion outside the family and were increasing absorbed in the escalating problems with their children.

EXAMPLE 85

The school finally puts pressure on Rosanna and Dan to seek help for Robin, their eldest son. If his behavior doesn't improve, he will have to get special education. Already at this point, Rosanna realizes that Robin is not an ordinary child, and that his temper, bed-wetting and anxieties are not due to her mistakes in his upbringing. In the end, what Rosanna had been dreading proves to be a blessing from heaven: Robin is thoroughly examined and significant conversation ensues. Robin is diagnosed with Asperger's syndrome; he proves to be very intelligent but emotionally quite young and vulnerable.

Rosanna reads three books about Asperger's and is moved to tears. All the things she was so ashamed of—thinking she was a failing mother, all her child's anxieties but also his endearing behaviors—are described in the books. She finds out that she has been doing precisely what one should not do, like getting angry, yelling and punishing her son. But somehow it no longer feels like an accusation.

The teacher is now eligible to receive help with Robin in the classroom, and for some time Rosanna and Dan watch training videos showing daily situations, showing just how Asperger's families are different. Best of all is the parents' group Rosanna joins. All five mothers (the fathers don't show up) have a child with Asperger's. Rosanne feels supported, not only by the subjects discussed, but because she feels seen. She can laugh with the other mothers about the bizarre situations that can arise with their children, things that used to bring Rosanna to despair. A close friendship grows between Rosanna and one of the other mothers; years after the parents' group, they still do things together now and then, and they call each other regularly. With all of this Rosanna no longer feels like an outsider everywhere.

She finds a trained person to help in the family which enables her to take artistic therapy that gives her the feeling of coming to herself again. In due course all the family members understand better how they can interact with Robin. It is like a load off their shoulders, and the other two children are now doing much better too.

See also the exercises in Chapter 17, Sections 17.3 and 17.4.

PART 3

Rising up out of Ashes
On the Way to Recovery

"Good morning," said the merchant.

This was a merchant who sold pills that had been invented to quench thirst. You need only swallow one pill a week, and you would feel no need of anything to drink.

"Why are you selling those?" asked the little prince.

"Because they save a tremendous amount of time," said the merchant. "Computations have been made by experts. With these pills you save fifty-three minutes every week."

"And what do I do with those fifty-three minutes?"

"Anything you like..."

"As for me," said the little prince to himself, "if I had fifty-three minutes to spend as I liked, I should walk at my leisure to a spring of fresh water."[44]

---

44 Antoine de Saint-Exupéry, *The Little Prince*, New York, 1943.

11 Getting better step by step

The third part of this book is devoted to recovery from burnout. It may be used by people who are burned out as additional support with therapy or coaching. For people who are on the way to burnout, it may be useful to help them prevent complete burnout. And finally, this part may help you if you simply want to take better care of yourself. The corresponding exercises are in Part 4 and may also be useful to therapists in helping clients in their recovery process.

11.1 Taking time to recover

To prevent and also to recover from burnout, it is important to pay attention to the different levels of your symptoms. In the early phase of burnout it makes no sense to do all kinds of processing exercises or have intense conversations; this will just aggravate the exhaustion. Similarly, it is not advisable when you are still in the midst of burnout, and you are very tired and downcast, to make important decisions regarding your work life or to make changes in it.

First of all, you need rest; you need to create space and time in which you can work on your recovery. The best thing is to begin with concrete measures and exercises at the level of your body and your vitality, if necessary supported by medication. This will lay a basis for the second phase, on which you can work on what you are experiencing at a soul level and how to process it. In the last phase you can work on questions regarding making a fresh start with work in which you have a better chance to set your own course and in which you can find a better balance between your ideals and the realities of your (work) life.

In the different phases, as I will describe them, the emphasis is successively on the body and life energy, the soul, and the "I." This does not mean that the first phase ignores soul symptoms such as sadness or anger, or that in later phases there is no need to continue exercises to keep your life energy in balance, for old habits are strong. Attention to life energy is needed throughout the recovery period, and also thereafter, to prevent relapse or repeat burnout. In this way the objective of burnout therapy is to achieve lasting changes in the way you work with your body, your energy, and your soul forces. How and how soon you recover depends a great deal on the seriousness of the symptoms, your age and your personality, but also on the way you are coached through the process.

A true recovery means not only that after the burnout you can go back to work with new energy, but also that you have learned a new way of living with yourself, and that you approach the challenges and hurdles of life in a different way than before.

11.2 Coaching and support

If you have devoted all your forces and energy to your work for years without holding back, it is a huge change suddenly to be thrown back onto yourself and to face the limitations of your capacities in such a painful way. It is also very difficult, when the compelling structure of working life falls away and you are exhausted and in the dumps, to build a new, healthier structure into your daily life. Because in this condition of exhaustion you have lost your structure and overall picture, because you have lost all sense of self-worth and have no energy left, it is most probably too great a task to try to recover all on your own. It happens repeatedly that people who are burned out sit at home somber and exhausted for the first few weeks or months, nothing really changes and they get no adequate help. Doing nothing, the big empty hole and the inner chaos make many people with burnout even more tired and, what is worse, even gloomier. Most of the time, therefore, just sitting at home does not lead to recovery.

For this reason it is advisable to look for an experienced coach or therapist from the start. The sooner you start working with a coach or therapist, the better are the chances of recovery. The coach may be a social worker, counselor, therapist, physician, psychiatrist or natural healer; the specific profession is not the important thing. But what is critical is that this is someone who has insight and experience in working with burnout— someone who understands the interaction between body and soul and the effect of prolonged stress on it; someone who makes time for you and can console you when the pit proves to be very deep; someone who does not consider it his or her job to get you back to work quickly, but who can give you hope. And most of all it should be someone who helps you transform a burnout experience into a meaningful inner travel experience, from which you emerge as a changed and more mature person.

This person's first task is to help you structure your daily life, set boundaries and recharge so that your inner store of energy can recuperate. In order to keep from falling into a big empty hole, it is important to pay attention right away to meaningful, constructive things to do. Besides, a good coach gives explanations regarding burnout and support in the mourning process. For having to face the situation, your "failing" in your work and the loss of ideals evoke a lot of sadness, pain and anger, certainly since work no longer provides any diversion. And to prevent social isolation and foster positive experiences, it is important to call on a social network and on sufficient support from family and friends. The primary focus in this first period is on the here and now.

EXAMPLE 86

> Malika is 31 and a manager in a publishing firm when her physician urgently advises her to stop working for a while. She seeks help from a therapist who tells her that she is burned out and explains the symptoms to her. That is a relief for Malika, because she had begun to think she was going mad since she forgot appointments all the time and could not concentrate. The conversations and practical guidelines for daily life help her on the way to recovery, and give her hope for the future, which is key, for she feels as if she will never be able to "climb out of this miserable pit." Malika gets a list of rules for daily life: walking an hour in the morning, a nap of an hour after lunch, doing something nice and relaxing in the evening instead of slumping in front of the TV. The conversations and explanation enable Malika to understand how burned out she really is. The instructions are so practical and don't take much extra energy. They give structure to her day again.

Although there are courses and programs that tell you differently, in my experience it takes at least a year, in most cases, before someone who is really burned out recovers sufficiently to resume full-time work. But it may take longer, or prove to be impossible, to completely pick up the former job again. If you go back to work too early and too little has changed, the result is often a repeat burnout within a year. It is therefore important that the physician assess the situation realistically and work together with the coach, so that both are actively engaged in the reintegration process.

People who call in sick because they are overworked, but not yet really burned out, can go back to work much sooner. People with less serious complaints may also make changes before they fall ill, and thus avoid burnout.

11.3 The body: For some ailments you need a doctor

Because most people with burnout have a number of physical complaints and often also untreated ailments, it is important to recognize and address these. Ask your physician for a full examination and blood work to determine what is really going on. As was mentioned before, many physical diseases may cause fatigue: anemia, diabetes, a sluggish thyroid, heart ailments, cancer, hepatitis, Lyme disease, and others. It is important to rule out physical ailments before reaching a burnout diagnosis.

Of course it may happen that someone with a physical disease also becomes burned out. There are several stress-related physical illnesses, such as high blood pressure and thyroid problems, that regularly go hand-in-hand with burnout. In such cases it is important that these be medically treated separately.

EXAMPLE 87

Besides the psychologist, Charles also sees his physician because he suffers from very high blood pressure. This requires treatment first of all with medication and, subsequently, relaxation exercises.

EXAMPLE 88

Liz has pneumonia which, even after antibiotics, is not properly cured. She visits a naturopath for further treatment and is given a number of minerals and vitamins to build up her resistance again.

11.4 Actively creating rest

To most people it seems as if burnout hits them from one day to the next, and it feels like a big shock and disappointment with themselves. In this crisis situation the first necessity is to create inner and outer quiet and stability. You don't simply do that by not working because all the other stresses in your life are still there. Your constant worrying, your family life, the mental and social pressures of obligations, and dealing with the backlog and the mess at home keep the vicious cycle of stress, restlessness and powerlessness going. It is therefore necessary to actively create rest. This is often a difficult process of making decisions and keeping away from situations that you know will drain your energy.

Your Work

A first steps is disengaging from your work situation. This means handing over your tasks and other obligations and creating an appropriate distance from your workplace and colleagues. For most people that is already a big job. Sometimes it is nice if colleagues call in or visit now and then, but most people experience even this as a confrontation and fatiguing. For this reason a burned out person should not be contacted too often by a boss, colleagues or others, let alone be put under pressure to come back to work too soon. Before you know it the conversation with a visiting colleague will return to the restructuring or your problems with the boss. And most of the time you find that all kinds of work-related things that are important to your colleagues don't interest you much anymore. This, in turn, stirs up all kinds of emotions and guilt, and often anger and powerlessness, which are not good for your recovery.

EXAMPLE 89

When she has been at home for six weeks, Joan gets a visit from a nice colleague who comes with a big bunch of flowers. Although she still doesn't feel well, Joan tries to show a good front. She puts on a nice dress and makes tea. She doesn't feel like talking about herself, so the conversation soon turns to school and the new education system that was introduced a year ago. All kinds of things in the lives of other colleagues also come up. Before she knows it two hours have gone by. The colleague leaves happy and tells the people at school that Joan is getting better already.

Joan, however, is completely exhausted after this visit. That night she sleeps badly and has confused dreams about school. She also starts worrying again about certain students and about the new system. It takes her a week to recover from the visit.

At first, you really need to distance yourself from your work and other obligations so that you can concentrate on yourself. As part of that, perhaps you arrange not to have any contact with your employer and colleagues for some time. You might also agree to have one person who contacts you at pre-arranged times. With your partner and friends it may also be a good idea not to talk about work and its frustrations, but only about pleasant subjects or neutral events.

Maybe this sounds exaggerated or strange, for isn't it a good thing to talk about problems and get them off your chest? No, sometimes it isn't. Often it turns into endless repetitions of all the wrongs and problems. And for the body it makes no difference whether you are actually caught in the situation or just talking and thinking about it. The memories and inner pictures you make of it immediately put your nervous system, your heart and other organs into a state of alert and stress again. A well-intentioned visit or phone call may, therefore, just as in the case of Joan, even aggravate your feelings of frustration and powerlessness.

At Home

If you have shouldered important obligations at home or for relatives, such as taking care of an ill parent or other family member, it will be necessary to consult together how the efforts you have undertaken can be brought into better harmony with your own condition. Other family members or professional help may need to take on some of your tasks. If the routine household and family tasks are also too much, it is advisable to call on help from friends or home care.

EXAMPLE 90

Lois has to accept that she can no longer intensively care for her mother-in-law, and that she has to transfer this to professional caregivers. She also withdraws from the business and tries not to involve herself with the coworkers. She also realizes that she no longer wants all the social obligations she has entered into and hands her activities for school and daycare center over to others. She does manage to take care of the children and the household. She finds that this actually helps her through the day and keeps her from woeful worrying.

Sometimes it is quite a job to create order in the chaos that has grown over time. All kinds of tasks weigh on you, but you don't know exactly which ones are the worst. Although you keep worrying about it, you try right away to push those thoughts aside and think of other things. In the meantime the unrest about all the things you know you have to do—stacks of mail, appointments, the dentist, a present for a friend, getting the car serviced, your child's birthday party—keeps growing because you also know you don't have the energy for all of them. To help you to get this situation under control, you will find an exercise in Part 4, Section 17.2, to actively create rest. This can be a help in making decisions as to what you want or don't want to take up, what you want to postpone and what help you need to get.

INTERMEZZO

An interview with a physician for psychosomatic and developmental questions

Burnout is a crisis in the relationship between soul and body. Listening to the body is necessary for recovery.

When a person becomes burned out, the body gives up. "I am dropping out," is the message. The body no longer supplies its energy. It is a crisis in the relationship of trust between you and your body that can be restored only by listening very closely to that body.

I regularly ask people with burnout: What does your body think of this? If someone does not *invent* what his body thinks but lets the answer *rise up in himself*, it is usually a surprising answer. And then I know right away that the answer does not come out of thinking but from the body or, as I call it, from the "body being." You can have a conversation with that body being. Just try it. Ask your body how it feels when you are taking a nice, elaborate shower.

The body is wiser than many people realize; your whole history lies anchored in that body. You can see from the outside if a person is often irritated; irritation changes the physiology. You can tell by the features of the face. The function of the body being is to preserve the beauty and harmony of the body. People who sit and are stressed at a computer all day are not working in harmony, on the contrary. If you structurally hollow out your body, there comes a time when the body being demands recovery. It wants to get back to the greatness and beauty it once had.

People with burnout often stay reasonably healthy; by that I mean their organs are not damaged. They just don't function very well.

Their heart runs wild or they are short of breath; their complaints are usually psychosomatic. In a certain sense the body being still takes care of the body, but to the soul it says: "You really have to stop now. You always have me running on and on, you mistreat me and refuse to listen to me. On vacation you have good intentions, but nothing comes of them. Right now is the moment when your body needs all your attention to be able to recover."

Sometimes such a moment happens very unexpectedly. For example, a physician friend of mine easily worked eight to ten hours per day for a long time—until he had a small conflict with someone, and suddenly he could not even manage to climb the stairs in his house.

I define burnout as a crisis in the relationship between body and soul. Such a crisis takes a long time developing and always has to do with the fact that someone is not leading the kind of life she is really meant to lead. If you do too many things you don't really want to do, your motives stop coming from inside and you quench your inner fire. You become overextended, you lose all pleasure in what you are doing and lose the connection with your own will impulses.

First, the question is: How do I make it to my vacation? Later the question becomes: How do I make it through the week? The body suffers increasingly from the situation. You drop everything you used to do for fun. The next phase is that you spend part of the weekend slouching on the sofa. Recovery takes more and more time, and in the meantime the relationship problem muddles on, until the day when one says to the other: "You were a great guy when I married you, but now we are at the end of the road." In burnout the body gives up in its relationship with the soul, refuses to function adequately, sulks and looks the other way. It can recover only if the relationship problem is squarely faced and acted on, just as in a relationship between spouses.

In burnout a person has to develop renewed respect for what the body is telling him, so that the body may recoup its trust in the soul. Step one is, therefore, doing what the body needs. Sounds simple, but for people who have lost contact with their body it proves to be quite hard—doing what the body needs means doing things you enjoy. Enjoyment is something that happens in the moment; so we need to stop and become conscious of the moment again. In times when you are enjoying something, when you feel comfortable, there is a healthy connection between your body and your soul. You could say that you sink down into your body; you are not outwardly focused, neither on the future nor on the past. You are *in the moment.*

My role during this phase of the recovery is to be the champion of the body. I am, as it were, the attorney for the body being. And that is necessary, because many people don't know how to listen to their body; all they want to know is how they can be whole again as soon as possible. Thus I advise people with burnout to do what they enjoy and makes them feel comfortable as much as possible. The person has to stop and remember what it is that could make her feel comfortable.

Once a lady client of mine said: "I can't think of anything other than going to Nordstroms and ordering a cup of coffee and cake." "Fine," I said, "then that's what you are going to do." Someone else may like puttering and working around the house. What is important is that you don't set any goals for yourself. Nothing needs to be finished, for that brings in an element of compulsion again. As much as possible, do what comes up as an impulse. Follow what your body is showing you; follow the direction indicated by your impulses. Start with clearing the table and if while you are doing it you think of something else, go and do that. Maybe later you will get an impulse to finish clearing the table. It is those needs, those impulses that you need to learn anew to feel and follow, because in that way the connection between body and soul grows again.

Listening to your needs can be quite difficult, particularly for women. It is very hard for them to put their obligations to the family aside. It is precisely those obligations have to come off. As soon as you succeed in experimenting with enjoyment, and you shoulder the responsibility for it yourself, your energy level will rise. Then you are ready for the next recovery phase.

During the first phase of the recovery process, I work with my clients on the relationship between soul and body. After that we focus principally on what is going on in the soul. What caused a person to lose the connection with his own will impulses and thus wander off course? As a consequence of how our society functions, we are no longer able to be in the moment and enjoyment has become a chore. Burnout is an opportunity! Together we look back and find all kinds of things, and eventually we look ahead in order to see what the person wants with his life from this point on.

The biggest misconception about burnout is that it means you are a failure and that it's a stupid or sad event. I find it most interesting to see through the layer of misery and recognize the opportunities. If after burnout you say that you have become your old self again, as far as I am concerned, the process has been a failure. For then you once again do not do what you really want. After a good burnout something new is born; it is like giving birth. A less hectic lifestyle, a job change, more inner calm, self-respect, space to enjoy things— these are all things people make room for in their lives after burnout. Actually, these things really wanted to be born long before, but no one was listening. Then followed burnout and saying yes to the new. It evidently takes a lot to reach the new.

12 Life forces: Nourishment, boundaries, protection

As was described in Parts 1 and 2, your vitality in burnout is profoundly affected. Your life forces are burned up because you have lived with too much stress for years. Because of excessive demands imposed by others or yourself, because of a work pace with no breathing space, and because of growing frustrations and disappointments you couldn't get over, you have undermined yourself. Before you can begin to work on the deeper causes of your burnout, you first have to recharge the battery. You do this by nourishing and protecting the life body and drawing boundaries around it.

12.1 What nourishes your life forces?

What nourishes the life forces is in part the same for all of us, and in part an individual matter. Universally healing are things such as resting, healthy food, a good day-and-night rhythm, and a nice place to live. Living in the here and now and enjoying what we do have a positive effect on everyone. That which nourishes us as individuals is connected with what we like and has our interest. One person likes to visit a museum, another hates it. For one person it helps to train in a fitness center, another prefers a walk in nature.

It is important to work from the beginning on restoring your rhythm in life and your vitality. The motto is: Don't spend more than you have. Everything you do has to serve your reconstruction. For most people with burnout, this is extremely difficult. In Part 4, Chapter 18 you will find exercises that can help you with this.

EXAMPLE 91

Liz likes to swim and used to go to a nearby pool regularly. She has resumed her swimming in order to get more energy. But Liz notices that she is exhausted when she comes back home and she is reluctant to go again. When she works with her energy situation (Exercise 18.3) she realizes that she has energy when she is on her bicycle on the way to the pool, but by the time she has put on her bathing suit, she is already dead tired and would rather go home. When she examines the moment when she feels her energy flow away, she finds that it happens during the time she changes in the changing room, which is filled with exuberant adolescents. The many people and the noise are exhausting for her. She asks the attendant when it is more quiet and learns that there is a time for people aged 50-plus, when there are few people. Even though she is much younger than 50, no one considers it a problem if she comes then. In this way Liz can quietly enjoy her swim, and when she comes home she is tired but not exhausted. She lies down for an hour before doing something else.

This chapter will discuss a number of generally nourishing activities:
– healthy rhythm in life
– nourishment
– meaningful exercise
– enjoyment and meaning during the day
– living attentively in the here and now
– healthy inner pictures

12.2 Healthy rhythm in life

When you become burned out, your normal life rhythm is disturbed and you have to find a new rhythm because you have stopped working. Some people stay in bed for a long time in the morning and think that is restful. The opposite is true. By staying in bed too long, you disturb the biological state of balance, for instance the level of melatonin. To restore your sleep rhythm is a priority. Even if you don't fall asleep right away, it is important to go to bed at a set time (not too late) and, even if you did not sleep well, not to stay in bed too long in the morning. It is better to get up at a set time even if you still feel tired. This helps the body adjust to a normal day and night rhythm so that the biorhythm can recuperate.[45]

---

45 With some sleep problems, for instance trouble falling asleep or habitually falling asleep very late and waking up late (delayed sleep syndrome), it is helpful to take melatonin as a sleeping aid. This is a hormone generated by the body that plays an important role in our biological clock.

Closing Your Day

Toward evening you should not be doing busy things; no extensive conversations or phone calls, no enervating television programs—do something nice and relaxing. Try consciously not to think of a lot of conflict and aggravation, but of pleasant things. Eating late is not a good idea either because then your metabolism will still be busy when you go to bed. Drinking coffee or black tea (for some people any time after 4 p.m.) will keep you awake because caffeine disturbs certain neurotransmitters and breaks down melatonin. In the evening it is also better not to read difficult books, work at the computer, watch TV or have intense conversations, because these activate you and fill your head with thoughts. Moreover, watching a lighted screen disturbs the melatonin level, resulting in sleeping problems.

Try to close the day on a quiet note, write something down, take a little walk or do something else that relaxes you. A review of the day helps getting away from persistent thought patterns.

Getting Sufficient Sleep

If you don't sleep you can still practice letting your body rest. You don't do this by worrying about lying awake. Make sure you are not too cold or too warm, and that you are lying comfortably. Do some relaxation exercises and think of good things. An afternoon nap may help you get an extra hour of sleep, but don't stay in bed for hours—it should be one hour at most, and at the same time every day, preferably right after lunch. Don't focus too much on sleeping; just make it a habit to relax and rest, even if you don't get to sleep. In Part 4 you'll find exercises to help you relax and fall asleep.

If you suffer from persistent sleeplessness, you might consider getting a referral to a specialized sleep clinic.

Besides taking care of your sleeping and waking rhythm, a healthy life rhythm also includes regular meals for which you sit down and take time, while giving attention to what you taste and allowing time for digestion. Eating while reading the newspaper or watching TV disturbs the digestion.

Moments of Inner Concentration

Brief moments of inner concentration during the day are a help in maintaining a healthy rhythm. If you have ever attended a string quartet performance you may have noticed that the musicians retune their instruments between parts of the music, so that they sound right when they start playing again. Such "tuning in between" is also a good habit for our organism: a brief pause to find balance again. Incorporating moments of rest and retuning, when you pull back from the stream of activities and focus your attention inward, has a harmonizing effect and is a proven anti-stress remedy. You can do it with a meditation or some slight physical exercise, or by just briefly enjoying the moment. These things strengthen your life forces and create rest and balance for your organism. You can find small exercises for this in Part 4, Chapter 21.

Also make sure that you aren't always running hither and thither, hurried and stressed. Part of a healthy rhythm is scheduling rests between your appointments and projects. This means not filling your day up completely and leaving plenty of time to get to your appointments so you can enjoy the scenery on the way, whether urban or rural. Taking a leisurely walk when you can relax and let your thoughts come and go creates an opening to come back into balance. Running nervously around while at the critical moment you can't find your keys, driving like a maniac to gain an extra minute, and irritation at having to wait in line, all because you are nervous about arriving late, produce stress reactions all along the line, and it takes your body hours to process those.

12.3 Food and stimulants

When you give attention to healthy food and take the time to digest it quietly, you support the process of restoring a healthy state of balance. The same is true for discontinuing the use of alcohol, drugs and all kinds of medications that artificially stretch your limits.

Healthy Food

During a period of recovery from excessive work and exhaustion, it is good to eat particularly healthy foods and a wide variety. Food builds up the body. Not only is it important what and how much you eat, its quality is at least equally critical. Organic food absorbs different life qualities than conventional agricultural products, and therefore it supports the life body better. And it is also important how the food is prepared. In my opinion, fresh food, vegetables and fruit of the season are the most natural and therefore the best nourishment for the life forces.

Another thing to watch is having your meals with regularity and taking the time to absorb what you are eating and digest it. When we are under stress we do not absorb food well, and our metabolism of sugars and fats becomes disturbed. Chronic stress therefore increases the risk of excess weight, hypoglycemia and diabetes.

In stressful periods your body may need extra vitamins or minerals. You may want to take certain supplements. However, it is not a good idea to just get these by yourself. Consult a competent person for this, such as a physician, naturopath or dietician.

Common Stimulants

Our sensitivity to caffeine often increases in situations of excessive stress and burnout. Caffeine is in coffee, cola, black tea and some painkillers. Especially people who feel anxious and on edge would do better to skip the coffee and other caffeinated substances.

Caffeine influences the neurotransmitters and makes you active and less sleepy. It inhibits adenosine, a sleep hormone, and stimulates adrenalin and serotonin which make us active. It also increases the level of cortisol, which can aggravate stress reactions. People who are under stress often get heart palpitations due to coffee. Caffeine may also lead to hypoglycemia, or low blood sugar, which makes you feel even more tired. If you drink a lot of coffee to stay awake and alert, your body may have become used to the caffeine. You notice this when you get a headache if you don't drink coffee in the morning, or when you become very sleepy without coffee. In such a case you will do better to reduce the quantity of coffee, tea or cola gradually.

Other things you can take to increase your level of energy are sugar, chocolate and nicotine. Eventually though these disturb a healthy state of balance in the body by influencing the way the body handles sugar, as well as neurotransmitters and hormones. Sugar raises the serotonin level, and chocolate stimulates endorphins, with the result that we feel better in the moment, but at the cost of addiction.

Alcohol is usually taken to calm us down; it dims the brain. In the run-up to burnout, it often happens that people start to drink more than before. It is a good idea to stop this promptly, not only because alcohol is addictive and your body soon gets used to it and demands ever more for the same effect, but also because of its negative effects on the brain and the immune system. In the short term it seems as if alcohol has a positive influence because it relaxes us and reduces anxiety, but as a matter of fact, alcohol will eventually aggravate anxiety, and it disturbs our sleep.

12.4 Meaningful exercise

Exercise, especially outdoors, is one of the best ways to restore your life forces. Exercise will also help you fall asleep, even hours later. Taking a walk every day at a measured pace, with an interest in observing your surroundings such as the quality of the light and the natural changes through the seasons, strengthens the life body. It can become an important contribution to recovery from burnout. Walking is a smooth, regular and rhythmic movement that makes a natural connection with the earth and quiets your thoughts. Later, when your condition improves, you can try other forms of sports and exercise that take more effort.

Most important of all is that you enjoy it. The point is not to do this fanatically and with a goal in mind, but to do what feels good while you also build in moments of rest and don't push past your limits. Excessive effort does not reduce stress; it just adds one more obligation.

You may also choose more meditative forms of movement that restore the connection between body and soul. Eurythmy, certain slow forms of yoga or chi gong may be helpful. Find someone who can help you find a form of movement that is good for you. One person may prefer a trainer in a fitness center, another a eurythmy therapist or a dance teacher. Daily practice furthers the restoration of life energy.

EXAMPLE 92

Charles opts for a trainer in a small group to build up his conditioning again, first in a fitness center and later by running and exercising outdoors. It helps him to be coached in this and to make clear agreements. It is also nice to do it together with the other participants. He particularly enjoys being outdoors and feeling that his condition is improving.

EXAMPLE 93

Johanna, the nurse, also starts out in a fitness center, but soon finds that she isn't getting better. She feels dead tired there, not because of the exercises as much as the environment. Although it is a small center, it has three television screens, all with different programs. Even with the sound turned off, world news, attacks, accidents and disasters, nature, a quiz— it all comes in, wanted or not, and she cannot really shut it out because the screens hang right above the exercise apparatus. There is also loud music that she dislikes. As a result, Johanna notices that she loses all her energy in the fitness center.

She consults her physician, who suggests a walk or bike ride every day and therapeutic eurythmy because this specifically enhances the growth of life energy. Besides, there are eurythmy exercises through which she can learn to shield her life body off from extraneous influences. Very soon the daily fifteen-minute practice becomes a source of relaxation and restoration and, indeed, her vulnerability to outside impressions decreases.

12.5 Enjoying what you are doing

Whatever you choose to do, it is important to enjoy things again and to do things less out of duty or habit. Think of what you would really like to do, and also try to take pleasure in little things. This means becoming attentive to your surroundings and to the small blessings of every day. Physical and artistic activities, such as gardening, cooking, music making or sewing, may help restore your sense of balance and overcome the spiral of stress. They focus your attention on the here and now. You may also enjoy a visit to a museum, photography, poetry or listening to music. It is good to choose something that demands a certain inner activity but not a lot of energy. Passive distraction by a movie or television, or by surfing the internet, are therefore not suggested. Whatever activity you choose, do it with purpose and in moderation!

EXAMPLE 94

> Malika says about the recovery from her burnout: "It turned out to be a prolonged, painful process I had to go through. All my certainties were gone; the only thing left was a 'naked Malika,' which I had to face. My therapist supported me, but she also helped me to go and do nice things that gave me pleasure, preferably together with a friend. We both agreed not to talk about all the problems but to focus entirely on enjoying the moment. I realized how long it had been since I had made time for such things.

You often have to learn to arrange activities so they don't break you down, but rather nurture you. That means slowing down the pace, taking frequent breaks and stopping before you get too tired. Ask yourself regularly whether an activity was good for you, and whether it generated or used up energy. For people who are burned out and have systematically ignored physical warning signals for years, resulting in a disrupted sense of life, it is difficult to find this limit, and even more difficult to stay within it.

EXAMPLE 95

> Susanne, the reporter who was bullied by her colleagues and has been sitting at home with burnout for a few weeks, is advised by her physician to take a walk every morning. When the doctor asks her two weeks later how she is doing, she says the walks make her dead tired, but that she is persevering every day. It turns out that she has chosen a considerable distance that she tries to accomplish within a certain time. She thinks this will build up her condition and make her better sooner. Despite the fact that walking this way is doing her no good, she fanatically persists until the doctor asks her about it and Susanne becomes conscious of an old pattern of persisting until you drop.

Spending a Meaningful Day

When you have been used to putting all your energy and strength into your work all day long, it is hard to give meaning to the day when you are suddenly home on sick leave. It is therefore important to look as soon as possible for a way to spend the day that enhances your vital forces and interest in life. A meaningful activity does not need to be useful in the sense of being productive; the point is that you like doing it and that what you are doing has meaning for you In this way you connect your activities with your inner world and you perform them with attention. So you are no longer acting out of a sense of duty, but out of your own free will and enthusiasm for what you are doing.

Manual work, performed at a measured pace without pressure to get something done, is perfect for this. In such work you are present in the here and now in a natural way; it helps you avoid brooding and worrying. The quiet attention and the work of the hands enable the soul to connect with the world again. People who have a family with growing children at home may be able to find such a way of spending the day by doing nice things with the children, or in household tasks such as baking bread or doing odd jobs in the house. Working in a garden can also be very relaxing.

People with burnout tend to work very slowly; they have trouble planning and keeping the big picture in mind, and therefore benefit from a limited project. It is often impossible to carry the full load of a household. It is therefore advisable to arrange for achievable tasks with the other members of the household. If you are thinking of outdoor activities, try to find something close to home, and don't let yourself get exhausted or pressured by performance goals and the like. And all the while it is still important to create moments of being alone and resting.

EXAMPLE 96

Eric is a burned-out high school teacher. When he's at home, he has next to no energy for almost anything. He finds that he likes cooking, but can't manage to do the shopping for it. He has lost the overview of what he needs for the day and, as a result, has to make repeated trips to the stores. A list is no help because he always forgets to put things on it. All the shopping wears him out. He decides to have his purchases delivered after his wife and he have decided on the menu together. Before he starts cooking, Eric makes a list of all the separate things he has to do for the menu. Then he takes ample time for cooking and tries to perform all the steps in the written sequence without haste. And when he is peeling potatoes or cutting vegetables he also tries to give all his attention to these tasks at hand.

No matter how worn out you are, doing nothing is in most cases not the best solution. On the contrary, it is important for your recovery not to end up in a kind of social isolation. Especially people who live alone will run this risk; when you are so tired it is really hard to maintain contacts with friends, and talking about your condition quickly feels like whining. Meaningful activities outside the home prevent isolation and distract you from always brooding and worrying about your job and yourself. There are many charitable organizations that offer opportunities for people to work as volunteers. Here too it is important to pace yourself and stay within your limits.

EXAMPLE 97

After Charles had been at home for three months, he found a volunteer job at an educational nature center. Four mornings a week he worked there in the garden, and he enjoyed being in nature and among other people again. Two months later he was asked, since he is a biologist, to give some courses to school children. Before he knew it he had agreed, but once he was getting some materials for the first course, he realized that he had bitten off more than he could chew. He was unable to get the preparations properly organized.

12.6 Living attentively in the here and now

Living in the present, focusing on what you are doing, and not worrying about what was or is going to be is an art which, when you work at it, immediately calms the body. You switch off your alertness and move into an observant state that is concerned only with the now—what do I experience now, in my body, in the world, in my thoughts? By doing this you connect in a different and more intense way with your body, your surroundings and what you are doing in the moment.

Wisdom about the life body and life energy has existed in Oriental traditions and medical practices for thousands of years. In cultures where Buddhism is strongly developed, care of one's own life forces is an integral part of life. In their languages there are many words for life energy that are completely absent from Western languages.

---

46 This movement is called *integrative medicine*. About ten years ago it was included in what was being taught in twenty American medical schools, and there has been much research into its results. Jon Kabat-Zinn and his colleagues, for instance, have done research into the effects of mindfulness training on the brain and the immune system, with special focus on stress reactions. He has published essays on its effects on depression, psoriasis and patients with borderline personality disorder.

In the last forty to fifty years, training and forms of meditation to practice inner calm have been coming to the West from the Orient. For about the past twenty years, these ancient practices which help people live more in the here and now have to some extent been Westernized and have become a part of conventional medicine.[46] Thus we now see more and more group training programs in mindfulness and attentiveness based on Oriental meditation and yoga practices, but integrated into a Western model.[47]

EXAMPLE 98

Eric, the history teacher, has followed a weekly mindfulness course for two months and meditates after getting up in the morning for half an hour every day. He also does yoga exercises and practices consciousness in the little things during the day. The course is very systematically structured. There is no discussion of any problems, but techniques are taught to live with thoughts and feelings in a different way. Soon he sleeps better and stops taking wine as a sleeping aid. He likes meeting other people and hearing how they also have difficulties in performing ostensibly simple tasks and, most of all, persevering in them.

12.7 Healthy inner images

In a condition of burnout you are hyper-sensitive to impressions from outside. It is therefore good to be selective in the impressions you want to take in, especially in the beginning. Limiting media is the first step. Television, radio, newspapers and the internet constantly bring all the wretchedness of world events into our homes. These are pictures that do not nourish and instead they promote unrest without creating any opportunity to contribute to a solution.

People with burnout are at first often obsessively occupied with frustrations around their work. Their thought life shrivels up. All their thinking solves nothing; it merely exhausts them. By evoking imagination and positive, mobile images it is possible to bring your thoughts into movement again and to nourish them. Healthy, healing pictures from fairytales, stories, poems and children's books have a nourishing effect on the life body. At first, reading a book is next to

---

47 Zindel V. Segal & J. Mark G. Williams, *Mindfulness-Based Cognitive Therapy for Depression*, New York 2013.

impossible due to an inability to concentrate; when that is the case it is helpful to take one image at a time and contemplate it, deepen it. Beautiful pictures in children's books appeal not to the intellect but to the imagination, and they nourish the inner child. (See also Chapter 18, Section 18.8, *Nourishment in the Form of Images.*)

Observing nature and engaging in artistic activities such as drawing and painting also enrich the inner life and strengthen the life forces. When your energy level has risen somewhat you might also try meditative exercises.

12.8 Therapies for strengthening the life forces

Medication and Remedies

Regular medication is frequently used to combat the symptoms of burnout, especially sleep aids, tranquilizers and antidepressants. Antidepressants cause an increase in cortisol receptors in the hippocampus, and the LHPA axis functions better. From the point of view of the restoration of life forces, we may well wonder whether it is a good thing to use these remedies at an early stage, because they generally end up aggravating the exhaustion and hardening the life body. Moreover, they often have troubling side effects and it may take great effort to discontinue them later. If burnout is viewed as a meaningful life crisis, these medications may disturb the process of self-knowledge and inner enrichment with their suppressing effects.

Natural remedies such as anthroposophical or homeopathic medicine, as well as herbs, can provide a healthier approach to supporting the life processes.[48] Talk therapy, meditation, yoga and other therapies may also have a positive influence on cortisol levels and the LHPA axis. Chronic stress affects both digestion and the body's constructive forces, therefore resulting in deficiencies even if we are

---

48 In anthroposophical medicine there are special remedies for vitality (such as Levico comp by Wala, which supports general vitality) and for the restoration of the function of organs and biorhythms (for instance Hepatodoron, which supports the liver and often helps with sleeping problems, and Cardiodoron that strengthens the heart, both by Weleda). Besides, it is good to look for specific remedies for your particular constitution and complaints. St. John's Wort is an herb that is often given to people with depression and stress complaints, and a lot of research has gone into its effects. In the right dosage it works just as well as chemical antidepressants.

eating well. In such cases it may be good to temporarily take food supplements to offset these shortages. Eating fatty fish and/or taking fish oil may improve our mood and also enhance resistance, because Omega 3 favorably affects the working of some neurotransmitters.[49] When there is a shortage it takes a few months before improvement occurs. There are also supplements that support specific functions such as blood sugar level or the immune system. It is important to get the help of a person competent in this field and not just try a range of supplements or self-medicate.

External Therapies

External therapies may be very helpful to stimulate the life forces. These are therapies that are applied directly to the body, such as rubbing, massage or baths, in which vitalizing essential oils are often used. There are many forms of relaxing and activating massage which focus on the restoration of balance in the body, for example, anthroposophic rhythmical massage especially for the organs, and shiatsu massage focused on energy points. Then there are bath therapies with essential oils that bring relaxation and have a strengthening effect (see Part 4). Acupuncture is another beneficial external therapy. All these measures stimulate energy points or organs, bringing sluggish life forces into movement and revitalizing the body.

EXAMPLE 99

Mae is very tense. She can hardly eat and keeps on worrying. She looks pale and skinny and always feels cold. Twice a week she gets rubbed with prunus oil after which she lies wrapped in a sheet and a blanket for half an hour. It does her good. After three weeks she is less cold and begins to eat better.

EXAMPLE 100

Hank's muscles are cramped, especially in his neck and back. He gets rhythmical massage with an essential oil and a special rub of lavender-gold-rose oil for the heart. At first he finds it hard to relax but after a few times this gets better. He notices that he is less tense at night and is sleeping better.

---

49 For the nervous system fish oil with an EPA:DHA ratio of 3:1 is especially effective. In case of heart problems the DHA content has to be higher than the EPA. On the internet one can find much information on the effects of Omega 3 and fish oil.

Art Therapies

All art, and especially active engagement with art, nourishes the life body. Art therapy exists in many forms and is practiced in many ways. The basic elements are:

- visual arts: painting, drawing, sculpture, pottery, etc.
- movement: eurythmy, dance, drama, tai chi
- speech
- music: singing, instrumental music

Every basic method has different forms for different purposes. Many therapists use several methods in conjunction to address the particular condition of a patient. Every art therapy can be used in two ways: inwardly and outwardly.

When you work inwardly, you use art like a medication. A therapist will choose a method, material or movement form that is especially effective for your situation. He gives you precise instructions as to what to do. He asks you to work with a particular color or rhythm, or you learn specific movement exercises. The purpose is to strengthen specific parts and functions of the life body. For instance, observant drawing of a simple object works well to alleviate nervousness, and dynamic drawing enhances inner mobility. There are eurythmy exercises that help to insulate the life body and make it sturdier. By doing voice and movement exercises you can work on your vitality. Because the life body has a close connection with the physical body, these methods also have a healing effect on physical processes, such as immunity, blood pressure and muscle tension.

EXAMPLE 101

Lara, the kindergarten teacher, feels exhausted. She likes to work in an artistic way to recharge, and takes art therapy each week for six months. At home she practices daily by observing a plant and drawing it. During the sessions she learns wet-on-wet painting, a watercolor technique with natural paints. In the beginning the therapist tells Lara quite exactly what she should do and gives her specific colors to work with. Lara likes that because she has so little energy. Her creativity is far gone. With the aid of the therapist she makes, to her own surprise, beautiful paintings related to motifs from nature and the seasons. This does her much good. Inwardly Lara is letting go of school and learning to enjoy the moment. It strikes her that she is seeing more color in nature around her and feels more interested in the changing seasons. For a long time, her art lessons are the high point of her week.

Outer art therapy begins with the soul. You bring your inner world to expression through movement or pictures. In this way you can express yourself without words. This stimulates creativity and is akin to the work of an artist. In this form of therapy it is important to not only express yourself artistically, but also afterward look back on the process and express it in words.

Of course, these two forms cannot be kept absolutely separate; even in executing the most precise instruction, you will express yourself to some extent, and when working outwardly the technique, color and materials will have an effect on your life forces.

INTERMEZZO

An interview with a psychotherapist who is also an art therapist

Pictures speak the language of the inner world.

Art has a remarkably healing effect because pictures directly reflect our inner language and they touch a very deep layer. Of course this is also true for people with burnout. One characteristic of clients with burnout is that they are out of balance; they no longer know what they want, cannot think straight, are overwhelmed by feelings or, conversely, no longer feel anything. I try to restore balance between thinking, feeling and the will with them. The artistic approach offers many possibilities. For instance, if someone is overwhelmed by feelings, I let her work with clay because it helps to give form to something.

Observation exercises such as drawing a spoon or a matchbox also help to connect yourself with the world again in a healthy manner. When you are burned out your relationship with the world around you is often upset; you take in too many impulses and have trouble focusing. Accurately observing and faithfully rendering a simple object enhances an inwardly relaxed focus and therefore a more balanced relationship to the outside world. Just try it yourself. Make a drawing of your shoes, and after this exercise you will notice that you experience your surroundings differently. By looking carefully and rendering the object faithfully, you come to know things anew, and you develop a new, more realistic relationship with the outside world.

I often begin the first hour of a consultation—the sessions take two hours—with artistic work. Many people like that because then they think less. When you express yourself through your hands in painting, sculpture or drawing, you let go more easily of everything going on in your head Your experience, your heart, all the places where your true colors show are more directly addressed by art than in conversation.

During burnout treatment, which takes some three to five months, a thorough "spring cleaning" takes place. Burnout complaints are often a consequence of undigested events that happened earlier in life, such as a divorce, a mother who died too young, or chronic money problems. Unprocessed business takes a lot of energy, it blocks the flow and development in life. Clients "clean out their closets" together with me; first they have to look at all their old stuff and sort it out, then there is space for the new, for new steps and a new future.

I know the process from personal experience. I was born in the hunger winter[50] and, thanks to a couple of "crises," I have been able to digest the fear and terror I carried in me from my early youth. I came to understand what caused my own heaviness. I now stand much lighter in life. People with burnout often carry around a kind of heaviness. I try to help make this digestible. Facing the chaos during the time of crisis is part of the creative process and, in the end, generates great inner abundance and freedom. People who complete this path are nicer, more creative persons and more genuinely themselves.

The clean-up process gets going because during the artistic work and the conversations someone's entire life story, including all essential subjects in it, is reviewed. Sitting on the sofa at home and musing about things is also very important. I also give homework such as visiting a museum, with the assignment to bring home pictures of two paintings: the most beautiful and the ugliest. In this way clients can explore their inner world, their thoughts, feelings and impulses in a refreshing way.

Every treatment is individual, but I do work with a number of general themes. The first consultation is always about the person's physical and material world. How do you handle possessions? How often did you move? How did you experience those moves? What are you attached to and what leaves you cold? At home they keep musing about these questions.

---

50 See note 25

Another theme has to do with the way a person works with time and rhythm, a timely theme because we are all very active and outwardly oriented while taking little time to process everything our body, soul and spirit have absorbed. I teach people to make some breathing space, for instance by asking them to take walks in nature with a sketchpad in their pocket to draw a flower or different leaf forms. With such an exercise it becomes clear that you can only observe something well if you take the time to stop and really see what you are looking at.

The subject of "connection" also always comes up. How do you enter into connections and how do you work with them? Together we try to discover what kind of behavior is really natural to a person. What attitude and manners are experienced as right? People with little appreciation of themselves are often much too subservient to others. This means that no one knows them; they are, in a certain sense, ignored and end up in a vicious cycle.

A person can work on this by making herself conscious step by step of her thoughts, feelings and impulses. If it appears that there is a big gap between how a person feels and what she does, I give her an exercise to find the middle between extremes. I ask the client to paint on one sheet how he feels and on another how he acts. This makes "tangible" the difference between feeling and acting.

Then I ask them to take a blank sheet and paint on it the connection between the two. The conversation about the manner in which the connection comes into being may be a real eye opener. Sometimes it is only then that a person realizes that he isn't reacting out of himself, but, because he longs to be appreciated, he is doing what he thinks someone else is expecting of him.

The combination of artistic work, conversation and homework is surprisingly effective. In the process, one gets more and more self-knowledge and develops a better connection with who oneself really is. A re-ordering takes place in the inner world. The artistic assignments especially help people to take their own process actively in hand, perhaps because these help them without words to recognize themselves and find the way back to those selves.

During my training as an art therapist, I learned to move from psychology to the language of pictures and vice versa. I also learned to understand picture language. You can tell a lot from someone's use of color, and the composition or amount of detail can also be a telltale indicator. Often I see a sharp division between below and above, where the above is very busy with clouds and sun. This often indicates a "busy head."

When I ask people to paint a landscape, some start from the center. These are people who tend to view themselves as the center of the world. In this way psychology shows up in picture language. Even people who lack all artistic talent still have their own style. This style reveals everything about who they are and how they stand in the world. For clients, this recognition is often a miracle to behold.

13 The soul: Finding a new state of balance

In burnout, and also in the period leading up to it, feelings, thoughts and impulses of will have grown out of balance and are no longer under the control of the "I." Self-image has incurred a big dent, and there is a lot of anger and regret about one's work situation. All these things undermine the strengthening of our life forces, so let us now explore the factors that can either support or undermine your well-being. They may involve the following:
- the hidden significance of work;
- learning to handle stress;
- overcoming negativity and practicing positivity—in your own thoughts and toward your environment;
- conversation with your different selves and listening to your inner voices.

13.1 The hidden significance of work

Not to be able to work anymore is a great loss. This evokes anger and sorrow, and there must be space for support and processing. If you have doggedly tried for years to keep your head above water, and have been living more and more for your tasks out of a sense of duty and responsibility, it is a big undertaking to find joy and satisfaction again in life as such, and in things that are not productive. But the significance of one's job in giving us a sense of fulfillment in life has frequently grown out of proportion for people who become burned out, so that a life without work, even if temporary, seems impossible.

Besides the importance of the work itself, one's job or business has another, more hidden and existential meaning for us. A successful career means that you are important; being seen at work gives you a sense of being good at it; having a teaching job proves that you're not dumb; disagreeing with your boss or surviving in a tense environment proves that you can stand your ground.

Most of the time unprocessed sadness from long ago will emerge in a crisis; the entrance to parts of the soul that had been covered over lies open. Besides the fact that this is a painful process, it also makes it easier to become conscious of these usually hidden meanings that your work has acquired and that have pushed you forward to achievement. By talking about and processing sorrow and frustration in your current situation, and by making connections with life experiences of past times, you will become more aware of how former situations and patterns in your work, relationships and childhood continue to influence your life today. This will gradually bring into view all kinds of unfree patterns, for instance being unable to say no, feeling responsible for everything, playing the part of the victim, or being unable to let go of details. In this way you may develop insight into your own role in the experience of the situation as it has grown at work, so that you can then break through unfree patterns in which you have become stuck.

EXAMPLE 102

Step by step Charles became able to recognize how he was still battling his father. When he was allowed to feel sorrow for the lack of intimacy and affirmation in the relationship with his father, and for the latter's early death, it became possible for Charles to build a more positive inner relationship with him. As a result he no longer had to prove all the time that he was no pushover. By the way, this also helped improve his relationship with his girlfriend's son.

See Exercise 19.8 in Chapter 19 about identifying old patterns in the now.

13.2 Learning to handle stress

For people with burnout or on the way to it, it is important to pay special attention to learning how to deal with stress. When you learn to work better with your life forces, you will notice a big improvement already. But many sources of stress lie hidden in the psyche, such as expecting too much of yourself, criticizing yourself all the time, habitual worrying about your appearance or performance, not daring to say no out of fear of rejection, fear of making mistakes— these are just a few of the many possibilities that may exhaust us. For example, you may need to learn not to take remarks and situations so personally; it helps to view them as having more to do with the other person than with you.

What is important is that you begin to judge yourself more realistically and above all more gently, and that you become able to forgive yourself for mistakes. Once you realize that taking risks, and therefore making mistakes, is part of life, and that you can't get ahead without making mistakes, you will give yourself an easier time. Mistakes are there to learn from, not to bash yourself on the head with. It may also be important to become more assertive. This means really saying yes or no, as the case may be, and instead of avoiding an answer, clearly expressing what you want. See the exercise in Section 19.3, *Allowing Yourself to Make Mistakes*.

EXAMPLE 103

Jack, the clinical psychologist, takes a special course in which, together with other partners of people with borderline personalities, he learns how to handle his relationship with his wife better, and especially how not to get upset himself. In addition, he has a number of private sessions in which he explores how he deals with demands and frustration, and how he can practice not getting stressed out all the time but staying inwardly calm. It helps him to make use of a little instrument that keeps track of his heart rate, because it makes him more aware of the effects of stress on his body and when it occurs.

EXAMPLE 104

For Phil the business always came first; he never said no and never noticed that he was going way overboard. And he felt that his wife was nagging when she complained that he was rarely home. He goes into cognitive behavior therapy and learns to observe himself better. He learns how to connect his thoughts, feelings and behavior, and practices watching his own limits and not feeling guilty when he says no. At the same time, communication with his wife becomes more open so that she no longer needs to nag him and he is better able to express what's going on with himself.

EXAMPLE 105

Mae is unable to handle her tasks in the daycare center because she never dares to disagree with anyone and is immediately upset when she is criticized. She takes an assertiveness course and learns to stay in touch with herself, even when someone is angry with her. She realizes that the anger of parents sometimes has more to do with their own situations and feelings of powerlessness than with her performance. She practices not saying yes right away when asked to do something, but instead to ask for time to think it over so that, depending on the situation, she can clearly feel, and answer, yes or no.

13.3 Overcoming negativity

Chronic worries and somber, negative and angry thoughts undermine the life forces. We have also seen how people like Charles, Tony and Liz become obsessed with resentment at colleagues, bosses and employers. Talking about this makes sense if it is in service of ordering and processing feelings, and discovering how you fit into the whole. But to keep repeating it and fruitlessly dreaming of revenge only hurts yourself.

This is why it may be a good idea to practice the "thought stop" when you find yourself brooding, in other words, to put a stop to the constant repetition of the same thoughts, and to set fixed times when you want to think about work and everything around it and when you don't. It is a way to regain control over yourself and lessen your tension level. It may help to write things down in a notebook; after a while you can decide to close the notebook and put it away. If you are in the habit of worrying a lot at night, it may help to make a conscious decision to do that at a particular time during the day, and to read a beautiful story or recall happy memories before going to bed. See the exercise in Section 19.4, *Thought Stop*.

EXAMPLE 106

Tony realized how much energy it took, without any real benefits, to keep inwardly venting his rage against the school, the other teachers and the headmaster. His therapist helped him by letting him express his anger and frustration, but she also forged a link to his sorrow. Tony, who had functioned perfectly as a schoolteacher for years, had to face the fact that his ideas and manner of working no longer fit into the policies of the school or with the government regulations. It was useful to him to spend an hour every day writing his ideas in a notebook, and on the facing page how these ideas related to current policy. For the rest of the day he practiced stopping his thoughts about school by telling himself that he would give time to that later; right now he wanted to think of nicer things. To his surprise, within a week he succeeded in thinking much less about school. In addition, his thoughts about school became much less negative now that he was able to write them down.

Practicing Positivity

For many people it is hard, particularly when they are in a somber mood, to have positive thoughts about themselves, daily experiences and things around them. If you have experienced a lot of spoken or unspoken criticism like Johanna has, it is fatal for your self-confidence. And if, like Susanne, you have been the whipping boy (or girl) for a long time, your ideas about your own performance are confused. It is useful in such cases to practice looking consciously for positive things in yourself and your life situation. You might, for instance, every evening write down one thing that happened during the day about which you were really happy, or make a list of your strengths and notice when and how you make use of them.

Sometimes it helps to do this together with your partner. You might also practice a consciously neutral or positive view of the world. You can do this by taking a set time of the day to let go of all the criticism you are feeling and make a conscious choice to see or look for a positive element in every situation. This might sound rather artificial at first, but you will soon notice that it is possible and has an immediate relaxing effect. See the exercise in Section 20.2, *Positivity*.

13.4 Conversation with your different selves— listening to your inner voices

If we look at our inner world as a collection of selves which our "I" has to control, it can be enlightening to hear what all those different selves have to tell us. Through drawing, writing and modeling exercises, but especially with the help of a trained counselor, you can learn to let these parts of your personality speak. For most people it is quite easy to learn to listen to their inner selves. It works surprisingly quickly and directly. By concentrating on a specific personality part, and really giving it some time, you can discover things you had not realized before. The trick is to listen without judging to what the inner voices want to tell you, to listen to them and not condemn them or instruct them to be different from what they are. For that is what we do all the time in daily life, especially with our rejected selves.

Most of our personality parts came into being at some point in our lives to help or protect us, and if we discover what their task is, we can make new choices. Perhaps that protection is not needed anymore or not in such a forceful way; perhaps we may want to give other hidden selves more acknowledgment. There are a few relevant exercises in Chapter 19.

EXAMPLE 107

Joan is being coached by a person who used to work in the educational system and now works with voice dialogue therapy. Joan makes contact with her various selves, and finds it interesting to look at people and their inner development in this way. After a year and a half she goes back to the school, but for fewer hours and in a different function. Three days a week she teaches children who need special attention. She makes house calls and supports colleagues with advice. In addition, she decides to take training in voice dialogue. A few years later she decides to leave the school to start her own coaching practice, which is soon successful.

13.5 Therapy for the soul—psychotherapy and art therapy

Psychotherapy

By focusing on your inner world and putting into words what you experience, with support from a therapist and in a safe place, it is possible to reflect on yourself. You can thus become conscious of your patterns of acting, feeling and thinking, and experience underlying feelings and choices. This may open the door to making different choices and trying out new ways of being.

In the first phase of therapy the emphasis is on support and being able to rest, and on forming an overall picture of yourself. Later comes learning to experience your emotions and express them. Even as adults, we can still be stuck in old patterns and anxieties or unprocessed sorrow—"overdue maintenance" that has to be done by processing our biographical experiences. Beginning to recognize connections between your situation today and your history creates space for something new. This may relate both to your childhood years and your life as an adult. A period of burnout is an invitation to explore these things in yourself. You may then still succeed in processing old wounds and transforming such ballast into something that can be fruitful for the future.

There are many psychotherapy forms and schools, for individuals and also for couples, families and groups.

EXAMPLE 108

Rosanna gets individual psycho-synthesis therapy. It gives her for the first time an opportunity to actually feel her old pain caused by the death of her little sister and her unreachable parents, and to process it. After mourning what was, she takes a new look at herself. A year after she became burned out, she decides to do something she really likes, something purely for herself.

EXAMPLE 109

Susanne, the journalist, cannot forget the bullying by the other editors. She gets special therapy to process her memories. In six sessions she is able to put her traumatic time in the department in its proper place. She is no longer allergic to good-natured teasing by her friends, and can now look back on that awful period without heart palpitations and anger.

EXAMPLE 110

Liz went into group therapy. "It was a great support to exchange experiences with others, to cry together and also laugh a lot. I also learned a great deal, such as what my own values and standards are, and that I can change those if I want to. Through the feedback from others I saw how I had exceeded my limits in my dealings with the boss, and how I often did this in all kinds of situations. I learned to recognize patterns and, with the help of the others in the group, I developed the courage to say no more often. By doing group relaxation and meditation exercises, I learned to listen better to signals from my body. I still have a couple of good friends from that group."

Expressive Art Therapy

In addition to conversation, the process of gaining insight into oneself can be supported by expressive art therapy methods such as painting, sculpture, movement and music. In these forms of therapy you make connections with your inner world and express these. You choose your own materials, forms, colors or gestures. It is essential to put your experiences into words afterward and to share them with a therapist or other group member.

Different kinds of exercises are possible in art therapy. Active interest in the world can be practiced to overcome feelings of being subjected to impressions, tasks and obligations imposed from outside. Non-verbal methods of exploring inner processes and experiences often go deeper and are more effective than talking about them. Through art therapy this can take place in a non-threatening, imaginative manner. Direct experiences emerge more readily this way than by talking. Stories, poems and song lyrics may be used as supporting elements in this therapy. It is also effective to work in a group and to share and discuss experiences with each other.

EXAMPLE 111

Rosanna also has art therapy. The therapist employs a variety of techniques, but the object is always to explore how Rosanna experiences things and what her feelings about it are. For the first time in many years, she brings her feelings to expression again in paint and clay and starts to write again. She talks with the therapist about the things that occupy her mind, which results in new assignments. An inner creative source begins to flow again.

Rosanna realizes that she has worked all her life to "keep things going." After the death of her sister and things went from bad to worse at home, she devoted herself to keep her parents' store going. Dreaming, stories and drawing were taboo. Her little free time was devoted to school work because her parents said that was important. Life had to be taken seriously. Also in the community Rosanna was always taking care of others.

Rosanna realizes that it's been ten years since she has done any drawing, although that used to be just as important for her as breathing. She signs up for the Art Academy and enjoys the courses there and her old/new creativity.

INTERMEZZO

An interview with a physician/biography consultant

My own burnout has been one of the most important learning experiences of my life.

Burnout has tremendous potential—a new chance to get back on course. I like working with clients who have burnout. They are strong personalities. You can only burn out if you burn. I like people who are passionate, for they strive to change something in the existing order, they want to turn something to the good. Sometimes that leads to a break in their career, and no matter how unwise that may seem, their passion is more important.

I know the phenomenon of burnout from the inside. About twenty years ago I was run off the road on my bicycle. I sat on the pavement and suddenly felt totally exhausted. I was smacked back to earth. What was I doing? My physician said I was "overworked." After a brief period of rest, I had an idea of what was happening. I had seen two professions go up in smoke, but because of the burnout my true ideal, my deepest motive became visible. I became conscious of what I had always wanted to do in my earlier professions, namely helping people on their way to unfold activities through which they can give the world the best of themselves.

A little more than a year after the fall off my bicycle, I was working people with burnout. It was a variant of what I had wanted to do as a general physician—not just fighting the symptoms of the umpteenth ear infection with medications, but discovering together with the patients whether the ailment of the moment could be some sort of signal; whether they were still on course in their lives. And it was an extension of my work as a coach for students, helping them find their way in themselves and in life.

I begin every case by making a map of the here and now. First the breaches in the walls have to be closed. If someone is stressed out about a particular thing, I explore that with him. Then we look back together. There is a good reason for this: An essential feature in people with burnout is that the will is stuck; they have given up on everything. The only way to reestablish contact with the will is to look to the past. The future is shrouded in mist, but when you look at the facts of the life that lies behind you, you become visible as a human being with all the values and things you believe in that give direction to your life. The facts are there.

The question of *how* you look at those facts is of great importance. Do you view yourself as victim, as actor, or are you "co-author" in that story? If you want to take life into your own hands again, it is necessary to view yourself as a creative, and not only as a suffering person. For that reason I explore with people what in their past unmistakably carries their own signature. Then we try to find in what way and in what setting they can give this a new form.

An example: I worked with a teacher who became burned out when his headmaster did not support him when he was unjustifiably accused of inappropriate behavior with students. He turned out to be very concerned with his students' well-being, but his colleagues no longer appreciated the way he expressed this well-meant closeness. This led the man to have grave doubts about himself. Exploring his past we saw that he had always offered intimacy, and in complete integrity. As a result of this review he was able to connect anew with who he was, namely a person of closeness. That is his signature. From there we arrived at the question of where he could find a proper place for his qualities. Where will his "product" fit? He did find that place.

In former times, people found their meaning in faith; today this is different. For many people faith no longer provides direction in their lives, and therefore they have to find their "rock" out of their own biography, their own story. It is my conviction that we have all been given a task; and this story, our reason for being here, is something we have to discover from life itself.

When people are at about the middle of their working life, if things go well, they make a change from "outside in" to "inside out." When we start working we are focused on what is expected of us. But the time comes when we need to orient ourselves "inside out," to wonder who we are and in what way we can come to optimal expression. A person who does not make that change out of herself may benefit from burnout. It is like a second chance when you have missed the exit from the freeway. People who are already "inside out" do not burn out.

During burnout, people also develop great doubts about their own abilities. That is the reason why I do a "competence analysis" with all my clients. People have to become conscious of their own strengths and talents again, and remember all the ways they are perfect for certain functions, so they regain their self-confidence.

I rarely work with a person longer than six months. The first three months are dedicated to mapping the past and discovering the person's deepest motivation. Because this motivation proves to be visible throughout the course of life, very often clients don't change jobs but just start doing their work differently. With clients who do want different work, we take a walk into the future—literally. Together we look into the distance and notice what obstacles we meet on the way. Having ideals is, after all, not enough to reach your destination; you also need a sense of reality. The point is that a person, when responding to his deepest motivations, also learns to take his own potential and limitations into account.

In my practice I often encounter whistle-blowers. Time and again these are people who do not understand that others do not always share their ideals. For example, I once worked with a tour bus driver. Because he expressed the opinion that the bus company's buses were no good, his colleagues started to badger him, and he got the worst schedules and buses. The complaint against him was that he had aired the dirty laundry and jeopardized the jobs of his colleagues. He eventually burned out. It totally escaped the man that he was the only one who thought it was important to drive a vehicle in top condition instead of one with worn tires. By looking back over his life, he discovered that justice and responsibility had always been very important to him; he could not compromise on those. In his youth he was always the one who was sent to the headmaster because he stood up for other students.

As a result of this review he saw that this sense of responsibility was an asset of his. Next time he encountered such a situation, he would definitely expose it again, but he would handle it better. He is now looking for a job and in his applications he mentions that integrity and openness are very important values for him. He gets positive reactions to this; evidently there are companies that also attach great value to that.

Your ideals are often so self-evident to you that you can't imagine that others don't have them. The last thing a fish gets to know is the water in which it is swimming. People with burnout are like fish lying on the bank who are given a chance to discover what element they want to swim in. Their next step is to look for some water.

I have hardly any clients who have relapsed. Where there is a will there is a way. And when people feel inspiration once again, they want to put it into practice. And that is wonderful thing to watch.

14 The "I": In search of your own motivation

In the recovery period after burnout, we are constantly working to find our balance between ourselves and the world. We begin to listen more consciously to all our various soul voices and do exercises to nourish our life forces instead of exhausting them. The goal is to get a grip on ourselves and our life. We try to achieve a better balance between connecting and letting go, between autonomy and being part of a social community, between fulfilling obligations and making our own choices.

Keeping the balance between our various impulses, feelings and ideas, between our own interests and those of others is a matter of the "I." It requires putting some distance between ourselves and what lives in our soul. Self-reflection is a peculiarly human property that no animal possesses. After everything is said and done, it is this conscious "I" that can weigh one thing against another and make choices. You can never do the exercises mentioned in the two previous chapters without engaging the "I"; and it is our "I", no matter what phase of life we're in, that guides our continued development.

14.1 Practicing balance

The tension between our own capacities, wishes and longings on the one hand, and the demands of family, work and the culture around us on the other, often generates an unhealthy dichotomy. Practicing the art of finding our own boundaries—even though there are countless necessary, useful and fun things to do—is an important source of life forces in this regard. There are many ways in which we can practice this sense of balance. For instance, we can build into our daily life moments of choice, by stepping back and asking ourselves, "Do I really want this?" or "Does it really have to be this way?"

Similarly, looking back on the day in the evening with a question, not a judgment, strengthens the capacity to reflect and the art of making adjustments. Consciously beginning an activity and then stopping it at an agreed time strengthens the "I" and counters any addiction to internet, television and telephone. Chapter 20 has a number of different exercises for this.

14.2 Doing what you want and wanting what you do

Finding satisfaction in your daily work forms an important pillar for a healthy work life. This is only possible if you are doing something you believe in and really want to do, in other words, if you are really motivated for the duties of your job Of course you don't feel the same motivation for everything you do; the point is to feel generally connected with your tasks and to be committed to them, whether at home or at work. If that is the case, it will be possible to face inescapable unpleasant things and to *want to do what you must do*, also even if it is not the most appealing thing you can imagine.

For all of us, part of our motivation comes from outside: money, affirmation, reputation. But here we are talking about our own inner motivation. Without inner motivation all work becomes a rut that cannot give much pleasure. With our own motivation we are able to face unpleasant things without affecting our life forces. But too much unfree, fanatical motivation, such as that displayed by people with a strong inner terrier, will tip the scale and exhaust vitality.

Just before burnout you tend to feel that everything you do, you are doing because you have to; it's all just your duty, and you have lost all inner drive. The things you still want go awry, and in the end you want nothing anymore. Many people then develop a state of constant inner resistance against what they have to do. You start an inner dialogue in which you keep telling yourself that you don't want it or can't do it, or an angry outer dialogue with colleagues or family members in which you call them names and rant and rave at them. These take a huge amount of energy which is of course completely wasted. In a sense you are building an obstacle for yourself that you're constantly running into.

Stopping this kind of thing can be learned. Every time you notice a stream of destructive and negative thoughts building up, you can deliberately turn your attention outward and look for something positive. You can try to rejoice at the amazing variety in the song of the mockingbird, or at the fiery autumn leaf that flutters down at your feet, or at your colleague who pleasantly surprises you with a cup of coffee.

See also the exercises in Section 19.4, *Thought Stop*, and in Section 20.2, *Positivity*.

14.3 From powerlessness to autonomy

The feeling of lacking all power over your own situation, and the impossibility of doing your work the way you want to do it, lead in the first instance to a feeling of pointlessness and powerlessness. A burnout period may be a challenge to develop more inner autonomy and thus become less dependent on your situation and on approval from the people around you. This frequently means changes to a job where you can work more in harmony with your own ideals and potential. Sometimes that is not an option and it becomes necessary to make changes in the work you were already doing. But this works only if you develop a certain measure of autonomy in relation to the world around you, and if it serves your own goals. It means that you have to start setting your own goals for yourself, and that you periodically review them and use them to evaluate your performance.

Nelson Mandela related an extreme example of this in his biography.[51] After a number of years in captivity on Robben Island, he and other prisoners are penalized by having to work there in the salt mines, where life is almost unbearable. Still, the group enjoys the fact that they are now taking daily walks through nature instead of being locked up inside all day. They manage to disconnect their feelings about the situation from the pressure of the environment which is telling them: "We are doing this to further humiliate and punish you." They succeed also to focus on the positive aspects that the situation offers and not so much on the many negative parts.

---

51 Nelson Mandela, *Long Walk to Freedom*, Little, Brown and Company, 1994.

In striving to make an autonomous decision, you practice being an independent person rather than a victim. When you can determine for yourself how you feel, and not allow yourself to be totally conditioned by your surroundings and the expectations of others, the feelings of senselessness and powerlessness evaporate. You then stand actively in the situation, not only in *what* you do but especially in *how* you do it. You actively connect with your own life situation, whatever it may be.

EXAMPLE 112

Ever since her husband fell ill, Lillian has had no enjoyment in her work. She is constantly worried. She takes a meditation course and practices living more in the present moment and paying attention to the positive things that happen around her. When she does this her work seems more like a diversion, and it helps her handle the situation at home.

A prerequisite for autonomy is the ability to experience your own identity, to be yourself. This is not a foregone conclusion for everyone. As we have seen, past experiences are important factors in the growth of our personality, and sometimes expectations of others and old patterns become so tightly woven into ourselves that we view them as our identity. In actual fact we are then merely strongly identified with certain of our part-personalities. Burnout can offer a great opportunity to deal with questions such as, "Who am I and what am I capable of? What do I want to develop?" Burnout may thus help us get to know ourselves better and to discover our identity so we can develop further.

EXAMPLE 113

Tony, the devoted schoolteacher, was a war baby and was named after his mother's twin brother, who was shot by a firing squad shortly before Tony was born. He discovers that a lifelong theme for him has been making up for losses. He had been the child who would make everything good again after the war. Tony realizes what an impossible task that really was, and begins to take a new look at himself and his ideals. He was focused too intensely on his ideal of making his students' classroom experiences fun, resulting in tensions that did nobody any good. His anger against the headmaster and the whole world may well have to do with all that powerlessness in his childhood. He finds that he still tries to put his mother, who died long ago, at ease by saying things like: "I am doing fine, Mom, don't worry about me." But at the same time he noticed much too late that things were not at all fine with him.

Tony discovers that at last he wants to lead his own life. He participates in a group with other former war babies and finds a good way of saying goodbye to his role of peacemaker. He is astonished when he finds out that the uncle for whom he is named was only 36 when he died, 19 years younger than Tony himself right now. He then respectfully takes leave of the uncle, and although Tony is already 55, he suddenly has a strong feeling that it is not too late.

14.4 The art of setting your course in life

As we become more conscious of ourselves, we become able to set our goals more consciously and to become more independent of the voices and habits of our past as well as the expectations of the people around us. This is actually a lifelong art: neither letting ourselves be overwhelmed by life nor tenaciously holding onto old certainties, identities and relationships. Saying yes to what life brings while at the same time always developing and therefore changing. Taking up themes and also letting them go again. We then become more and more the conductor of our own life, setting and adjusting our goals while consciously engaged in a lifelong process of development. Part of this is also learning to deal better with disappointments.

Dealing with Disappointment

Disappointments may be caused by actual shortcomings in yourself or colleagues, but they can also be projections. For instance, if you strongly idealize a colleague, friend or partner and ascribe characteristics to them that are not grounded in reality, the day will inevitably come when they can no longer live up to that image and have to disappoint you. Or if you are living so strongly with an ideal that you lose sight of inconvenient reality, sooner or later you are in for a disappointment.

It is the task of the "I" to explore regularly what the state of things really is. Are giving and taking still in balance? Are your ideals and goals realistic in view of your capacities? What wishes and anxieties am I projecting onto the other so that she becomes unfree and I am disappointed? If you succeed in making your goals more realistic, you have a better chance of achieving them. If you can have clear expectations, express and test them, you reduce your risk of being disappointed. If you can recognize projections, they have a story to tell, mostly about yourself. Mutual difficulties and disappointments will then cease to be energy destroyers but, on the contrary, may create the possibility of relating better to yourself and to others. And if it is really a case of a constantly disappointing work environment, it is better to leave and look for other work.

See the exercise in Section 20.1, *Reflection—are you still on course?*

Practicing Presence of Mind

Finding your way through life is a matter of consciousness. We can practice this through regular moments of self-evaluation, but also by practicing presence of mind during the day. Living in the here and now, calm observation of the situation in which we find ourselves without pressure or anxiously looking backward or forward, is something that is practiced in many meditation schools. It means being completely awake in the now, being calmly anchored in the body, and facing the situation that exists without prejudice, irritation or anxiety. The better we learn this, the more solidly we can stand in life without stress.

See the exercises in Chapter 20.

14.5 Therapy focused on the "I": From therapy to inner development

Therapy means treatment. Most people who go into therapy do this because of an illness, a disorder or something that troubles them. They do it when something has gone awry, when they want to change things, or when they are stuck in old patterns and can't make a change themselves. Therapy therefore has to do with growth, a desire to change yourself, inner development. Most people don't want to have to get sick before they change. They want to remain in development as healthy persons. They consider inner growth as a prerequisite for a meaningful life. When in such a process you look for a coach or counselor, it should not be someone who focuses on what is sick or disturbed, but rather on that which is healthy and wants to be strengthened. Then you are making a step from fighting disorders to functioning in a healthy manner and, concurrently, preventing diseases such as burnout. This is called *salutogenesis*.[52]

The word *salutogenesis* is a composite of the Latin *salus*, health, and the Greek *genesis*, origin. Salutogenesis explores and strengthens the origin of health. The word pathogenesis means the origin of illness or disorder. Pathogenesis therefore focuses on the origin of an illness or disorder; it has been the central subject of Western medicine for centuries.[53] Both strive for health, but the difference lies in the focus of attention. In the pathogenetic concept, health is the absence of disease. In order to get and stay healthy you have to combat disease. In salutogenesis health is an active state of well-being that transcends the mere absence of disease. You focus on the sources of health and try to strengthen those. Development and change are fundamental concepts in this approach: growing stronger as a result of obstacles, illness, frustration and stress by learning to deal better with yourself and the world around you all the time. Salutogenesis therefore means ceaseless inner development. Therapies and coaching directed toward the "I" are usually salutogenetic in nature.

For instance, in biography work and therapies that help people find meaning, the counselor helps a person explore his biography and develop a new orientation in life. Psychotherapy too, although initially focused on the soul, will in the last phase often turn its attention to finding a new course in life. This is also of importance to prevent another burnout.

For exercises in self-direction, finding meaning, and spiritual nourishment, see Chapter 20.

---

52 Dr. Aaron Antonovsky (1923–1994) was an American-Israeli sociologist and researcher who explored the relationship between stress and health. He introduced the term *salutogenesis* in 1979. See his book, *Unraveling the Mystery of Health: How People Manage Stress and Stay Well*, San Francisco 1987. See also http://en.wikipedia.org/wiki/Salutogenesis.

53 Pathology and pathogenesis are therefore the principal subjects in medical schools, while salutogenesis is not taught at all. In case of an infection, the question of pathogenesis is who or what infected the ill person and what medication will combat the germ of the illness. Out of salutogenesis the questions are: Why has this particular person contracted the illness, whereas other people have remained healthy? What has protected the others from this illness? How can I strengthen the sources of health for the ill person? In this sense, pathogenesis and salutogenesis complement each other.

15 Burnout as challenge for change

15.1 Back to work—trial and error

Just as becoming burned out is a process that takes a long time to develop before you finally hit the wall, recovery from burnout also takes time. It is a process of trial and error. At first you feel you can't do anything anymore, and it is an accomplishment even to get some sleep, to make it through the day and to do anything useful or, most of all, pleasant. With the aid of the various therapies, by staying away from anything to do with work, and by resting, you will begin to feel better after a few months in terms of your physical symptoms, sleep patterns and vitality. Life energy is returning. You no longer just feel dead tired and you start feeling like doing something again.

When they start feeling some vitality, many people are so happy that they immediately overdo. They take on too much, try to help others, or stop napping in the afternoon. Especially if their slave driver or worker bee have loud voices, they go back to work too soon. For this reason the recovery from burnout is most often a period of trial and error.

EXAMPLE 114

Joan's recovery period was one of intense fluctuations. Even after several months, days when she felt much better alternated with days when she felt awful again. Her moods also went up and down for a long time. Although she used to be able to withstand a good deal, she now noticed that she was oversensitive to stress. Just the thought of work, such as after a well-meaning phone call from a colleague, was enough to upset her whole stress system and keep her awake at night. When she had a setback such as a canceled vacation, or when she was at odds with her adolescent daughter, she was immediately upset. But also things that happened in the world—a distant war, a disaster, new money-saving measures in the schools—generated more anxiety and anger than before and could cause a relapse.

Although things such as a mandatory call with the boss may be the cause of new tension and anger, they may be unavoidable, and therefore it is much better to use them as "practice material" to stay in yourself and keep a handle on your stress, rather than to avoid them or allow the anxiety and anger they generate to get the better of you.

Some people maintain that while recovering from burnout it's better to stay in touch with work the whole time. Some employees are obligated to report regularly to their team and pick up some part-time tasks as soon as they have a little energy again. In my own experience this is not a workable strategy. It is confrontational, often aggravates the situation and also creates confusion among the colleagues. It often causes more stress than pleasure and, in the beginning stages of burnout, people need to be fully focused on recharging themselves. There are already plenty of frustrations to cope with without such contacts.

This strategy does help, however, for a person who is overworked but not yet really burned out. In such cases her workload needs to be reduced, but she isn't in immediate danger of falling into a deep hole. If she receives coaching on learning to relate to people differently and to handle her limitations better, carefully managed contact may prevent burnout.

I advocate giving people who are genuinely burned out plenty of time to recover. In most cases it is necessary not to work at all for at least three to six months, and not to think of work too much. After that, if the person's vitality permits, work may be carefully resumed. If there was a lot of tension in the workplace, it is first necessary to find out if a solution was found to the spark that set off burnout. It is often better to let a person resume work in another department or different position.

When you are once again functioning reasonably well at home, and if you can start working again in a harmonious situation, you will discover how hard it can be at first. Things you thought nothing of before are now suddenly huge challenges. Background noise, the sound of many people talking, people walking in and out—they are all much bigger distractions than before. Conversations, meetings, multitasking, and planning are all difficult, and you quickly lose focus. After a morning's work you are exhausted. These are common experiences; they are par for the course. They are no reason not to resume work; they're just telling you to take it easy. At this point the emphasis must still be on restoring, on building up, and not on spending energy.

EXAMPLE 115

Susanne found a new job with a weekly paper. In the beginning it took great effort for her to trust her colleagues; she felt skittish and not at ease. She had lost her self-confidence and writing an article took much more effort than it used to. With the aid of a good coach, and because of the good atmosphere in the new department, she made it through this phase, and six months after a cautious beginning, she was able to work full-time again. As things developed, she was a good fit for the team, and no one found her odd or bullied her. That was a big relief, but she did notice how sensitive she still was to jokes and good-natured teasing.

In the reconstruction period it is important to spread out the work. Working four half days is better than two whole days, because you can rest at home in the afternoon and take a nap. If you have to begin with full days, try to build in long breaks during which you can leave your desk for a while. If you have your own office, you can take a siesta by turning off the phone and closing the door, and have a real rest or even a nap.

Some jobs are so hectic that it won't really work to go back to them. The solution may then be to begin with something else, possibly within the same company; but sometimes it is necessary to re-integrate somewhere else. With the help of a coach you can learn to protect your boundaries and use your time and energy better. Night and evening shifts are not advisable. In some professions weekend work may help one return to work, because things are usually less busy on weekends and the mood is different.

EXAMPLE 116

At the end of a recovery and re-integration period of a year and a half after she had left her department, Johanna started work in an outpatient clinic of the organization where she had worked before, but now with a different manager and new colleagues. She had only day shifts and did not need to solve crisis situations. She was also free on weekends. Only after a year was she able to take an evening shift again. She absolutely did not want to go back to her former position.

15.2 Setting your own course—finding a new direction

Burnout is a cultural disease and simultaneously an individual life crisis. A period of burnout inevitably signifies a confrontation with personal values, standards and behavior that used to be self-evident, but now apparently require change. A burned-out person goes through a deep valley. Afterward, many people find the path has led them to a deepened self-knowledge and view of life, and looking back they see this period as having enriched their life. Burnout then leads to a rethinking of the way they stand in relation to life and work.

For this reason, burnout and recovery often have radical consequences for people's lifestyles and orientations. The ability to be more aware of your limitations and to refuse to overdo things will affect your entire way of living and working. It may be that your new way of being will not fit in with your former work situation, or even with your profession or your relationship. A large number of people who became burned out opt for radical change—in work and sometimes also in their personal life. Others stay with their professions, but put new life into them.

If your former vitality does not completely come back after some time, you will have to take that into account by working less and/or taking on less at home. But in many cases, one also witnesses a change in mentality, a change in attitude. You realize there is more to life than working hard and achieving things. You have made a more realistic estimate of what you can handle so that it is still pleasant. There prove to be things other than work that make life worth living, things that are more constructive but that also require time if you want to give them your attention. For this reason, it is more reasonable and healthy if after burnout you work less or enter into a less stressful profession or position, and if you can view this as a choice and not as some kind of disability.

EXAMPLE 117

Malika realized that she had found many things satisfying about her position and tasks at the publishing firm, but that deep down she had been brooding for a long time about the meaning and significance of her work. She decided to follow her heart and turn her hobby of cooking into her new profession. Now, two years after she became burned out, she works three days a week in a small Iranian restaurant. In addition, she does freelance editing work for the publisher. The direct results of her new work and the pleasure she gives others by cooking delicious things inspire her again and again. She likes to visit her sisters and their families, and sometimes visits her mother.

EXAMPLE 118

For Lara it took a long time before she was able to let everything around the school go, but when she succeeded, she enjoyed her own children more than ever before. Thanks to her art therapy, she discovered that there was an artistic trait hiding in her which she wanted to develop further. When her energy came back, she took a year-long art course and made room at home for painting. Using her many years of experience with toddlers, she also started writing and illustrating children's stories and found a publisher for her wonderful picture books.

EXAMPLE 119

After nine months Charles feels enough energy to begin teaching at the nature center. But whenever he thinks of his old job, he immediately feels tense again. After a while he discovers that he likes teaching much better than the idea of going back to his former employer. He takes a course for teachers and finds a job in a high school. Here he can give free rein to his enthusiasm and creativity again. But he also watches his boundaries more carefully than before.

In a therapy or coaching program you can become conscious of old survival mechanisms and choices you made in the past. Whereas before you were driven by performance and the judgment of others as a matter of course, you can now arrive at a better balance between the demands of the outside world and your own desires, capacities and ideals. Unfree patterns from the past can be overcome. And you can also practice becoming more free of compelling cultural norms and taboos. This requires living less in habits and routine, being more consciously present in the here and now, letting yourself be surprised by little daily miracles. The result is a path of inner development with daily moments of reflection that nourishes the life forces in a lasting way. Finally, consciousness of your life ideals and your own spiritual tendencies may be a help in making new choices in your professional life.

EXAMPLE 120

Jack, the 50-year-old clinical psychologist, was working as a manager in a large hospital when he burned out. In the succeeding year he reflected with the help of a biographical counselor on his life and work, and examined his own interests and talents. He realized that, although he is a good manager and can earn a lot of money doing that, his real interest lies in psychotherapeutic work with individual clients. He decided to shed many of his tasks, to work part-time and take one day a week to develop a private practice for psychotherapy and life questions. He also wanted to be at home one day a week with his wife and little daughter. His own practice soon grew, and 18 months later he resigned from his job and now enjoys working with people directly on a small scale.

Many people describe how after a period of burnout they are more oriented toward inner values and experience more balance between work and other elements, such as family, nature, art, and their own inner development. This feeling of inner equilibrium, this greater enjoyment of life and faithfulness to their own values are experienced by many as a profound enrichment of the quality of their lives and of their relations with other people.

EXAMPLE 121

After the fact, Malika experiences her burnout period as a tough reprimand by her body, because she just kept on wearing it out. She is happy that she has been able to change her life and that in this way she has gone through important inner development. She still takes her walk in the morning, and in the evening she looks back on the day with a specific question. "To be happy I no longer need to be the perfect woman, lover, friend, sister and manager; I am now more focused on my own inner goals." And yet, she also has a sense of loss: "The way I was before my burnout I will never be again. The landscape before the pit was hard going, rough, but good and wild; the landscape after the pit has gently sloping, beautiful fields where I love to be, but sometimes I am a little homesick."

15.3 How do I avoid (repeat) burnout?

Descriptions of the burnout and recovery processes easily lead to insight into effective preventive measures. The point is to find the balance between work and relaxation, between external obligations and inner motivation. Working hard is not bad in itself, but it is important to take breaks during the workday, and to close the day properly. If you have your own business or work freelance and have irregular hours, it is good to plan one fixed day off, so that you can work that into your social planning. At least one truly work-free day per week is a good habit. Let it be a day when you have no work-related phone calls, no report writing, meetings or planning, but will be able to focus your spirit on entirely different things.

Also in the course of the year, we all need periods of rest in which body and soul can recover. How long those periods should be depends entirely on the individual, but even one week of doing something completely different, perhaps going on a hiking trip for a few days, can work wonders. Maybe you can make your vacations longer and less hectic, or rather, take more frequent shorter times for a break together with your partner or a friend—without laptop and files. You could also go on a solitary week-long retreat every now and then, to reflect on yourself and your work.

We all have our own individual warning signs that start to flash when we're under too much stress. For some it is work-work-work and not sleeping well, for others it is migraines, depression or drinking. It may also happen that you feel too empty and exhausted after a regular day's work. It is good to learn to recognize such signals and, when they occur, take appropriate measures. In most cases it is enough to take out your calendar and cross out superfluous things, or arrange for a week off to take care of backlog. But pay special attention to the tasks you plan to focus on during that week; instead of constantly assisting others, make sure you spend enough time doing things to recharge your batteries. In the end it is better to report sick for a week when you feel dead tired or sickly than to have to go on disability for months later.

Nature is a source of restoration and health. You need to find your own way of connecting with nature, whether it's watching the changing seasons with their particular colors, plants and birds, or tending your garden or the plants on your balcony. By consciously entering into an inner relationship with the landscape around us, by really observing it and participating in it, we recharge ourselves. We can do this with a little walk, but also by actively watching the natural world around us when we move through it.

The experience, and especially the practice, of art also nourishes and heals our life- and soul forces. Sing in a choir, join a weekly group to paint or sculpt, or start reading literature or poetry with some people. The main thing is to engage in activities that awaken your creativity—things that have nothing to do with any obligation, but which you do alone or with others purely for your own pleasure, and not to achieve any goal.

Finally, it is beneficial to do the ordinary things in life in such a way that you feel they are helping you in your development. Build in moments of reflection, when you consciously choose to do certain things and leave others alone, and when you regularly make time for yourself: time to think, contemplate or meditate. When we work on our own inner development, the "I" connects with the soul, with the life forces and with the body, and we improve our ability to remain true to our own motives in life without exceeding our limitations.

The exercises in the last part of this book are offered as aids on this path.

PART 4

Exercises

16 The ingredients of the exercises

This last part of the book offers exercises that relate to the text, but can also be done by themselves. The exercises have different characteristics. Some relate to Parts 1 and 2; these are intended for self-examination. They serve to find answers to questions you may ask yourself after reading the text, such as the following: What is the state of my energy level? Am I burned out or on the way to it? How do I work with my energy? Am I doing enough things that recharge me? How much stress do I have in my work and private life? What are the things that relax me and help me preserve my equilibrium? What about those various inner voices, which ones are getting me riled up and why? Are there selves that get too little attention? Are there old patterns that keep on working unconsciously in me and cause me trouble? Is my heart in my work?

There are also exercises for Part 3. These are meant to help you actively practice standing more solidly in life. They can help you recover from and prevent burnout.

You don't need to do all these exercises, certainly not in sequence with the chapters. Just choose the ones that appeal to you and which you think may be helpful at this time. It may also be interesting to do an exercise that, at first sight, repels you. Frequently, dominant personality parts such as the slave driver or the perfectionist are the ones likely to reject certain exercises because they don't fit in their ballpark.

Whatever exercises you choose, don't think of them as drudgery or self-imposed duty; try to do them in a mood of being kind to yourself. You might also enjoy doing certain of them together with someone else and share your experiences. Feel free to change, expand or shorten the exercises any way you like.

This chapter contains a few fundamental exercises. We describe the basic principles and give examples of the following:
- grounding
- relaxation
- observation
- focused concentration or undivided attention
- visualization

16.1 Grounding

Grounding means creating a good connection with your own body, the earth beneath you and heaven above you. Through inner pictures you make contact with those realms, body, earth and heaven. Grounding means being at rest in yourself with a spirit that is awake. There are many ways to become grounded. It is something you can do as a relaxation exercise before a meditation, visualization, conversation or a difficult task. Grounding helps to experience yourself as calm in your body, and to be unprejudiced and open-minded to what life brings at the moment but also, if needed, to screen yourself from myriad impressions or demands. It forms a preparation for the following exercise, in which you turn inward and concentrate on yourself.

There are a lot of very different grounding exercises; we describe one here that you can change, expand or shorten to fit your style.

Grounding exercise to connect with the earth and heaven and the heart as center
- Sit comfortably. Make good contact with the chair and with the surface under your feet. If you wish, close your eyes.
- Feel how your feet rest solidly on the ground.
- Feel the heaviness of your body and how the chair, and the earth under it, carry the weight of your body.
- Entrust the weight of your body completely to the earth; let the earth carry you.
- Let your feet become very heavy, then you lower legs, your thighs, your pelvis. Let your vertebrae come solidly together, lower your shoulders, relax your wrists, let your hands rest in your lap. Loosen your tongue and jaw, let your eyelids become heavy.

- Surrender to gravity, the pull of Mother Earth.
- Now focus your attention on your feet, the soles of your feet. Try if you can to open them to the earth, so that you are in direct contact with the earth and its life force.
- Feel the forces of the earth stream up and fill you with their vitality. Feel this energy stream through your feet, legs, pelvis and abdomen up into your heart.
- Let your heart be a chalice into which you can receive this vitality. Let this energy flow and fill the chalice.
- Now bring your attention to your crown and the space above it.
- Connect with a pure energy above you. Perhaps it feels like a radiant light or color.
- Let this connection grow.
- Let this energy stream over and through you in light, color and feeling.
- Let this energy fill your heart.
- Let this energy stream through your entire body.
- Now experience the two streams concurrently: the force of the earth beneath you that carries and nourishes you with its vital energy and the light force above you that fills and inspires you.
- Feel how these two streams meet in your body. Experience your heart listening in the present.

16.2 Relaxation

Relaxation exercises quiet the body and the soul, and thus serve to build vitality. When you are relaxed it is easier to watch inner pictures and to work out of your dream consciousness with an awake spirit. If you do relaxation exercises daily, in between other things or before going to sleep, your ability to bring yourself back into balance will grow, even when you feel stress rising during your daily life. You can use them for brief relaxation during a busy day, as a help to fall asleep, or as preparation for other exercises described in this book.

Here is a brief relaxation exercise.

Seven-step relaxation exercise

This is a simple relaxation exercise in seven steps that you can do while standing or sitting at home, at a bus stop, at work, in the middle of a store, wherever you want. As with everything else, practice makes perfect. If you do this exercise regularly, slowly twice a day to begin with, it will work better and better, even if you have just a few minutes for one sequence. You learn to turn inward for a moment, to calm down and relax, and subsequently you can apply it in all kinds of situations.

- Sit quietly and straight in a chair. Close your eyes if you want, or stare at a neutral spot on the ground in front of you. Relax the breath and breathe in and out a few times. Then focus on your body. Keep breathing quietly.
- First you direct your attention to your feet and lower legs and, while breathing out, let go of all tension in them, saying to yourself: 1.
- Then direct your attention to your upper legs, pelvis, lower back and abdomen and let go of all tension there: 2.
- Now move your attention to your chest, shoulders, arms and back and let tension flow away there: 3.
- Give your attention now to your neck, throat, face, cheeks, jaws, eyes, eyebrows, forehead, the entire head, and relax: 4.

Next you go back, in the same way but in reverse. Try to deepen the relaxation with every step:

- Direct your attention again to your shoulders, arms, back and chest, and deepen the relaxation. You relax on an out-breath: 5.
- Then you direct your attention to the lower back and abdomen, pelvis and upper legs and increase the relaxation on an out-breath: 6.
- Finally you give your attention again to your lower legs and feet. You increase the relaxation and connect again with the earth. Let the earth absorb any remaining tension: 7.

Repeat this sequence a number of times. Always end with number 7, back on the ground. Stretch and move around a little.

The seven-step exercise connected with a meditative text

You can also connect this seven-step exercise with a verse by Rudolf Steiner about finding quiet as an active force in yourself—quiet that you can mobilize with inwardly-focused willpower.

> Quiet I bear within me.
> I bear within myself
> Forces to make me strong.
> Now will I be imbued
> With their glowing warmth.
> Now will I fill myself
> With my own will's resolve.
> And I will feel the quiet
> Pouring through all my being
> When by my steadfast striving
> I become strong
> To find within myself
> The source of strength,
> The strength of inner quiet.[54]

After you have practiced the seven-step exercise by counting 1, 2, 3, etc., now after every step, say a part of this verse instead, as you connect inwardly with the content.

- Direct your attention to your body. Breathe quietly. First give your attention to your feet and lower legs. While breathing out, let go of tension there and say:
  Quiet I bear within me.
- Then move your attention to your upper legs, pelvis, lower back and abdomen; let go of all tension there and say:
  I bear within myself
  Forces to make me strong.
- Now focus on your chest, shoulders, arms and back and let tension flow away; say:
  Now will I be imbued
  With their glowing warmth.

---

54 Rudolf Steiner, *Verses and Meditations*, London 1961.

- Go to your neck, throat, face and head, let tension go and say:
  Now will I fill myself
  With my own will's resolve.
- Move your attention again to your shoulders, arms, back and chest and deepen the relaxation:
  And I will feel the quiet
  Pouring through all my being
- Focus on the lower back and abdomen, pelvis and upper legs, deepening the relaxation:
  When by my steadfast striving
  I become strong
- Finally direct your attention again to your lower legs and feet. Increase the relaxation, reconnect with the earth and let any remaining tension be absorbed by the earth:
  To find within myself
  The source of strength,
  The strength of inner quiet.

This may be repeated a few times. After some practice, just saying or thinking the text alone in silence will bring you calm and relaxation with an awake, open spirit.

16.3 Observation

Many exercises begin with conscious and attentive observation; observing yourself, your body, feelings, thoughts and behavior, but also observing other people or situations, and observing your own reactions and interactions with those people or situations.

The purpose of some observation exercises is to learn to know yourself better. Observing your body serves to become more conscious of tension, relaxation, pain, fatigue, hunger or pleasant feelings in your body. The life body can also be more consciously observed. Can you be aware of fatigue or vitality? What makes you tired, and what gives you energy? How sensitive are you to impressions in certain daily situations, such as at work, at home, in stores? In what kinds of interactions are you involved, and how do these affect your vitality?

Such physical and energy observations may help you become more aware of the signals your body gives you, and thus also of your limitations. How do you handle your vital forces? Do you listen to your body?

You can also observe soul processes. What kinds of inner dialogue take place in you? How are you undermining your own functioning with negative thoughts about yourself? Which habitual patterns in your daily life are helpful to you, and which hinder you?

Many people find it difficult to observe themselves (and others) in a balanced, unprejudiced way. They immediately feel all kinds of judgments, guilt, explanations or self-criticism—a constant stream of comments on what they do or don't do. This inner commentary is a form of reflection on yourself (and on the world around you) that most of the time is largely unproductive and often has a negative connotation. It therefore contributes to exhausting you. For this reason it is good to silence this stream of commentary from time to time and be open-minded when you watch a situation and yourself, or make a conscious decision to look for the positive side of things. By actually registering such observations, you can gradually transform and change certain patterns and stand in a more positive and constructive way in your life.

Finally, there are observation exercises focused on the outside world, such as when making a drawing in nature. These are often short exercises that you can do quickly in an idle moment, instead of letting yourself be distracted by worries or a constant stream of thoughts. They help you concentrate on something objective, often positive, outside yourself. They have a stress-reducing effect and help increase vitality because they calm the psyche.

16.4 Focused concentration or undivided attention

Focused concentration or undivided attention means directing all your attention to awareness of your body, your breath, a sense impression in your environment such as a sound, a movement you are making such as walking, or an action such as washing your hands. You can also focus fully on a subject, a text or poem, prayer or verse. The point here is to generate great, focused concentration without judging or changing anything, without criticizing yourself, without any interfering thoughts, without forcing yourself. This self-directed concentration creates inner calm and is good preparation for meditative exercises and visualizations. It sounds simple, but for most people it is something they can keep practicing for the rest of their lives.

16.5 Visualization

Visualizing means creating pictures in your mind. The Latin word *visus* means "seeing, vision"; but here we are talking about pictures that you not only see in your mind, but that are supported by sense impressions as much as possible. For instance, if you evoke an inner picture of a river, it is good to see the flow of the water. What colors do you see in the water? Is the sun shining or is there a mist? Is anything floating on the water? Can you see the banks? But also, can you hear the sound of the waves lapping on the banks? The birds singing in the bushes? Can you smell the water and the grass? Can you feel the cool water on your body? In your imagination, can you take a mouthful of the water and taste it? The more senses you use, the livelier the picture becomes and the stronger the effects of the visualization will be.

Inner pictures, including memories and dreams, come from our life body. We let them rise in our soul, in our day consciousness. If pictures remain only in our life body, we cannot take them into our day consciousness. Both with dreams and with visualizations it is difficult to hold on to the pictures in our ordinary consciousness. We forget them, they slip away as soon as other impressions enter our consciousness. If you want to remember the pictures of a dream or visualization, you might write down a couple of key words or images. For dreams this works best if you keep a little notebook by your bed and jot down a couple of images in the dark. Through associations with what you wrote down you can then later call up the pictures again and work with them.

With this sort of images it is absolutely not required for you to remember them the way you remember facts, appointments or mathematical formulas, but to build them up again from scratch. As soon as you do that, they begin to work anew. The same is true for recalling songs, poems and stories. It is not the words that help you along, but the inner pictures you built up. And because the pictures come out of your life body, you can, by nourishing yourself with positive images, nourish and strengthen your life forces. Inversely, you undermine your vitality by always imagining negative pictures, especially pictures of your own failings.

By creating an imagination of a future encounter or other event, you can prepare yourself for such a situation. When it then occurs in reality, it will take place in a more satisfying way. You prepare your life body through pictures you consciously evoke, with the result that you are better able to structure the event and place yourself into the real situation. This works even more effectively if you do it the evening before, or even repeat it several evenings before. You then take the pictures with you into sleep, which makes them stronger. You can practice this as a teacher by imagining the content of your next lesson, the students and yourself while you are speaking to them about an interesting subject. It can also be useful, for example when you're facing a difficult discussion with your boss, to call up a lively picture of yourself speaking in a relaxed manner with the person. Therapists use this technique by making brief inner images of the patients or clients they will be seeing the next day.

It also works when you are having difficulties with someone, for instance a colleague or a problematic child in the class. In the evening, make a picture of this person the way he or she is. Try to make the picture as detailed as possible; involve as many of your senses as you can. Do not get your feelings involved, but stay with the picture of the person without your own judgments or anxieties. If you succeed in this you will notice that your problems with the person will lessen and that you will better relate to her or him.

Visualizing is something we can do spontaneously; we do it when we look forward to a vacation or recall good memories. You can also cue yourself: Vacation photos, pictures in a book and many works of art are in fact aids for calling up inner pictures. It is not the photo that makes us happy but the memory of the beautiful waterfall or that nice meeting; the photo helps to recall the situation.

Words and text can also help, for instance a verse, poem or song. Not only the words themselves have an effect, but the pictures evoked by the words. The psalms in the Old Testament, the *suras* in the Koran, the words of the Buddha—these are examples of texts that call up inner images and have inspired strength in people for hundreds, sometimes thousands of years. Legends, myths and fairytales also have this effect on our soul and our life forces. It may therefore be a good thing, if you are burned out, to nourish yourself with such healthy inner images (see Section 18.8).

For many people spoken images work even better than words you have to read. You can do this by memorizing a text and speaking it aloud to yourself. The words then come out of your head and enter into a different layer where they work as images from the heart (learning by heart).

It may also be very effective to have someone else read a text to you. The more the reader calls up for himself the images he is reading, the more effective it is. This is why stories work so strongly on children and adults, and why in many streams spoken visualizations are used to allow participants in a course or training call up their own inner pictures (in which case it is important to keep the pictures so open that everyone can call them up and fill them out in his own way).

17 Observing yourself: Registration exercises

The principle of registration exercises is that you choose an aspect of your life and give that your special attention for some time. To begin with, you change nothing, you only register how you handle this chosen aspect. You can do this with:
- behavior: sleeping, eating, hurrying, work efficiency, saying yes without thinking, etc.
- thoughts: negativity, worrying, brooding
- feelings: fear, unrest, enthusiasm, gratefulness
- relationships with others: interactions, being too nice, quarrels

Frequently you will also register a combination of behavior and the corresponding thoughts and feelings.

It is important to have a little notebook with you and to write down what you register at set times, for instance three times a day, or right away after an observation. By doing this you will become more conscious of certain patterns. What happened unconsciously and you used to take for granted is now brought to light through your attention. Sometimes this alone can become an occasion for a change in behavior, but most of the exercises that begin with registration are followed by an evaluation, at which point you can choose to make changes and practice them. This chapter describes a few registration exercises, but you may also develop them yourself and apply them to aspects of your life that you want to examine.

17.1 Questions for self-examination: Am I (almost) burned out?

Perhaps you are reading this book because you are concerned and want to know whether you are experiencing symptoms of stress or burnout. Or maybe you are a caregiver and want to know what to watch for and what questions to ask to ascertain whether somebody is stressed or burned out. In both cases you can use the list of questions on the next three pages. Read the symptoms and behaviors in the question list and fill in the boxes with numbers 0 to 3:

0 = no problem
1 = little problem
2 = some problem, troublesome
3 = big problem

Because others can sometimes see things more accurately than yourself, or answer more objectively, it may be good to ask your partner or another trusted person to take the survey too, and then compare their observations with your own.

Total scores:

0–25   Don't worry. You may have some symptoms of stress; try
         to take care of them one at a time.

25–45   Be careful. You have too many stress factors and too little
         relaxation. Watch your equilibrium and try to take more
         time for relaxation and having fun.

45–80   You are in the danger zone. You are overworked or on
         the way to burnout. Make changes in your way of life and
         work and start doing relaxation exercises. Potentially,
         speak with your manager at work or your partner at home
         to get coaching help.

80 +   You have (serious) symptoms of burnout.

Self-Examination Questionnaire

Physical Complaints

- ☐ I feel that my condition has deteriorated.
- ☐ I have less resistance, I am more prone to catching colds, flu and infections.
- ☐ I am experiencing worsened premenstrual syndrome, difficulty achieving orgasm, or impotence.
- ☐ I am having frequent headaches.
- ☐ Sometimes I am dizzy or have attacks of dizziness.
- ☐ I have heart palpitations and/or hyperventilation.
- ☐ My blood pressure is too high.
- ☐ I have intestinal and/or digestive problems such as stomachaches, gas, food intolerance or diarrhea.
- ☐ I have stomachaches and/or nausea.
- ☐ I have muscle aches and painful or stiff joints.
- ☐ I have recently developed the following conditions, or they have worsened:
  diabetes
  elevated cholesterol
  over- or underactive thyroid
  cardiac complaints.

Total this section_____

Vitality

- ☐ I constantly feel tired, even after getting plenty of sleep.
- ☐ I have trouble falling asleep, my sleep is too light and/or I wake up often, or wake up very early in the morning.
- ☐ I don't feel like making love or I have no energy for it.
- ☐ I can't concentrate as well. I forget appointments. I am always losing things.
- ☐ I have problems absorbing and remembering information.
- ☐ I am more sensitive to sounds, light, smells, etc.
- ☐ I feel under stress all the time; I don't know how to relax anymore.
- ☐ I catch myself in random hyperactivity; I sometimes run around like a chicken with its head cut off.

- ☐ I have started consuming more coffee, nicotine, candy, chocolate or alcohol. I need sleeping aids and painkillers to make it through the day.
- ☐ I have less time for my hobbies and spend more time in front of the TV and/or on the internet. Without outside pressure, I don't accomplish anything.
- ☐ After the workday or some activity, I feel completely exhausted.

Total this section_____

Soul Life, Emotions
- ☐ I have very little desire to do anything for fun or enjoyment.
- ☐ I regularly feel weary and empty; somber thoughts predominate.
- ☐ I feel anxious more often than I used to and/or I am troubled by bad dreams.
- ☐ I feel unhappy in my work and/or life situation.
- ☐ I regularly feel frustrated and angry with people around me. I regularly feel angry with managers and colleagues and I am disappointed in them.
- ☐ I don't manage to do the things I have to do. I often have a feeling of failure and falling short. I am constantly afraid of being caught short in something.
- ☐ I have noticed that I often react too emotionally. I am often irritated by little things. I am less stable than I used to be.
- ☐ I am getting involved more often in conflicts and arguments— at home, in traffic, at work.
- ☐ I regularly feel powerless and in despair about my own situation at home and/or at work.
- ☐ When I think about my situation and all the tasks that are waiting for me, I start to panic.
- ☐ I feel guilty about all the things I never get to.
- ☐ I increasingly try to deny or avoid problems. I find myself avoiding situations or people to evade confrontations or questions.
- ☐ I feel easily hurt by others and unappreciated for my abilities.

Total this section_____

Self-Direction and Motivation

- ☐ I am less enthusiastic about things I used to feel involved with. I notice that I am less motivated at work.
- ☐ I find it more difficult than before to see through complex situations and judge them correctly.
- ☐ I notice that I don't plan as well as I used to, and as a result I often arrive late or not at all for appointments.
- ☐ I have a hard time making decisions and don't dare take risks. I get into things before having weighed the pros and cons adequately.
- ☐ I no longer react with flexibility and humor.
- ☐ Others find that I hold onto my principles for dear life.
- ☐ It is as if I am racing around in a broken-down car and can't find the brake, and the steering wheel doesn't work properly.
- ☐ I keep on going despite difficulties and/or physical signals, even when I am really too tired.
- ☐ I find I am less creative than before.
- ☐ I feel cynical and indifferent more often than I used to.
- ☐ I am beginning to lose my self-confidence, and I often have negative thoughts about myself.
- ☐ I catch myself with thoughts of death as a solution. Sometimes I have suicidal feelings or plans.

Total this section_____

Overall score _____

17.2 Active calm—separation of tasks

Do you keep postponing things at home or work because you don't have the energy to take care of them? Such things as paying bills, collecting things for recycling, sewing on a button, checking the oil in the car, taking your child to the barber, hanging a picture…? When you postpone such things all the time, they continue to bother you, keep you from sleeping, and cause constant unrest and tension at the edge of consciousness.

The following exercise can help you make choices. The purpose is:
- to stop worrying about all the things that have to be done and don't get done
- to consciously choose activities
- to delegate

The exercise:
- Make a list of all the tasks and activities you really have to do but never do because you dread them and keep postponing them.
- Put the list on the refrigerator and add things as you think of them.
- After a few days inspect the list; take ample time for this.
- Take three sheets of paper and give them the following titles:
  A. Things I can delegate in whole or in part to someone else, or that don't need to be done at all;
  B. Things I have to do myself but can postpone;
  C. Things that can only be done by me and cannot be postponed.
- Divide the tasks and activities of the first list into the three new lists.

During the succeeding week, work with these three lists. Everything need not be done at once! Set a specific time during which you want to work on these things, not more than an hour. Then stop. Rest until the next day.

List A.
Things I can delegate in whole or in part to someone else or that don't need to be done at all.

STEP 1 Determine for each item to whom you could delegate it, and how and when you could ask that person.

STEP 2 Ask these persons whether they are willing to do these things for you. Perhaps someone can't; don't let that discourage you. Ask someone else.
Delegate the tasks.
If you are too tired to do it yourself, ask someone to help you get it organized, for instance, by making calls or writing emails.

List B.
Things I have to do myself but can postpone.

STEP 1 Determine for each item the maximum time it can be postponed and note this on the list. Tell others who are involved that you are postponing these things. If necessary, ask someone to make the necessary phone calls or send emails.

STEP 2 Write in big letters on the list: I won't worry about these items until their time has come. Give yourself permission to really postpone these things. Look through the list again and make a conscious decision to let these tasks go for now.

STEP 3 Put the list away someplace where you can find it again. Write in your calendar the designated date and time that you'll look at the list again, and make sure you have the time for it. If in the meantime you start worrying again, remember your decision and the fact that the list is in the place where you left it until the set date. Let it go.

STEP 4 When the time for the first item has come, get the list and decide anew which tasks you are able to do, which ones can be postponed again, and which ones are no longer necessary.

List C.
Things that can only be done by me and cannot be postponed.

STEP 1 Examine the list and discuss with partner, family members, colleagues or coach what is needed to make the tasks you want to do soon and yourself less stressful.

STEP 2 Create a timetable for the tasks you actually want to do, with a well-organized but not crowded work plan. Perform the tasks, but at a measured pace; plan to do one or two of them per day. Put these activities on your calendar on the dates you have performed them, so you can see what you have accomplished.

STEP 3 Check each task off on your calendar when it is done. Celebrate when you have finally accomplished something that looked difficult and was often postponed.

STEP 4 If you can't manage to get a task done, ask for help and transfer the item to list A. Don't start fussing about it.

If needed you can repeat this exercise from time to time.

17.3 Examine your energy and lifestyle

This exercise is a good one when you feel you might be on the way to burnout but aren't there yet, and also for when you're on the road to recovery.

For one week keep a record of the balance between your stress and relaxation. In the little notebook you keep with you all the time, take two pages per part of the day (morning, afternoon, evening) and write on the left the moments of rest, pleasure and relaxation, and on the right the moments of pressure, hurry, irritation, stress. Note it down right away, don't wait till evening.

Assign a score to each part of the day by writing a number on the left-hand page expressing how relaxed you got and on the right-hand page how stressed you felt. See whether the numbers are equal (in balance).

If they are out of balance, consider how you could change something. Are there things on the relaxation side you could add, or on the stress side you could eliminate? You may also find that it is not so much a question of adding or eliminating, but that you can do the same things in a different manner.

In the example, the person might make the following decisions:
- There are things that simply have to be done; I will make time for those instead of letting myself get frustrated by the work I had planned but now cannot get done.
- Even if I arrive at the swimming pool late, I will still enjoy the children or get into a nice conversation with another parent.

Monday morning

Moments of rest	*Moments of action and stress*
I slept well last night.	6:30 Was jerked awake by my partner's alarm clock, but fell back to sleep.
7:10 Woke up slowly, had tea in bed, got dressed.	7:30 Breakfast with the kids, made their lunches and sent them to school on time.
8:30 Quiet drive to work.	
10:45-11:00 Coffee break; watched birds outside.	8:45-10:45 Lots of stuff to do, phone calls; can't get to the things I had planned; frustration.
12:30-1:15 Nice lunch and brief walk with Anne; she listens to my gripes and makes jokes.	11:00-12:30 Difficult restructuring meeting; boss is stressed, his manners annoy me; I feel kept on the run and I worry about the future of the department.
Score: 7	Score: 8

Thursday afternoon

Moments of rest	*Moments of action and stress*
2:00 Good work discussion with Pete; laughed a lot.	3:00 Quickly finished things so I can leave early to take Laura to the dentist. Hurried her up, left just on time with an anxious child.
6:30 We are coming home; the house smells good; dinner is ready and everyone is in a good mood.	4:00 Crowded waiting room, dentist late; I'm irritated to have to wait because I won't be in time for Bill's swimming lesson.
	5:15 Indeed late, drove too fast; teacher angry at Bill who can't do anything about it; I feel guilty and angry.
Score: 6	Score: 10

17.4 How strongly does the screen attract me?

Many young people, but also adults, are addicted to a screen, be it TV, computer or phone. It may be that evening after evening you sit switching channels or surfing the internet or playing games. You are glued to the screen, spend hours per day with it and go to bed much later than you had planned. Frequently such a pattern can sneak up on you, and you will not be conscious of it. With this exercise you can gauge to what extent the TV, computer or phone are in control.

Record for a week how many hours you spend with TV, computer or phone—games, surfing, email, texting, chatting. Make a note of the times when you begin and end; do this right away and don't wait till later, because that will distort the picture.

Questions to consider:
- Are you irritated when you can't watch, text, chat, etc.?
- Do you switch channels or do you just stay with whatever happens to be on?
- Do you determine ahead of time what you want to watch, or do you go from one program or website to another without making a conscious choice?
- Who is in charge, you or the screen?
- Are you able to stop playing games or surfing once you have started?
- Are you honest with others regarding the time you spend with TV, computer or phone, and about what you are doing during that time?
- Try to look back after an evening spent that way. How do you feel (your head, your body) and what impulses do you experience? What did you see, and what do you think of those programs? How important was it actually to watch them?
- Also try to look back at the end of the week. Can you remember what you watched? Which programs have stayed with you, and which disappeared like snow in the sun? What did the screens bring you in the way of relaxation/tension, satisfaction, development? How important is that in your life today?

- How much time would you save if you got rid of the TV, and would you miss anything?
- How much time would you save if you did not use the computer for a while, and how many essential things would you not do or miss? Could you do something else to relax in the time you'd save, such as have a conversation, read a book, do something cultural or social or artistic, or get some sleep?
- Try to live without TV and computer for a week, and register what you do with the time on your hands. Do you feel different? If so, how?
- Determine how much time you want to spend with the TV and computer—and stick to it.
- To offset the effects of the screen, try to make time every day to consciously take in images of nature or art and to generate your own inner pictures.

18 Exercises focused on the life forces: Inner observation and nourishment

18.1 Becoming conscious of the effects on the body of stress and of good memories

- Start with a brief grounding exercise.
- Make contact with your heart, breathe a few times toward your heart.
- Become conscious of your body and observe whether and where you feel tension and where you feel relaxation.
- Now recall, without opening your eyes, a recent situation when you felt tense, angry or anxious. Preferably take a very common and recent case, for example when you were in a tearing rush and afraid of being late, or got frustrated in traffic, or couldn't finish your work, or someone was rude to you, or you got angry at your partner or children. Any situation when you felt tension, irritation or fear is good for this exercise. Imagine it all as concretely and realistically as possible.
- Relive the situation—what did you see, hear, smell? What did you feel? Stay in this unpleasant place for a few minutes.
- Direct your attention again to your body and observe what you feel. Where is there tension, what is happening to your concentration, your thoughts and feelings?
- Register it and make a note of it.

Now do the same thing again and this time with a recent event when you felt happy, grateful or loving. Make a note of this too.

End the exercise and review your observations. What is the difference? Become conscious of the effects of purposely recalled memories on your body. Become aware of the effects on your body of daily aggravations. And also of the ways in which you can relax your body by recalling positive images and memories.

18.2 Energy leak

STEP 1 Wearing your pajamas and socks, sit down in a comfortable chair in a warm room. Do a brief relaxation exercise. Close your eyes and concentrate on your body. Slightly curve your hands and explore your body at about a half inch distance from your skin. You don't touch yourself, but you do feel differences in warmth and cold in different areas of your body. Take your time to carefully observe which areas are vulnerable or cold. Note if you can feel where your body loses energy.

STEP 2 Put your hands on these areas and feel if that offers protection. Keep your hands there for some time, protect and warm yourself. Note what it feels like when you cover, protect, enclose these areas.

STEP 3 When you have observed these vulnerable areas, you can give them extra attention and protect them for a week by wearing an additional layer of clothing, a scarf or a hat. You can do the same by rubbing the areas with a relaxing and protecting ointment or essential oil such as lavender or rose oil, or a combination of these. They help keep your energy more in yourself and close you off. You can reinforce this by speaking an appropriate affirmation while you apply the oil or ointment to these areas.

STEP 4 For a week record in what situations and where in your body you feel energy escaping, and how it feels to protect yourself from that. What is it that helps you? For instance, you could experiment with the distance you keep between you and another person. If you feel that you lose energy when you come too close, add some distance a bit, or during a conversation put a little table or something else between you and the other.

Decide at the end of the week if you want to keep taking these protective measures as a matter of habit, and evaluate this now and then.

18.3 Energy balance

This exercise requires three quarters of an hour to an hour of undisturbed work. You need:
- Colored pencils or pastels. Preferably, use the flat side of the pastels or use shading with the pencils (to keep you from producing a line drawing).
- A board and three sheets of letter-size paper.

The exercise works best if you don't look ahead, but do it step by step, without reading the next step before you have finished the previous one. However, do read each step entirely before you start doing it.

STEP 1 To begin with, take five minutes for a brief grounding or relaxation exercise, during which you make a conscious connection with your body. Perhaps you have your own way of doing this; you may also apply one of the basic exercises.

STEP 2 Eyes open. Take a sheet of paper and your pastels or pencils. Bring your attention to your home situation, your private life: the place where you live (house, garden, surroundings), what you do in your leisure hours, tasks, favorite spot, your family, chores waiting for you, things you want to do. Muse about these things rather than think about them, as if you wander through life in a sort of dream. Taste the atmosphere in your home, directing your attention both to the things you experience as positive and to those you find difficult or that cause you trouble.

In the meantime pick up pastels spontaneously, without thinking about it, and let them speak on the paper (with the flat side). Don't draw anything, and certainly don't try to make something beautiful. Taste or smell the atmosphere of what arises in you, and let the color play on the paper to give expression to whatever has your attention at the moment.

Whenever another aspect of your home situation comes up for you, without thinking, pick another "right" color, and let this speak on the paper. Take five to ten minutes for this.

STEP 3 Look at what you have made, at the different aspects of your home life that have become visible. What is the status of things? Which items give you energy and which take away energy? Review the scores; are they in balance? The chart below might be helpful.

Write down the various aspects of your private life and ask yourself whether they give or take energy. Indicate this by a check mark in the corresponding column. Most things can both take energy and give it; examine them to see whether or not they are in balance. If they give as much energy as they take, they are neutral; indicate this with a check mark in both columns.

Now put this drawing aside.

STEP 4 Turn to your work situation and do the same thing on the second sheet of paper. In your mind wander through your job: your commute, colleagues, appointments, tasks, expectations, encounters, phone calls, social aspects, sticking points, pressure, workspace; taste the atmosphere and make it visible in the colors on the paper.

Take five to ten minutes for this.

STEP 5 Use the second chart to see if your energy situation at work is in balance.

STEP 6 Go back to the first drawing. Forget for a moment how you made it and just look at what you see on the paper in the way of color combinations, contrast, movement. How does it look as a whole?

Ask yourself what this picture is wanting, what it needs. Perhaps a particular color is lacking, or perhaps you feel a need for more (or less) contrast or depth of movement. One part may dominate, while another part is too thin. You might experience too much, or too little, air or space; weight at the bottom of the page; connection between the parts; substance; structure. Try to simply look at what the drawing is asking for and see whether you can supply it by changing or adding something.

Now stop and review what you have done. What is this change you just made in your home situation? What quality have you changed or added? Try to name this for yourself; write down a few keywords.

STEP 7 Let this drawing go and go through the same process with the drawing of your work situation.

STEP 8 Write something down for yourself about:
- The status of your energy balance at home and at work;
- The changes you have made in them;
- The effect of these changes on the energy balance.

Try to transform the entire exercise into concrete changes at home and/or at work.

Energy Balance in Private Life

Aspects of my private life	Gives energy	Takes energy

Energy Balance at Work

Aspects of my work situation	Gives energy	Takes energy

18.4 Doing things for pleasure

Make a good cup of coffee, sit down in a comfortable chair and take your time. Make sure you are not disturbed. If you like, turn on some good music and do something that is restful and centering. Let pictures arise in you of activities you enjoy, or enjoyed when you still had energy and time for them. Perhaps you used to like to paint, or work in the garden, take a walk, dance, or read poetry. Create a lively imagination of doing this activity by using your good memories of it. You thus imagine yourself while painting or walking.

Now feel what takes place in your energy and mood. Sometimes the mere recall of the atmosphere connected with an activity will give you a nice feeling. Choose one or more activities and decide to do these, preferably for an hour on two days in the coming week. Also choose a couple of little things you can do for five minutes every day.

Maybe you are thinking: That is all well and good, but I don't have any energy for it. However, try to overcome that feeling by choosing something and simply start doing it.

− Carefully plan the moment in time.
− It may help to explain to your partner or family why the activity is important to you.
− Ask them for their support or, at least, to respect your wish and therefore not disturb you or ask for attention just when you are making time for yourself.
− If the preparation takes too much energy, ask someone to help you.
− Sometimes it helps to schedule an activity with someone else, such as a walk or a swim.
− It may also be important to plan to be alone for a while, turn on some favorite music and perhaps dance around the room by yourself, with no one watching.

Do the selected activity, and afterward do a brief energy balance exercise. Pay attention to the circumstances and moments when your energy level increased or decreased. Make notes if that helps you. Frequently, one part of what you are doing is nourishing, while another part feels exhausting. For instance, it may be that you really like the activity you chose, but that it was too much for you (the walk was too long, you swam too many laps, or you stood painting at the easel too long). It is often difficult to sense the moment when nurturing/just right changes to exhausting/too much.

If you want to direct this exercise at your soul, try paying attention to your various selves. Atlas, for example, will say that you are not allowed to do something for yourself, especially since you are already shortchanging other people. Perhaps you want to take a walk and your guilty one is afraid of running into someone from work; and what might that person think seeing that you are not suffering at home, but are doing something nice, while all your colleagues are hard at work! Or the perfectionist says that the painting has to be very beautiful, and the slave driver exclaims that if you have energy for dancing, you might as well do something *useful,* while the critic sniffs that you never get anything right.

Try to consciously engage other personality parts. Let your bon vivant enjoy himself for a change, and give the hermit his much-needed rest.

Try to tune what you choose to the energy you have available in the moment. Encourage yourself with the things that went well and that you enjoyed. And before you go to sleep, recall the image of the bright-colored the bird you saw or how great it felt to be dancing.

After a week, review what you have done, the little things and the longer activities, and choose something for the next week. Try to plan such little gifts into your day and week regularly, preferably daily.

18.5 Hidden energy consumers

Some people are very sensitive to background noises, magnetic and electrical fields or a particular kind of light, transmitters and receivers, and magnetic fields around equipment such as computers, telephones and lamps.

Our environment is full of constant background noises. The humming air conditioner, the washing machine, radios, neighbors, traffic, a construction site, passing airplanes—they can all be sources of stress we're barely conscious of, but to which we expose our bodies every day. Too much light at night may disturb our sleep and for some people it constitutes a hidden source of tension and stress.

Give some thought to these kinds of hidden energy consumers; how many are there in your work environment and at home? How sensitive are you? Do you feel better when you don't have some of those buzzing sounds or certain transmitters or lamps in your vicinity? Is there something you can do to improve your environment in this regard? How is the air quality in your house and workplace? Is it possible to let in sufficient clean, fresh air? Can you consciously look for places or create places that feel healthy to you and where there are none of those interferences?

18.6 Do you get enough sleep?

Insufficient sleep often has to do with an inability to let go. Besides, we are so used to it that we don't really know how many hours of sleep we would really need in order to function effectively. It may be that you find it hard to let go of the workday and transition to rest and sleep; or your partner needs less sleep and so you both go to bed later, with the result that you constantly get too little sleep. Perhaps you put a strain on your body too late in the evening, asking it to process impressions or digest food, so that it can't make the transition to the biorhythm of the night. All kinds of concerns living in the soul may also raise your stress level and keep you awake. And finally, there may be interference from outside such as noise, light, or children asking for attention.

Questions to consider:
- How many hours do you normally sleep during the work week, and how many on vacation, when there is no alarm clock? How many hours do you think you normally need?
- Do you wake up in the morning because of the alarm clock or because you have slept long enough?
- Do you feel rested when you wake up in the morning?
- Are you giving yourself plenty of time to wake up or does the day hit you with a bang?
- Are you often disturbed at night or early in the morning by children who are asking for attention?
- Is there a time of day when you don't want to be disturbed anymore by the phone, email or anything else? If not, why not? Do you dare say no to people who are disturbing you?
  How hard is it to close the day, stop your waking life and decide to go to bed?

Do you lie awake for a long time before you fall asleep? If so, what causes it?
- My bed is not comfortable.
- I am too cold or too warm.
- I am having pain.
- I am anxious or angry.

- My partner is restless.
- Noise is keeping me awake.
- It gets light too early in the room.
- I am worrying and my head is still full of things of the day; I can't get rid of my anxieties for the coming day or days and worry about my work and the things I am not getting to; I am aggravated with myself because I think I am failing or not doing enough.
- I am worrying about my family and myself, and because things are irritating me.
- I am worrying…
- I am worrying…

Finally, you may wake up tired in the morning due to sleep apnea during the night, a brief period when your breathing stops and your brain receives too little oxygen. Snoring may indicate that this happens. You can ask your physician to examine you for it.

If you find that you chronically get too little sleep, the above questions will help you examine the causes. When you have trouble falling asleep, try to solve or change the things that keep you awake. Taking a walk during the day will help you fall asleep, even hours later. See if you can build in moments of relaxation or a brief siesta during the day.

Try for a week not to do any "awakening" things in the evening, such as watching television; using the computer; having serious conversations, phone calls or intense study; arguing; or visiting people. Instead, try to do relaxing things to close the day, such as reading a book, taking a stroll or a lavender bath, doing yoga or a relaxation exercise or meditation. Go to bed an hour earlier than normal and see whether this enables you to sleep longer and have more energy.

Help Falling Asleep
See to it that you are neither too cold nor too hot; use a hot water bottle if you're cold. Are your feet warm? Make your bedroom dark. If there is noise from outside, use ear plugs or sleep in another room. You might also try to just let the noises go by and not to be bothered by them.

Aggravation is an effective means of keeping yourself awake. Just before you go to bed don't work or talk intensively, don't drive a car and don't watch a screen. Take time to move from the day to the night. Do a review of the day or a meditation. Put clear closure to the day.

Make sure you don't have all kinds of concerns about the next day. Choose your clothes, prepare your purse and decide that you can't do anything about things now anyway. "Say your prayers and go to sleep; the morning is wiser than the evening."[55]

After you have turned off the TV, computer and phone, and are ready to go to bed, have a glass of warm milk or relaxing herbal tea. Sit quietly while you enjoy this. You can also take a lavender bath or do some eurythmy, yoga, tai chi or a meditation. All of this helps you be more relaxed as you begin the night, so you fall asleep more easily and sleep through the night.

Lying in your bed, do a relaxation exercise. Then recall beautiful and happy memories and see them before you in images. This is a kind of waking dreaming; the pictures will fade and turn into real dreams or deep sleep. Most of all, don't lie there getting agitated about problems; don't keep getting out of bed, but relax and remember that simply lying there, quiet and relaxed, will give your body much-needed rest. The same goes for when you wake up during the night. Don't get up and certainly don't turn on the light. Moments of wakefulness during the night are normal. If you don't get irritated, you have a better chance of falling asleep again.

Sometimes, if you really can't stop yourself from worrying, it may help to get up, get something to drink, and perhaps read for a while. This changes your thoughts and distracts you from your worries. Then go back to bed and do a relaxation exercise. This will often help you fall back asleep.

If you sleep in the same bed with your partner and are kept awake by his or her movements or noises, don't get aggravated but go to another bedroom or the sofa in the living room.

---

55 From a Russian fairytale.

18.7 Creating moments of calm and quiet during the day

In our busy, action-oriented culture we often forget to build in moments of rest. But for our life forces, vitality and mood it would be much better if we did this. Make sure, therefore, that you regularly make room for brief breaks during the day, moments when you detach yourself from your work or other activities. Take a little walk, do a brief relaxation exercise or visualization, or simply enjoy a cup of coffee. Although it is certainly nice to have your lunch together with colleagues, this could be a time to be alone for a moment. With busy conversation in a noisy cafeteria, it is hard to really calm down inwardly. If you take a stroll or sit down somewhere by yourself, it can be tricky not to keep thinking of your job and everything it involves, but to really let go for those few minutes. It may help to consciously take in your surroundings, a singing bird, a playing child, and give these your full attention.

If your work is so busy that you can't do any of these things and you also can't go outside, remind yourself that breaks are actually required by law, and that briefly getting away from work enhances concentration on your tasks when you go back to them. As a last resort you can always withdraw to the restroom to do a short relaxation exercise or visualization. Frequently we only think we can't take the time for a break, and then it turns out to be not so bad after all when we simply do it anyway.

Another way to create a restful moment is by taking a little more time for the things you have to do. If you leave a few minutes earlier, you don't need to drive like a maniac to make it to work on time. Time-wise, it's just a few minutes, but for your level of stress this can make a big difference. Also, when you take the time to do things calmly and with full attention, you create calm in body and soul and you nourish your life forces. Therefore, make it a habit to build into every part of the day a few deliberately chosen moments of calm and relaxation.

18.8 Nourishment in the form of images from fairytales and stories

Images are nourishment for the life forces. The more elaborate they are and the more filled with imagination, the better. Because of a lack of concentration, many people who are burned out are unable to read an adult-level book or even the newspaper. But children's books and fairytales with lots of pictures they can often still handle.

Choose a story that appeals to you. Read it slowly and let the pictures work on in you. Don't read too much, not one fairytale after another, but enjoy just the one story, and when you have finished it, try to recall the pictures in your mind once more. After reading, you might also make a drawing or painting of a scene that particularly struck you. Retelling the story to others or to yourself further reinforces the inner activity and life force. When you do this, don't try to retell the story literally; rather let yourself be led by your own inner pictures. Stay with one story for some time, perhaps a week.

This kind of exercise may also help you sleep more deeply and longer. By immersing yourself in the picture world, you strengthen your "dream self" and fall asleep more easily.

18.9 Affirmations—letting images sink into the life body

An affirmation is a sentence representing an image you have created, with which you work for some time to change certain habitual patterns of behavior, thinking or feeling. Everything we do out of habit, without thinking about it, is lodged in our life body.

STEP 1 Choose a theme you want to work with. For instance, you may want to be less nervous when meeting with parents of the children in your class; or you don't want to be so rushed in the morning; or you want to enjoy nature more instead of driving frantically around in your car.

STEP 2 Affirmations work on the life body, which knows no negatives. The life body works with pictures and, unlike negative numbers, negative pictures do not exist. If I ask you not to think of a red car, you will immediately see a red car. If I imagine that I am not angry or nervous, I first have to call up a picture in my mind of what I am.

The second step is therefore forming a picture of the way you want to be in the situation you are working on. You want to stand strongly on your feet and be relaxed when you speak with the parents; you want to take your time for breakfast and drive to work calmly; you want to focus your attention on birds and plants instead of worrying the whole time you're out for a walk.

STEP 3 Now turn this positive quality into a brief, active sentence. There are a few rules to this game. The sentence has to be in the present tense and has to contain the word "I"; after all, it is about you. It is important that it is an active sentence, therefore one with a verb. With an affirmation you begin a process of change, which needs to be expressed by a verb. The most important thing is for the sentence to evoke a positive image. You can't make an affirmation with an abstract or negative text. The point is really to mobilize positive inner images. An affirmation could, for instance, be: "When I work with parents, I stand solidly on the ground and remain friendly" or "When I drive to work, I take my time and enjoy the flowers and trees."

It often takes a bit of trial and error before you find the right sentence and it feels good. You have to remember that affirmations are not magic formulas. You have to set a realistic goal and corresponding picture, for even if you say to yourself for years, "If I do my best I can fly," you will never grow wings.

STEP 4 Now make sure to write down your affirmation and post it in places where you will regularly see it, for instance on the bathroom mirror, the refrigerator, the inside your front door, on the dashboard of your car or in your wallet. It is important to recall the affirmation—the text and especially the corresponding picture—a number of times per day and actively and intensely bring it to life in your soul.

If you want to transform something in the life body, you have to work at it intensively for at least four weeks. Out of that effort the new inner image will have an effect on your experience and actions. Therefore, practice your affirmation a number of times every day for four weeks, and you will notice that, through the power of the inner image you have created, changes will start taking place in the direction of that image.

After four weeks you may release this affirmation, and you may want to start a new one.

18.10 Nutritional and oil baths

One of the age-old ways to enhance your life forces is to take a bath with medicinal herbs or essential oils in warm water. A nutritional bath is a simple way to rebuild your vitality, to restore your forces and to increase your resistance to colds and flu. The ingredients for a nutritional bath are:
- A pint of milk, preferably raw and fresh from the dairy,
- A lemon,
- A large spoonful of honey,
- An egg.

Biodynamic, or at the least organic, ingredients work best; these will have a healthier and stronger effect on the life body than conventional products.

It is best to take a nutritional bath in the morning, but if that is not convenient, take it in the evening. Take such a bath twice a week for three and a half weeks (thus seven times), wait two weeks, then repeat the series of seven.
- Fill the bathtub with nice, warm water, not too hot.
- Beat the milk, egg and honey together in a bowl. Pour the result into the bath water and mix it into the water with a number of slow lemniscate (figure eight) movements.
- Cut the lemon in two and squeeze the juice into the water and also put in the lemon peel.
- The bath is now ready. Step into it and stay in the water for twenty minutes. Keep the water warm.
- When you step out of the bathtub, don't dry yourself off but wrap yourself in a big towel or warm robe and get into bed under a blanket for twenty to sixty minutes. (If in the evening, you can fall asleep after the bath.)
- Then get up and start your day.

Baths with Essential Oils

In addition to nutritional baths you can take baths with essential oils. Lavender has a relaxing effect and is therefore good before going to bed; rosemary wakes you up and warms you, and rose oil has a harmonizing effect.

Fill the bathtub with warm water. Take an empty jar and half fill it with warm water. Drop a little oil into this water, close the jar and shake it well. Pour the result into the bath water and mix it in by moving your hand in the form of a lemniscate (figure eight). After your bath, take a twenty- to sixty-minute rest under a blanket, or fall asleep if in the evening.

19 Exercises focused on the soul: Processing and changing

19.1 What keeps you from taking good care of yourself?

Make a list of all the things that relax you. Review it and notice which forms of relaxation you never practice. What is it that keeps you rushing around? It may be that there are certain anxieties and fears that have that effect on you. For instance:

- incessantly working hard for fear of not making ends meet or of losing affluence
- eating in the busy cafeteria with your colleagues every day for fear of rejection, though you dislike noise and would rather take a walk alone
- not walking in the woods for fear of getting lost or running into scary strangers
- not making love for fear of missing out on sleep, though you would really like to.

1 Look over your list again and decide whether those fears make sense. Do they actually serve to protect you and do they enhance your happiness in life? Or are they in your way, preventing you from enjoying things? Most of all, do they increase your feeling of being pressured and stressed out?

2 In the coming week, take one of these relaxing activities and decide to completely ignore your fear. For instance, you don't accept an extra order, even though you could make a profit on it; or you take a walk in the woods and decide not to be afraid of losing your way.

3 Review how this worked for you; for the next week, continue with this and/or choose another relaxing activity to enjoy anxiety-free and uninterrupted.

19.2 Expectations of myself and others

From "What I have to do" to "What I want to do" and what I'll need for that

We will illustrate the discussion of this exercise using the example of Rosanna (see EXAMPLE 2, page 25). A feeling of having to satisfy all kinds of expectations can often be a source of stress and tension. This exercise lets you examine your expectations of yourself as well as those of others, giving you the opportunity to handle things differently. There are eight steps.

STEP 1 Make a list of the expectations that (you believe) your family, colleagues, patients, clients, students have of you. Pick one of these expectations to work with, preferably one that takes energy every day because it causes aggravation, worries or conflicts.

STEP 2 Test the reality of this expectation. You do this by asking people around you concrete questions about it, for instance:
- Do your family members really feel shortchanged when the evening meal consists of some simple soup in lieu of the complete meal you always prepare?
- Do your colleagues really expect such an extensive, grammatically perfect report without typos, or would a simple memo be sufficient?

It may be that people actually expect these things of you. But you may discover that no one expects these things of you but yourself.

STEP 3 Check your own feelings in the light of all these expectations, either from you or from others (usually they are combinations of the two). It may help to make a drawing. Draw a circle and, using keywords, write in it a situation and the expectations connected with it, e.g., "My colleagues expect of me a complete, high-quality report of the meeting." Then draw a second, larger circle around the first one and write in it, again using keywords, all the thoughts and feelings rising up in you when you think of this situation. Permit yourself to have the most contradictory thoughts and feelings.

STEP 4 Draw a third, even larger circle around the second one and try to name all the various selves that relate to the feelings and thoughts you put in the second circle. These may contradict each other or reinforce each other. This will show you how your various contrasting selves are in conflict with each other or may even conspire to stress you out. If you are able to get an overview of the inner battles and interests of all the different parties, it is often possible to rise above that level and discover what you actually want in this situation.

STEP 5 Examine what you yourself want. Perhaps you also consider it important that the report of the meeting be as complete as possible, but you need more time to write it.

STEP 6 Explain this to your boss, colleagues, partner or family members.

STEP 7 Together with the other parties, or by yourself, examine whether you can be given more time, if perhaps someone else picked up some of your other tasks.

STEP 8 After some time, evaluate whether the solution is working.

The example of Rosanna

STEP 1 Rosanna makes a list and chooses the subject that currently causes her the greatest frustrations.

Rosanna is drowning in all the mess and chaos, especially at the end of the day. She is tired, the children are whining, and dinner has to be ready on time. She thinks that her partner expects all the toys to be cleared and put neatly away when he comes home. For he has said that he doesn't feel at home anymore and complains about the mess and the mountains of dishes in the sink. Rosanna feels guilty that she is not managing, but also angry about his "demands." It causes tension every day, and she works till late at night to get everything clean and orderly.

STEP 2 Rosanna tests the reality content of the expectation that the house has to be neatly organized.

Rosanna asks Dan what he thinks of the mess. Does he really expect all the toys to be put away before he gets home, and do the dishes in the sink bother him? It turns out that the mess does indeed bother him. He has worked hard all day and wants to come home to a nice house without having to step over mountains of toys. He doesn't mind cooking, but there is no room on the counter.

STEP 3   Rosanna checks her own feelings regarding this expectation.

Rosanna finds that she has very contradictory feelings. Part of her agrees with Dan's expectation. She also thinks the house is much nicer when everything is put away. The adapter in her has always felt that she should go along with his wishes to avoid arguments. There is a self that feels that, whatever she does, it isn't very important: "All she has to do is mind the children, and she can't even clean up after them!" There is also a rebel in her that finds the expectation totally ridiculous and therefore fiercely resists cleaning up. Why should Rosanna have to do that? Isn't she already coping with three yelling children all day? Isn't that work too? And what is he doing to make things nice in the house?

STEP 4   Rosanna tries to name the selves that are showing up. She makes the following drawing:

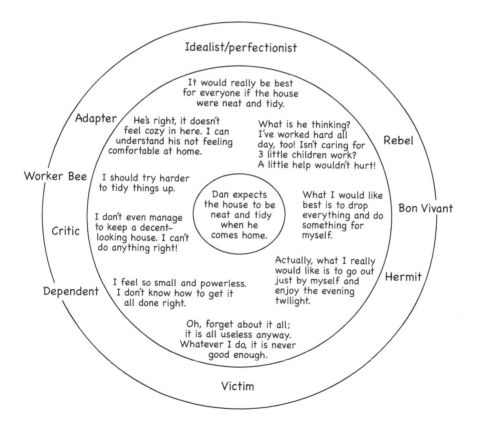

STEP 5   Rosanna examines what she herself wants and needs.

Rosanna can see the inner struggle that is exhausting her and preventing her from making an honest choice. To do that she has to take herself seriously, but also take the situation seriously. When she looks at the whole picture she can ask herself: What do I really want? What she wants is a nice atmosphere and some order in the house, but also time for herself and support from Dan with the upbringing of the children.

STEP 6   Rosanna takes it up with Dan and discusses her feelings and wishes with him.

She is now able to say to Dan that she doesn't want a mess in the house either, but that at the end of the afternoon she has no energy left to put things away, especially when their eldest son comes home from school tired and needing her attention.

STEP 7   Rosanna starts looking for a solution.

It has become clear that Dan's and Rosanna's wishes are very much the same; it has now become a joint problem rather than a daily row. They can now consider together what is needed to reach the goal. Having a more pleasant household will require more support from Dan, or from somebody else who will come in to help. They decide to buy a dishwasher and to tidy up the house together when he comes home.

STEP 8   After some time Rosanna evaluates the solution.

Rosanna is still tired at the end of the day, but she no longer wears herself out worrying and feeling guilty and at fault. Things are also tidier now that the rebel feels heard and no longer works against the situation out of spite.

19.3 Permission to make mistakes

Some people put themselves under enormous pressure because they do not permit themselves to make mistakes. This causes constant tension, especially in new situations and at work. There may be many reasons why you do not allow yourself to make mistakes. You may explore those in the following exercises: 19.8 *Discovering old patterns*, 19.5 *Dominant selves*, 19.6 *Suppressed and rejected selves*, and 19.7 *Your inner children*.

In the exercise at hand, *Permission to make mistakes*, the purpose is not to discover why you are not allowed to make mistakes, but to learn to permit yourself to make mistakes, to avoid getting into a panic due to potential mistakes, and to judge yourself more gently when you do make mistakes. You might even have some fun because of your mistakes. Allow a couple of weeks for this exercise. It has three parts.

PART 1 Make an affirmation (see Section 18.9) about mistakes and practice this for at least four weeks. After those weeks you might make another affirmation about mistakes. It may be an affirmation such as: "Everyone makes mistakes, therefore I do too; mistakes are there to learn from." Or: "Mistakes make development possible. I don't lose my dignity when I make a mistake."

PART 2 Think of the situations in which you are most afraid of making mistakes. Is it when you are standing in front of the class? Or is it a fear of being caught flatfooted in a social context, such as not being politically informed or not knowing which football team won yesterday's game? Or not remembering the name of the person you're talking to at a party? Is it making a wrong turn, or addressing someone in the wrong way, or simply saying something stupid?

Make a list of all the situations you are afraid of on the left page in a notebook and, on the right, the worst thing that can happen when you make that particular mistake, such as going down in flames, being laughed at, getting lost, losing face, getting fired, etc.

Now choose a situation you are not so terribly afraid of and begin the exercise. You decide to purposely make this mistake two or three times in the coming week. You might make a note in your calendar so you don't forget. Create in your notebook a "mistake log." When you deliberately make your chosen mistake, pay close attention to the way others react. Are they noticing it at all? Are they laughing at you? Are you being rejected or attacked?

Also watch what is happening to you: Are you blushing in shame? Are you stammering? Are you completely lost or can you ask someone for directions? And so on...

Choose two other mistakes you are going to practice next week.

PART 3 Finally, while you're busy practicing making mistakes, notice when others do too. Now you are the "public." What do you feel when someone says something incorrect, has lost his way, or can't remember your name? And watch how the other person handles her mistake. See if you can find people who are handling them the way you would want to, and use them as your role model. Maybe they can inspire you to make a new affirmation.

This is a good exercise to do together with other people who are also afraid of making mistakes. It may be really amusing while at the same time encouraging you to overcome some of your fears.

19.4 Thought stop

The thought stop is an exercise for stopping the incessant stream of anxious and negative thoughts that constantly run in your head, and to consciously make room for more positive experiences. It is a way to get more control over yourself and reduce tension. Thus the goal is to stop that stream of thoughts, but also to create set times when you allow yourself to worry and other times when you do not.

STEP 1 Take out your notebook and choose a fixed time each day to write down your worries, for instance from 10:00 to 10:45 in the morning, but in any case not in the evening before you go to bed. You can write them down at random as they occur to you, or you can also use a page for each subject you worry about: your family, your work, your house or finances, whatever gets you worked up every day.

STEP 2 Set a timer for 30 to 60 minutes (not longer) and during that time write down all the worries that are coming up for you.

STEP 3 When the time is up, close the notebook and put it carefully away. Then say to yourself: "OK, this was the worry hour. The rest of the day I am going to think of more positive things."

STEP 4 Now you actually need to do that! The moment you catch yourself worrying about something, you say to yourself: "Stop worrying. I will worry only between 10:00 and 10:45" (or whatever time you chose).
   If it is very difficult in the beginning to worry only once a day, you might choose a quarter of an hour three times a day, or half an hour twice a day. The point is to practice not worrying outside the set

time and as much as possible during that time. It may help to think of something you can use to distract yourself when you catch yourself starting to worry, something you really enjoy doing. You could also make a drawing of a plant or memorize a poem. The idea is to distract yourself in a pleasant manner and to stick strictly to the worry times, even if you don't feel like worrying. Observe the same times for a week and then decide it you want to change them for the next week.

You will notice that this helps. You develop control over your thoughts and most often can shorten the daily worry period after a while. If you tend to worry at night, this exercise will help you move your worry time to a more appropriate time of day.

19.5 Dominant selves

This exercise may be spread over a number of days. You can do it alone, but it is also nice to do it with a couple other people. During the role play identify with the various personality parts seriously, but laughing is permitted.

STEP 1 Act as if you are applying for a job. You are asked to put your seven best character traits on paper. Don't reflect on it. Just write down in key words your seven best character traits, in two minutes at most. (But do be honest!) It's a good bet that your dominant or "primary" selves are described on that page.

Live a few days with one of these traits. Try not to pay attention to more than one trait at a time. Observe in what situations this aspect of yours is prominent. What advantages does it give you and what disadvantages? Can you name a self with which this trait is connected?

STEP 2 Act out a one-person role play and take care that you have no one watching who could make you uncomfortable. Step completely into the shoes of this personality part. Enlarge its character traits so that you completely "become" responsibility or commitment, goal orientation, calmness, efficiency, care, honesty. Stand and move completely out of this self, speak out of pure responsibility, commitment, etc.

Sense how you dwell in your body when you identify one-sidedly with this energy. Keep doing this as long as possible and keep asking yourself a number of the questions below. You can give them brief written answers and then return to the energy you are examining.

- Of which parts of your body are you most conscious?
- Where do you feel tension?
- Where do you feel relaxed?
- What about your breathing?
- Are there parts of your body you are barely aware of?
- Are you warm or cold?
- Are you moving quickly or slowly, heavily or lightly?
- What do you want to achieve out of this energy?
- What do you want to avoid at all cost?
- What could be the unpleasant consequences if you were *not* so responsible, committed, etc.? What unfavorable thing could then happen?
- What does this energy protect you from?
- In what situations is this energy useful?
- How does it help you?
- What associations or memories come up in you when you identify completely with this energy?
- Do you remember when and in what circumstances you experienced this energy for the first time?
- Why did you need this quality at that time, and how did it develop later?
- Are you perhaps like someone you know or once knew?
- What do you long for when you have lived in this energy for a time?

STEP 3 Going strongly into one kind of energy this way often evokes its opposite quality. Notice whether this happens in you. If it does, examine this other quality or trait in the same way.

STEP 4 Then try to balance these two qualities. You might, for instance, put one to your left and the other to your right, while experiencing yourself in the space between. You might also form them in clay or draw them. What do you need to give both parts of yourself the space they need and keep them in balance?

In this way you can try to get into an inner conversation with your various personality parts. As your understanding of these selves grows—how and under what circumstances you developed these traits—you will get more of a grip on them. You will start recognizing when suddenly your dreamer or organizer jumps onto the stage and why he feels called on at that moment. You can begin to choose whether you want to leave things to the organizer or whether it is now perhaps the bon vivant's turn. It is a fun and playful way of getting to know yourself better that lets you gradually acquire more inner freedom and balance.

19.6 Suppressed and rejected selves

Think of someone who irritates you badly. It may be someone at work, a character from a TV show, a relative, a politician or actor, in brief, anyone. Imagine this person in great detail. Make a list of the character traits of this person that irritate you so much. These are ostensibly character traits you do not appreciate. They probably all have too much of something: too egocentric, too lighthearted, too careful, too childish, too angry, too sexy, etc. These character traits can function as the keys to discovering your own rejected personality parts.

Live with one of these traits for a few days. Ask what it would be like to have this character trait yourself. How would it feel to be so lazy, arrogant, weak, egocentric, etc.?

Now try this out in a little one-person role play. Step into the shoes of this egocentric, etc., person and adopt his or her attitude. Exaggerate a bit so as to feel it clearly. Look, stand, move the way that person does. Speak the way that person would speak and say the things he or she would say.
– How does that feel?
– How does your body feel when you identify with this energy?
– Do you become aware of parts of your body you aren't usually aware of?
– Where do you feel tension, relaxation or space?
– Do you feel lightness or heaviness?
– Are you using your voice in an unusual way?

- What bothers you about this attitude?
- What do you like about it?
- Are there any memories or associations that come up?
- Does it perhaps remind you of someone you knew in the past, maybe a very long time ago?
- Can you think of a situation in which you behaved that way? What were the consequences?
- Was there a situation in which somebody acted this way toward you?
- What were the circumstances and what were your feelings then?
- What unpleasant consequences might follow if you were to behave this way now?
- What dangers might there be?

We tend to have pretty clear judgments of our rejected selves; they are unwanted and condemned to a languishing existence deep in the darkest corners of our soul. And yet, they have important messages for us, and the more we refuse to listen to them, the craftier they become in their efforts to be heard. Unexpectedly they will raise their heads and cause havoc. Or we run into them mirrored in the behavior of our boss, our adolescent son, partner, mother-in-law or neighbor.

If we manage to enter into inner conversation with these rejected parts of our personality, it can turn into an important contribution to our inner equilibrium. It suddenly becomes clear why we always seem to attract those irritating people (helpless, cynical, egocentric, etc.)—they have something to teach us about ourselves.

Consider how you can listen to the rejected selves you have discovered and give them some more space.

19.7 Your inner children

Deep inside we all have personality parts that are connected with our childhood and carry good and bad experiences with parents, siblings and people outside the family. This is called the *inner child*. We most often have more than one inner child. Most people have an inner child that is injured, a playful or magical child that can play delightfully and endlessly, or a rebel who listens to no one and is a daredevil, or one who is terribly good and dares to do nothing wrong; a very small and anxious child, one who is so angry that he wants to howl and stamp his feet, or a magician who sees elves among the leaves, dragons in the clouds and monsters under the bed.

The energy of your inner children may have great influence on the way you stand in your work, your relationship and the world. If you regularly feel hurt or powerless, or you become terribly anxious or angry for relatively innocuous reasons, it may indicate that an unhappy inner child is calling for attention although you are completely unaware of it. You can check that by asking yourself: "How old do I feel when I yell at my adolescent daughter that way, or when I fearfully walk away from a confrontation with a colleague, or when I suddenly feel lonely and unhappy?" Most of the time you know right away how old you were—what your age was that fits this kind of behavior. This can help you find an inner child.

The energy represented by your happy and magical children has sometimes become deeply buried in your adult life. If you can liberate it and let it flow, it can help you be more joyful and creative.

This exercise lets you call forth two young inner children, enter into conversation with them and listen to what they have to say. You can do the same exercise with the school-age child and the adolescent in you.

You will need: Three sheets of drawing paper, pastels and clay, tissue or paper towel

In preparation, do a grounding or relaxation exercise for about ten minutes.

STEP 1 Let your imagination take you to a nice spot, one you knew when you were a young child (in kindergarten or grade school), a place where you liked to be and where you often went to play, in the house or outdoors. Imagine that you are in that spot again; look around you and observe everything. Recall all the little details of the place. What are you seeing around you, what sounds are you hearing? What smells do you detect? How does the ground feel under your feet—carpet, tiles, hard soil, soft grass, sand, dampness?

While standing in this place from your childhood, you hear a child laugh somewhere in the neighborhood. Look around you and see this child—this is you the way you were when you used to play here. Watch yourself enjoying yourself there. Observe yourself playing carefree and happy. How old are you? What colors are you wearing? How do you have your hair? What are you doing? Did you bring a toy or a doll or something else? Listen to yourself laughing. Enjoy your playing. Hold on to this picture of yourself, connect completely with this happy child and then come back to your observing self.

Now let your attention go to a different sound. This is the sound of a child that is not happily playing but is hurt and unhappy. The child is somewhere near, but you may not see it right away because it has hidden itself in a spot where no one can find it. But you know where to look, because this child is also you. Look for the child. Where is it hiding? What is this place like, where the child feels safe enough to give in to fears and worries?

Observe this child. What is its age? Look at its clothes, shoes, hair, gestures, movements. What is it exactly that this child is feeling—distress, loneliness, anger, fear, rejection, something else? Hold on to this picture and connect fully with this injured child. When you look back over your shoulder, you can still see your other child playing happily.

The time has come to leave this spot. Let the two children be in the places they choose, but take their pictures with you. Bring your mind slowly back to the here and now. Notice the sounds, the smells of the place where you are now sitting. Feel the chair you are sitting in, feel the solid ground under your feet. Bring yourself back fully into the here and now.

You have seen images of two children in your own inner world. Direct your attention to the child that stands most clearly before your mind and recall it as distinctly as possible before your inner eye.

STEP 2 Take the first sheet of paper and the pastels. First create the surroundings of this child, without any detail, just create a mood with the colors that belong to the spot, using the flat side of the pastels and rubbing the color with your finger or a tissue. Let the different colors merge into each other in this way. As you are doing this, concentrate on the image of the child who is in this place. Now and then close your eyes to recall the picture better.

When you have recalled the mood of the surroundings on the paper, let the child now come into the picture. It does not need to be true to life. What is important is that the child shows in some way who it is. Is the child large or small relative to the surroundings? Is it standing, lying down or sitting? Are the arms waving in the air; are they held behind the back or hiding the face? Is the head held up, down or hidden? Let the gesture of the child speak without too much precision. Choose one or two characteristics that really define this child, perhaps a toy or a typical sweater it often wore.

The nice thing about pastels is that when the picture doesn't come out right away the way you want, you can rub it out or change it. Play with it until you can recognize the child in the picture. If you like to work in clay, you can form the child instead of drawing it. Don't work too long on it; ten minutes is plenty. If you continue too long you can get caught in unnecessary detail and lose sight of the essence.

STEP 3 Step back from the picture and look at it. Try to find a name for the child, a name that seems to fit its personality. Imagine that the child could speak—what kinds of things would it say? Ask it some inner questions and hear what answers it would give—questions such as: What makes you laugh, cry, talk, keep silent? What are you afraid of? What do you long for and dream about? What do you need? What do you want to tell me? Just let questions rise up in you and listen to the answers. Perhaps you want to write down both the questions and the answers.

STEP 4 When you have given this child enough attention, close your eyes and recall the picture of the other child. Work in the same way with this second child.

STEP 5 There is a third person in this story. This person knows both children as no one else knows them and also knows exactly what he or she can do or say to give each child what it needs most. This is your inner wise woman or man. Perhaps you will want to close your eyes for a moment and evoke a picture of this old and wise one who knows every aspect of you like no other. When you have been able to form such a picture, make a drawing of it in the same way as you did of the two children. Maybe it consists of only colors, maybe a form emerges—let it surprise you.

Place the old, wise one next to one of the children. He or she knows what it needs. Try to hear what words the wise one wants to speak (consolation, advice, affirmation or something else), and how the child can receive this. Perhaps the wise one wants to give something to the child, something it lacks, or a symbol of a quality it needs.

If you wish you can also draw this or form it in clay. Look what difference it makes for the child to receive this object or symbol. If you have worked in clay, you can set up the three figures together. Try out different configurations and discover how they want to be placed relative to each other.

STEP 6 Reflect on the place these inner children (who are living deep in your inner being) occupy in your present life. You might write down whatever occurs to you. When do you feel that the inner energy of the injured child is activated in you? In what kinds of situations? How do you react? Do you give the child what it longs for, what it needs? Do you suppress the needs of the child? What do you gain thereby; what are the drawbacks?

When do you feel that the energy of the happy child is activated in you? In what kinds of situations does that happen? How do you react to that? Does this child receive what it needs or are its needs suppressed? What do you gain thereby; what are the drawbacks?

What feelings did you experience in the places you have visualized? What are your feelings now when you look back on it? What qualities do you experience in the old, wise one? To what extent and in what ways do the qualities of the old, wise one play a role in your daily life? When did you last have contact with these inner children? And the old, wise one, do you run into his or her gifts in your life? Or are they perhaps almost unrecognizably hidden in something else? Can you hear his or her wise words?

STEP 7 After you have done this exercise, try very consciously to maintain contact with an inner child for a week and ask yourself in all kinds of situations how it is reacting to them. Do nice things especially for or with your child, and console it when it is afraid or angry. Maybe your inner child can inspire you to handle things differently in your life, do new things, or stop doing some things.

19.8 Discovering old patterns in the here and now

With this exercise you can track down injuries from the past that put extra burdens on ostensibly innocuous events today—situations, occurrences, confrontations at work, at home or with friends; situations that touch you deeply and that, more than you think is reasonable, throw you off balance or make you feel powerless. You can examine events that steer you time and again into an old, fruitless pattern of behavior, and begin to understand the underlying dynamics. This can help you feel more free so that you don't keep falling into the same traps.

You will need: At least 6 sheets of paper, a few colored pencils and a pen.

STEP 1 Take a frequently occurring, real-life situation and live into it as much as you can. Where were you, who else was there? What happened exactly? What was being said?

STEP 2 *Sheet 1.* Make a quick, cartoon-like sketch of this situation, with pictures representing the people who were most involved in it, including yourself. This is not an objective rendition of what actually happened, but a subjective one—the way you experienced it. Exaggerate the proportions and expressions of the figures, play with the sizes of the figures and their positions relative to each other. (One may be ten times the size of another one, have twenty fists, a big mouth, no ears, or whatever, so that you get a caricature of the situation.)

Let every important figure in the drawing say something—*not what was literally said in the moment, but what you experienced as the underlying message,* purely subjectively out of your feelings ("You don't count. You don't get it, do you? There he goes again with his egoistic attitude. I can't do this any more"; etc.).

When you put yourself in this situation again, what is your inner, subjective, instinctive impulse or reaction to it? What comes up in you? The point is not what you actually did, but your *immediate, subjective impulse or reaction* that this situation evoked, such as hitting someone, walking away, crying, screaming, hiding, or whatever.

STEP 3 *Sheet 2.* Draw this impulse or reaction of yours in the same caricature-like manner. Also give yourself a spoken text. What words, directly from the heart, belong to this impulse or reaction? Look at this drawing and concentrate on the feeling you were experiencing. Try to recall that feeling. Where in your body do you feel this? How does it feel?

STEP 4 *Sheet 3.* Make a drawing of this feeling in your own body. What words belong to it? Close your eyes for a moment and concentrate on this spot in your body and on this feeling. Do you recognize the feeling? Does it have to do with a much older situation, from a prior job perhaps, or from your youth? Find the *oldest memory* that evokes this same feeling at this same spot in your body.

STEP 5 *Sheet 4.* Make a sketch of that former situation like you did in the first drawing—yourself and the others who were involved, how they related to each other in your subjective experience, not now but at that time, the way it felt then. Give these figures a spoken text, too—not what they said literally, but the underlying message as you received it.

STEP 6 Now look at the former situation from today's perspective; observe yourself there. What can help you here and now? You can't change the circumstances, but you can call up certain qualities that can help you—inner or perhaps outer qualities. For instance, what do you need—courage, love, space?

Sheet 5. Make a sketch of this. If you aren't sure of the qualities you need right away, you can explore while you are drawing. Try to find the words: What I need in this situation is …

STEP 7 Look at the recent situation again (Sheet 1). How can you apply the helpful quality of the last drawing to this situation? How can you create this help for yourself? What would this mean concretely?

Sheet 6. Write down in a number of key words what occurs to you.

20 Exercises focused on self-direction, meaning, spiritual nourishment

20.1 Reflection – are you staying on course?

With this exercise, work for a week on looking backward and looking forward.

What pictures did you have five or ten years ago of what you wanted to do with your life? What plans did you have then? Try to remember this and write it down in a notebook. Do this for a number of days for about three quarters of an hour each day. You might also illustrate it with drawings or just use colors.

When you have the feeling that it is complete, take a look at your current life and compare it with your past wishes, goals, plans and dreams of the past. Look at the way in which your life has actually taken its course in the past five years. Can you see any particular patterns? Does it show a particular "direction"?

In your notebook write on a left-hand page what has been realized of the plans you made and on the right-hand page what went differently and what didn't work out. And how about today? Have you remained true to your intentions? Did you stray without realizing it? Did you end up on a side track or at a dead end? Or did life develop very differently from what you thought, but actually feels right and fitting?

Notice also why you took certain turns. Sometimes you find that it took unpleasant things like a conflict or a burnout to muster the courage to make a change in work or lifestyle, although it should maybe have happened sooner than later. There may also have been a physical reason why you deviated from your plans, for instance, an allergy or surgery.

The next day, read through what you wrote yesterday and see if you want to add anything. Then look at your life as it has evolved and is now, and consider whether you are going in the right direction.

Which way do you want to go? What do you want to develop in the coming years? What inner goals do you want to achieve? Write these things on a new left-hand page.

At this point, consider how realistic these goals are and how you could achieve them. What do you need in your outer life to work on your inner goals? Try to form a concrete picture of how it will be in five years. In doing this, create lively pictures of yourself in certain situations and observe how they make you feel. For instance, if you see yourself in the same job you have now, how do you feel there? Or if you see yourself in a different house, what does that house look like, and how does that feel? Experiment with different pictures of different situations.

Do this each day for a few days. Review your work at the end of the week, and set yourself a course and direction, an intention for the coming five years.

20.2 Positivity

Many people find it difficult to think positively about themselves, about daily experiences and things around them, especially when they're feeling down. In such cases it is helpful to consciously practice viewing yourself, your situation in life and your surroundings more positively again. One way you can do this is by writing something in a diary or calendar every evening about:
- something you were really happy about that day;
- positive events of the day—a little miracle; a nice, unexpected encounter; a pretty walk you took; a beautiful sunset;
- your positive character traits, and how and when you can use them.

This means focusing consciously on the positive sides of your life and character, and giving these extra attention. It may help to give yourself a reward when you succeed at something. Sometimes it also helps to do it together with your partner or a friend.

You can also practice consciously making your view of the outside world more positive, for instance by taking a specific time of day when you let all the criticism you are feeling be what it is, and make a conscious choice to look for a positive element in every event. At first that may seem artificial, but you will soon notice that it is possible and that it has an immediate relaxing effect. When we try to view the glass as half full rather than half empty, we perform a good service for ourselves. The point is neither to deny the negative nor to ignore difficult life circumstances by magical thinking. The purpose of the positivity exercise is to discover something of value in every situation, even the unpleasant and painful ones.

This exercise has been taught and practiced in the great wisdom teachings of all times. In our time it has been demonstrated that positive images and ideas enhance our immunity against diseases, relieve stress and improve the overall health of the body. Regardless, you will notice right away that your moods will improve and that you take more pleasure in your life.

20.3 The significance of little things—an exercise to actively summon motivation

Sometimes we find ourselves in a work situation in which it is hard to stay motivated. There may be a reorganization with which you disagree, a negative atmosphere with a lot of grumbling or conflict with management's policies. In such a case it is not always possible to resign and leave. At the same time, however, these are circumstances in which you are at greater risk of burnout, especially if you are consistently at odds with what is happening but are unable to change it.

In such a case it will be helpful to consciously recall and create positive moments, moments when it was important that you were there and you did what you did. Moments, no matter how fleeting, when you felt genuine enthusiasm, such as a friendly word to the secretary of your colleague, a nice exchange with the doorman, a little help given to the patient who had to switch rooms, a cup of coffee with a new colleague. It is often just some little thing or interaction with another person. Try to focus your attention particularly on small things like this and, when you go home at the end of the day and look back, try to recall such moments that gave you personal satisfaction and a feeling that you mattered.

You can also create a project for yourself, or give yourself an assignment that no one else knows about and is just for you. In this way you make yourself more independent of the general atmosphere, expectations and vicissitudes in your surroundings. You start doing things because you want to do them and not because you have to.

Once when I had a new, busy job in a somewhat impersonal hospital, I decided to pay more attention to the plants in my office: I always forgot to water them and therefore had to look at those miserable, yellowing little plants. I bought a little book about taking care of house plants, bought a couple of nice-looking plants, and made sure I cared for them with love and attention. The plants grew and thrived and were a daily joy to see. To my surprise I soon had colleagues bringing me their pathetic, dying plants because they said I had a green thumb.

This gave me a nice feeling and, despite the fact that it had nothing to do with my daily work, I had created a situation that I could enjoy every day, completely independently of my tasks or what was otherwise going on in my department. This not only enhanced my feeling of autonomy, but also my motivation for the work.

20.4 Meditation

Practices of reflection and concentration have been taught and used in many cultures and spiritual traditions from ancient Egypt to the native American cultures, from the shamans in Siberia, Europe, Australia and Africa to the Jewish and Christian mystics, from the Oriental spiritual traditions in India to Sufism, the mystical tradition of Islam. Meditation has evidently been viewed for thousands of years, and in the most varied human cultures, as an essential part of inner life and schooling. It is also a method of healing and self-healing.

The word *meditation* has different meanings in different streams and for different people. Its core is a form of concentration focused on one's inner being. Concepts such as *undivided attention*, *mindfulness* and *visualization* are sometimes used as synonyms for meditation.

In the first instance, meditation means total concentration on a content, image, or one's body. While meditating, you focus therefore on one single item, and you let all other thoughts, feelings and impulses fall away; you don't give anything else any attention. That sounds easy, but it isn't. For, when we are awake, we are filled with thoughts, feelings and impulses that involuntarily well up in us in a constant stream of inner pictures, words and movements. When this stream stops we usually lose consciousness and fall asleep. In meditation we direct ourselves inwardly, remain alert, and focus on a self-chosen theme, image or text, while we remain lucidly awake.

Many of today's forms of meditation come from the Buddhist tradition. Their essence is complete concentration on the *now*, in full awareness. For instance, you focus fully on your breathing or on awareness of your body. Every time you notice that thoughts, feelings or will impulses well up in you, observe them, then let them go in order to return your attention completely to the here and now. You thus detach yourself from the constant stream of feelings and thoughts that occurs half-consciously in the soul. This technique is practiced in sitting meditations, but also in walking meditations and yoga exercises; it has strong, harmonizing and vitalizing effects.

In recent decades meditation as a daily practice has been a rising phenomenon in the U.S. and Europe. It is practiced by many people as an instrument of inner spiritual development. But it has also often been taken out of its spiritual context and used as a method for stress reduction, pain control, healing and relaxation. An example of this is *mindfulness*, a relaxation method widely practiced today developed by Jon Kabat-Zinn on the basis of Buddhist meditation. He writes: "In meditation the simplest techniques, such as being aware of your breathing, are equally healing and liberating as more complicated methods."

In his anthroposophical path of schooling, Rudolf Steiner emphasizes meditation as a training of sharper thinking and deeper feeling. He also teaches total concentration, not so much on the body and physical processes, but on words, inner images or considerations that are brought vividly to life in the soul. Take for instance the sentence: "Wisdom lives in the light." The goal is to think this single inner content in full concentration, and to bring it to life with corresponding inner feelings. The next step is to wipe away the content of the meditation, and then to observe what takes place in the soul with thinking, feeling and the will.

There are therefore many methods of meditation on practically any content or observation. You can take your bodily sensations or breathing, but also a prayer, a poem, a verse or a picture. Meditation demands discipline and perseverance. Sitting down for half an hour every day and concentrating on one single content is a tall order for most people. For people who persevere, it has a relaxing, healing effect on the body and enhances the strength of soul and spirit.

20.5 Connecting with content you are interested in

When you are tired or on the way to burnout, you are likely to do fewer things that are fun and have a constructive or relaxing effect. Also if your work is boring or you don't see any prospects for your life situation, it is easy to doze off and never do anything that matters. But in busy times or when you feel a lack of inspiration, it would be really good to pay attention to things for which you feel enthusiasm, things that have nothing to do with work, things you choose in freedom and for your own pleasure.

If you like gardening, make sure to keep giving it time and enjoy the flowers in your garden or on your balcony. If you play a musical instrument, practice every day, even if only for a quarter of an hour. If you like reading or studying, don't stop immersing yourself in books or magazines you find interesting. It often helps to start a project, long or short. For example, you are going to work with roses for a summer or immerse yourself in a particular subject for six months and read books about it. You might want to see all the films of Ingrid Bergman, or learn a particular drawing technique, or study Rembrandt for a day. You might practice a Beethoven sonata, learn a language or explore the history of a particular area, preferably by visiting it yourself.

Any subject is a possibility, as long as you are interested in it. The point is that you choose it yourself and no one pushes you into it, and that it is not a requirement for your work. In this way you create a free space in which you can indulge and nourish your own creativity and/or interest. A specific project will make it easier to take yourself seriously and stay true to your plans. It also gives more satisfaction than doing different things randomly. You will find that this enriches life and that you can detach yourself from all kinds of goings-on at work.

20.6 Active wonder

Find a quiet spot in nature where you can sit relatively undisturbed. Take ten minutes and very consciously use your senses. What are you seeing around you, what forms and colors, what movements? What sounds do you hear, what do you smell? Touch things around you— how do they feel, what temperature, what humidity? Can you notice more subtle things—movements in the air, light and shadow?

Close your eyes. What do you experience now? Can you recall the landscape around you? How do you relate to your surroundings? This may be very different from when you have your eyes open. Explore this. Does it feel as if you are vertical or horizontal, floating, hovering in the air? How far away or near do things feel when your eyes are closed?

This exercise can help you trust your sense perceptions, to take them as true: to recognize the wholeness of the world outside in the wholeness of your inner world, and vice versa.

20.7 An attentive walk with open senses

Take a nice walk in nature. Try to direct your attention outwardly to the things around you. What do you see? What do you hear? What do you smell? What do you feel?

If you want to, slow down your step so you are walking more and more slowly. Keep your gaze loosely focused on the path before you. Walk very slowly for a while so you become conscious of every step, your weight moving from one foot to the other and the moment of change from one foot to the other. Try to experience that the air you breathe in reaches all the way down to your feet.

Try to keep walking as attentively as possible, but focus on nature around you. What do you observe in the way of color, form, sound, touch? Then, continuing your walk, direct your attention inward again, to your own body.

Alternate this a number of times. When you are distracted by thoughts, don't judge yourself, but quietly return your attention to where it was focused.

20.8 Observing while making a drawing

This is a simple and pleasant way to be in the here and now. You don't need to be good at drawing; the drawing serves only to help you observe more carefully, completely.

You will need: Paper of any sort, possibly taped to a board, and a soft lead pencil.

Choose a simple object, not too big, not too small (an apple, stone, toothbrush, shoe, …). Explore it with as many senses as possible. Look at its different aspects, taste it (if you like), listen to it, smell it. How does it move? Touch it, feel its texture, temperature, elasticity, weight.

Place it in front of you and turn it until you find that it is positioned just right, and that you are observing it from the right angle. Look primarily at the object and only now and then at the paper. Out of movement (tracing circles or scratching or whatever seems to be right for the object), draw the general form of the object, including the shadow it throws. Try to draw the form to actual size.

Move your gaze alternately between the object and your drawing. Slow down the movement and adjust the drawing so that the form becomes more recognizable. Continuing to alternate your gaze between the object and your drawing, put in light and shadow spots, so that the form becomes still more distinct and acquires more substance. In doing this you may increase or decrease the pressure on your pencil.

Now look primarily at your drawing, only now and then at the object, and add a few details. Give the drawing a title, a title that not only indicates the appearance of the object, but also says something of its inner aspect, of what you have encountered in it.

It can be nicer to take a flower or a branch with flowers still in bud; or a young tomato plant that you can draw every day while it is growing, flowering, ripening and withering. In doing so you can discover astonishing little details and become a witness to a little piece of a great secret of life.

When you have connected with an object in this way a few times, it may also be interesting to draw it from memory. Close your eyes for a minute or so and recall the inner image of the object. Try to activate all your senses to make the inner picture as lively as possible. Then draw the object as it is living in your memory. As you are drawing it you can always close your eyes for a moment to re-enliven the picture if it is fading.

20.9 Preview and review

A good method to build or strengthen structure in your life is to look backward and look forward. In the preview you let the coming day quickly pass before you, preferably in as much lively detail as possible. Picture yourself while commuting to work, standing before the class, or picking up your children from school. What are your plans, what appointments do you have, are there things you must not forget? You don't need to spend hours on it; fifteen minutes is enough.

With this exercise you prepare your life body for the day, and you will notice that the day is less chaotic and that you forget fewer things.

In the evening before you go to bed, look back at the day. Let the pictures of the day gone by pass before your inner eye as if you were a spectator—no judgments or comments, just watching how things went. What did you do, what encounters did you have, how were you sitting at the table? You can make this exercise very extensive and let every detail parade before you; but you can also do it with a particular question in mind and focus on that. What did I really enjoy today? What encounters did I have? What was the color of the light today?

This exercise strengthens your life body, especially if you don't do it in the normal stream of time, but against it, thus going back in time from the evening to the morning. It is important that you observe yourself without prejudice and with interest, and that you make no judgments.

You can expand both the preview and the review to include a longer time periods, a weekend or a week. Or you might try a review of a particular period of your life.

20.10 Living in the here and now – presence of mind

Eckhart Tolle, a modern mystic, says in his book, *The Power of Now*: "The now can be viewed as the principal portal to being; it is an essential aspect of all other portals, also of the inner body. You cannot be in your body if you are not intensely present in the *now*."

Of course we live in the now; that is self-evident. The interesting part is that if you really observe to what extent you are actually present in the now, it is much less often than you might think. So many of our thoughts are about things that have already taken place and that still occupy our minds, and we are so often busily thinking ahead to what is still to happen that we in fact hardly notice the now. But the now is the only thing we have any degree of control over. We can invite the future to bring us certain things, but to what extent any of that is realized is something we hardly have any influence on. The past is over and done with, we can't change it anymore. But every new moment is ours to use the way we want to.

The now is even so full of potential that it has a strong influence on both the past and the future. We cannot change or erase sad or painful experiences from the past, but every moment anew we do have the ability to determine how we live with those memories out of the now. This awareness can give us a great feeling of liberation and self-determination. When we no longer live in the tension between past and future, but out of the awareness of the now, our experience of time develops a different quality. The now is so much broader than that which lies between past and future.

Almost all the exercises in this book are about being present in the now. It is so simple, and yet it turns out to be very difficult to do. Before you know it you are thinking back or thinking ahead again. The secret lies in the moment. You don't need to be present in the *now* all day long. It suffices to be regularly in the now for a brief time. Those moments will then expand naturally of their own accord.

A very simple aid may be to put a little piece of paper in a conspicuous place, such as your mirror, your computer screen or your wallet. When you see it, take a few deep breaths and focus briefly on the moment. More is not necessary.

20.11 Synchronicity—a little game: picking a card

We have all, from our childhood on, learned to think in terms of causality, of cause and effect. Causality follows the stream of time. It is shown in the effects of something that happened before. As a result, the *now* is the consequence of the past. But you can also view the relationship between events in another way, namely things that happen at the same time. Carl Jung, psychiatrist and founder of analytical psychology, called this the *law of synchronicity*, that which happens concurrently. Synchronicity goes against the stream of time and manifests in what comes to us out of what has not yet become. The *now* then bears the promise of the future in it.

You can become conscious of synchronicity by paying attention to small occurrences that coincide in time and have meaning for you. You are thinking of your brother in Canada when your friend asks: "How is your brother in Canada doing?"—and that evening he calls you on the phone. Through the law of synchronicity, we can experience a connection with our own unconscious, our dream layer, but also with the collective unconscious. Of course, events in our dreams are rarely comprehensible through causal thinking; dreams always have symbolic relationships of events and pictures.

Many people like to pick a card now and then, or every day, from a set of cards they like. When you draw a card that way, you create a synchronicity experience. You pull back and reflect for a moment and, if you want, ask yourself a question or think of a particular subject. While concentrating on what has reality for you in the moment, you pick a card. Depending on the cards you are using, you might read the word *purity* or the message, "In the end it is less painful to face your illusions than to cling to them." Maybe you see a picture of a fairytale prince, a white stag, a sword or an oak tree.

This is your picture of that day. It comes to you and is your gift for the day or for the situation. You have to realize that the picture is not a logical answer to your question; picking a card has nothing to do with magically predicting the future. You can carry this picture with you through the day, recall it a couple of times, without analyzing it or wanting to explain it. Sometimes the picture begins to speak, and gives you a new insight. At a deeper level you practice opening yourself in a playful manner to the processes *behind* things, processes that take place at a level akin to our life body.

.

21 FAFS: First Aid For Stress exercises

The following short exercises are intended to help you create more balance in daily life between activity and tension on the one hand, and moments of quiet and relaxation on the other. We assume that the moments of tension will arrive all by themselves; these exercises are therefore focused on relaxation.

Life is full of stressful moments and situations that often happen unexpectedly. It can be handy to have a few simple, brief exercises you can instantly use to keep yourself in balance.

21.1 Observing and creating your own reality while you are waiting

In our hectic life it is often irksome to have to wait. We become impatient and get aggravated—before a red traffic signal, in line at a checkout counter, in the waiting room of the dentist. But all this aggravation and impatience doesn't solve anything. It doesn't shorten the line or clear the traffic jam; it doesn't make the dentist work faster. Instead of getting annoyed, you can use such waiting times in to relax, for example:
- Thinking briefly of nothing, or of a nice weekend or funny incident.
- Looking around you and observing things without judging them. What do you see, what do you feel, smell, hear? Open yourself to your surroundings (see also the exercise for active wonder in Section 20.6).
- Doing a grounding or breathing exercise while waiting at a red light.
- In a long checkout line, thinking of your loved one, grounding and making contact with your feet, and thinking of something nice. Your body will relax immediately.

21.2 Nourishing the soul while you travel

While you are walking or commuting by car or train, you can easily observe your environment. Maybe you suddenly notice a remarkable tree, a pretty bird or a strikingly beautiful light. On the bus or train you may have a beautiful moment of contact with a child or another traveler. And instead of listening to the news or endlessly checking email and texts, you could bring a book to read, or an audio book in the car.

21.3 Tracking and letting go of projections

What others think and feel about you does not necessarily indicate how you are or want to be. The projection is part of the other person.

In community life with others we all project positive and negative character traits on each other. These projections strongly color our behavior and feelings toward others. Sometimes we are aware of this: You know that you dislike the woman in the ice cream shop because she reminds you of your ex-mother-in-law. Or you know you admire a certain colleague because she is very good at something you don't know how to do.

Most projections, however, are unconscious. We think we are seeing the other, but in actual fact we are seeing ourselves—or one of our selves—in the mirror the other unknowingly holds up for us. We can become conscious of our projections if, whenever someone stirs up strong positive or negative feelings in us, we deliberately stop and think of the significance the person has for us. Who does he or she remind us of? What do we expect of them? What do you think they are thinking of us? How old do you feel in relation to them? Do you feel strong or helpless? Do you feel large or small? And so on.

The other way around, other people project all manner of traits on us, or make assumptions about us, as in the following examples. Joan's neighbor regularly pours out all the miseries in her life to Joan. At parties she says that she has a wonderful neighbor who is always so ready to help another person. She projects the patient listener onto Joan, the savior who will make everything good again.

Malika used to be the child who did not cry at misfortunes and setbacks when she was growing up. At work she notices that colleagues always unload difficult presentations and negotiations on her because she "does them so easily." Apparently people project a certain strength and power onto her. In such cases it can be hard feel the dread or the wish not to want to do something, let alone to show that you're afraid.

The manager regularly asks Phil to work extra hours because he never has a problem with it and is always so sociable.

Chris's colleague who was passed over is furious; he finds Chris arrogant and unreachable. Whenever Chris tries to approach the man, it only seems to get worse.

Such positive and negative traits and qualities can be projected on or assumed about us by one or several persons. Projections often reinforce our dominant selves from a young age, but they can also be experienced increasingly as oppressive and unfree. Positive projections put people on a pedestal. Negative projections, when they become collective, may lead to bullying and exclusion.

Projections may take a great deal of your energy. They may "force" you to always behave in a certain old pattern; they may make you afraid of people or, conversely, cause you to have to save someone all the time, though you're dead tired and don't really want to. They limit you and often make you unhappy, and may contribute to burnout.

Projections in a marriage or work relationship (manager-secretary, teacher-janitor, coworker-branch manager) often complement each other nicely. But when one of the two changes and no longer wants to behave according to the other's projection, there will be problems because the other becomes confused, angry or unhappy and forcefully tries to restore the former character of their relationship. See the examples of Phil, who refused to keep working under the prevailing conditions, and Malika, who rebelled against her parents. It may therefore happen that, if you decide to stop behaving in response to certain projections, your perseverance will be tested. If you succeed despite everything, the result is often a more truthful, open situation and a better relationship for both parties.

If you feel inhibited in your work or private life by strong convictions and opinions of others about you, and you feel that these are forcing you into a particular type of behavior and making you unfree, the following exercise will be useful. You can also use the exercise to explore your own projections on others and let them go. The exercise takes about 30 to 45 minutes, after which you will need to put it in practice in daily life. You need a few sheets of paper, colored pencils or pastels, and a pen.

STEP 1 Make a caricature-like drawing in which you picture yourself in a typical situation with a person you feel is projecting onto you. Exaggerate the qualities, gestures, relationships of the two figures with each other so that they create a strong impression of the role/quality/characteristic being projected onto you. The point is not to picture the objective situation, but rather the opposite: your subjective experience, how you think that the other views you, what he thinks and expects of you, and how it feels to you. You may try more than one of these sketches. Also draw yourself, the way you stand in the relationship and react to the other.

STEP 2 Give the figure of the other an appropriate text, as in a cartoon. The text may consist of words she has actually spoken, but they may also consist of words that were never spoken aloud but express your subjective experience of how she views you. You might also give yourself a text that occurs to you in response to her text.

STEP 3 Now look at these two figures and explore what quality fits the spoken texts. What quality does the other project onto you? Write down those qualities you feel that the other projects on you. Then draw a conclusion: I am going to act … (submissive, arrogant, strong, sweet; or like a peacemaker, savior, rebel, pleaser).

For instance, Joan might write: *My neighbor projects a savior onto me, and I will behave like a savior.* And Chris: *My colleague projects an angry, arrogant boss onto me, and I will behave like a peacemaker to make things good again.* And Malika: *My colleagues project strength onto me, and I will look self-assured.*

STEP 4 Review this carefully to see if it feels right. If it does, check with yourself whether this is the way you want to be. At this stage it is important to realize that what others think and feel about you does not necessarily indicate how you are or want to be. The projection, whether positive or negative, belongs to the other. You need not accept it nor follow it; you need not behave in accordance with it or apologize for it. Now write a sentence in which you hand the projection back and express what you are going to do from now on in your relationship with the other person.

Write on another sheet: *I return to you, …(name)…, the projection of ……; it is your projection, and I will no longer follow it in my behavior. I am …(your own name)… and will from now on …(what you are going to do)…*

Joan: *I give you back, neighbor, the projection of savior. It is yours; I will no longer follow it. I am Joan. I am no longer going to behave as a savior when you knock on my door, but I shall ask for space for myself.*

Chris: *I give back to you, colleague, the projection of arrogant and impossible boss. It is yours. I will not follow it anymore. I am Chris. From now on I will no longer act the peacemaker, but will call a spade a spade.*

Malika: *I give back to you, colleagues, the projection of the strong woman who can do anything. It is yours. I will no longer follow it. I am Malika. From now on I will more freely say what I really feel.*

Now think of a number of concrete strategies you will employ to put your intention in practice and write those down. Decide whether you will do this by yourself or communicate your decision to someone else.

For instance, when her neighbor comes, Joan could say: "Sorry, not today" and close the door, but she could also explain in a conversation with the neighbor that she really is not eager to hear about her problems all the time.

When his colleague makes remarks, Chris can always remember that it is not his fault and let him stew in his own juice, instead of putting more and more energy into making things good again. Alternately, he can also get mad and become authoritarian.

Malika can come up with a pretext and refuse to do the presentation this time. She might also say out loud that she doesn't want to make presentations all the time, and that she is just as afraid as anyone else to handle those negotiations by herself and wants someone to go with her.

Giving projections back to the other

After you have practiced for a while and feel that the time is right, make a little ritual for yourself to say goodbye to the projection. You might burn the drawing or tear it up and bury the scraps. Take your time and possibly involve someone who is willing to be your witness and can help you when you fall back into your old pattern. To remind yourself of your decision, you might make a funny little poem and post it where you can see it regularly so that you can touch it when the old pattern raises its head again. Projection patterns are persistent. You might have to say the sentence with which you return the projection a number of times to yourself, and make up your mind to really do it.

Stop projecting on others

You can apply this exercise in the same way to examine what qualities you project onto others. In Steps 1 and 2 you would then emphasize your own behavior, feelings and thoughts about the person you are drawing, and add your own spoken and unspoken words as your text. Also give text to the other that indicates how he or she reacts. In Step 3, you write: *I project ...(quality)... on ...(person).*

Next you might examine what effect this projection has on your own behavior and self-image, how real the projection is, and whether you actually want to maintain it. Could you think and feel differently about this person? Also examine what your projection does to the other. This might result in your deciding: *I hereby take ... (the projected quality)... back and no longer project it on you.*

You may have to say this a number of times a day for a longer period of time, and make up your mind to actually do it. You can reinforce this intention by means of a brief ritual, as described above.

21.4 Breathing deeply, singing a song and smiling

When you feel angry, aggravated or frustrated, you actually commit an assault on your stress balance. You can practice letting situations that irritate you slide off your back and becoming less irritable. It sounds too simple to be true, but singing or humming a little song can be balm for the stressed-out soul and improve your mood right away. So, are you about to get aggravated? Breathe deeply a few times, hum a song and smile.[56]

21.5 Heart balance

The heart is the organ that most directly perceives harmony and its disturbance. All relaxation and meditation exercises have a direct harmonizing effect on heart coherence. Other situations that enhance coherence include enjoyment, being in nature, musing with the cat on your lap, and relaxing together with your loved one. There are gadgets like a little ear or finger clip that allow us to observe in what kinds of situations our heart beats coherently or chaotically. In this way those of us who feel comfortable with such devices can examine in what situations we experience physical stress, of which we may be quite unaware, and when we feel in harmony. It can also help train us to remain more in harmony and in a coherent heart rhythm during stressful events, such as a business meeting, a traffic jam, or a conflict at home.

21.6 Fencing off the surroundings

On a busy subway platform or in a crowded store you may sometimes have the feeling of being swept away by the multiplicity of impressions that are washing over you. People, sounds, smells, light everywhere. You feel as if you are being pulled out of your body. In such a place it may help to do a brief protecting visualization exercise.

---

56 Both breathing deeply a few times and smiling have an immediate, positive influence, through neurological circuits, on the stress balance, and also on the coherence of the heart rate.

You can also become conscious of the space you occupy. You sense how much of the space around you belongs to you, and fill that space with your presence. If you can't fill the space, you have made it too large; then bring the boundary closer to you. You might imagine that this space right around you is filled with your color, or with the scent of roses or freshly cut grass. See it before you, smell the scent. If you can fill your space with your own presence, you will notice that even on a busy sidewalk people will no longer bump into you but give you more space on their own.

When there is a lot of noise around you, you can do a listening exercise. First listen consciously to the sounds around you, then move your attention step by step to sounds that are progressively farther away. Stay with this for a while. Try if you can to hear a bird, or the wind, or the voice of a playing child. When you are standing at a bus station between three noisy buses and you suddenly hear a bird, or a church bell, you'll immediately experience more space and freedom.

21.7 Focusing on your goal

Recognize this? When you are walking through a supermarket countless bright colors, slogans, offers, sounds and strategically placed products compete for your attention. Before you know it you are caught in complicated comparisons and decisions. Or you are seduced by one attractive product after another and are fighting all kinds of impulses. When you get to the checkout you have spent another half hour and your shopping cart has more in it than you ever intended.

Try this a different way. Before you enter the store, know exactly what you came for and where to find it. Walk straight to the goal. You have promised yourself not to be distracted by anything, so take just what you need and go straight to the checkout to pay for it all. What a difference!

21.8 Humor

It was for good reason that the solemn, serious kings of the past had jesters who reminded them that everything is relative and that laughing is healthy and builds community. Humor is the perfect anti-stress remedy. But when you are on the way to burnout and are racing through the store just before closing, or are aggravated with your children for the mess they've made, or if you feel overwhelmed by all the demands your boss or your partner are making on you, humor isn't the first thing that comes to mind.

Especially in such cases, look for the jester in yourself and feed him or her. Step away from yourself a bit, look at yourself and have a laugh. Make sure you look for funny situations and try to view things with humor. Go watch a funny movie or visit an amusing friend and let them make you laugh. Make sure you can laugh wholeheartedly at least once every day. It helps you relax and keep things in perspective.

Index of examples

A number of case studies are included as examples to support and illustrate the text material. Below is an index of first names (changed to protect privacy), in alphabetical order, with the corresponding page numbers where they appear in the text.